Biographical Memoirs

NATIONAL ACADEMY OF SCIENCES

NATIONAL ACADEMY OF SCIENCES
OF THE UNITED STATES OF AMERICA

Biographical Memoirs

VOLUME XLIII

PUBLISHED FOR THE ACADEMY BY

COLUMBIA UNIVERSITY PRESS

NEW YORK AND LONDON 1973

CONTENTS

Biographical Memoirs

VOLUME XLIII

George W. Bartelmez

GEORGE WILLIAM BARTELMEZ

March 23, 1885–September 2, 1967

BY DAVID BODIAN

G EORGE WILLIAM BARTELMEZ became widely known as a brilliant and versatile microscopist, in the direct line of succession to those who created the sciences of cell and tissue biology. He made major contributions toward understanding the cellular mechanisms of menstruation, the structures involved in the transmission of nerve impulses from cell to cell, and the complex transformations of the embryo which lead to the development of the adult human nervous system. Few scientists and teachers have evoked greater personal affection, or greater respect for high standards of scientific scholarship.

Bartelmez was born and educated in New York City; he died in Missoula, Montana, at the age of eighty-two. A brief draft of a biographical sketch prepared for the National Academy of Sciences by Bartelmez in 1958 informs us that his father, Theodore Bartelmez—the son of a forester—came from the Schwarzwald of Baden and migrated to the United States in his teens. Theodore Bartelmez became manager of a lumber company and later married a Philadelphia girl, Caroline Osten. Writes Bartelmez of his mother, "Her father had come from Braunschweig as a boy of sixteen and reached the American shore in a breeches-buoy after the shipwreck of the schooner that brought him over. Her mother came from Rudesheim where her father had settled after serving under Napoleon."

Bartelmez continues: "My father had been the only member of the family who had more than an elementary school education but I was permitted to go to one of the newly established public high schools, a two-mile walk from home. My reading had been confined to my father's travel books and to the Sunday School library. School opened up an entirely new world that became increasingly more exciting with each new subject that was presented. During this period my grandfather became totally blind and I read to him for two hours after school—mostly German historical romances. Several summers were spent with old friends of the family, the Rev. and Mrs. F. W. Kirwan in Delaware County, New York.

"My desire to become a physician had been confirmed by the courses in Biology and I was enrolled in the medical preparatory course. At its end there were no funds for medical school tuition and Mr. Kirwan decided that I ought to go to college. He came to the city and talked with the teachers at the high school. They recommended my taking a fourth year to prepare for college and applying for the scholarship offered to the school by the University College of N.Y.U. It had recently been moved into the country (212th St.) but could be reached by streetcar and was within walking distance of home. At that time the college had about 300 students."

Bartelmez graduated with the B.S. degree from New York University in 1906, and continued his work there for a year as Assistant in Zoology with C. L. Bristol. He writes:

"After entering the laboratory of C. L. Bristol most of my time was devoted to biology but it was possible to enroll in any course that did not conflict with a required course so I was able in this and later years to take additional courses in English and German literature, in chemistry and in geology. Bristol had inherited the teaching methods of Louis Agassiz through C. O. Whitman, which involved a maximum of encouragement and minimum of supervision so that we learned to work independently. After the sophomore year Bristol invited me to help collect fish for the New York Aquarium in Bermuda and I became acquainted with the teeming life of the coral reefs and the ways of the fisher folk. A little experience with research on the toad, common in Bermuda, led me to abandon all plans for medical school."

While working in the research laboratory established by Professor Bristol, on White's Island in Bermuda, Bartelmez met both his wife-to-be and E. V. Cowdry, who remained a close friend throughout his life.

Bartelmez continues: "After another year with Bristol as a laboratory assistant he [Bristol] arranged with Whitman for me to be given a fellowship at the University of Chicago. It paid $320 per year of which $129 went for tuition. The opportunity of collecting a load of fish for the Aquarium netted $100 so that I had enough to pay expenses during the first year."

Bartelmez was appointed a Fellow in Zoology at the University of Chicago in 1907. At Chicago, Whitman, head of the department, prompted Bartelmez' doctoral work on the bilaterality of the pigeon's egg, for which he received his Ph.D. in embryology in 1910, the year of Whitman's death. The study, which was later extended to other bird species, demonstrated an interesting point overlooked by embryologists during the lengthy history of the study of the bird's egg: that the long axis of the embryo was related to the long axis of the egg in a regular manner. Despite a degree of variation of the angle between the two axes, the right side of the embryo, with few exceptions, faced the pointed end of the egg. Bartelmez made the significant inference that the basic bilateral symmetry of the embryo was determined in the ovum before ovulation.

Bartelmez writes of this germinal period in his scientific and personal life:

"On my arrival in Chicago Whitman took me into his home for a week, had a rig sent over so that his son could drive me about the neighboring parks and talked about universities and research. His advice was to concentrate on research, waste no time taking courses and avoid university committees and politics as well as social engagements. As to a research problem he said, 'Take the development of the pigeon's egg immediately after ovulation: there are many problems to be solved during that period.' He did not realize how abysmal my ignorance was in many fields of biology, especially in embryology, so I registered in Lillie's 'Physiology of Development' which was most stimulating and suggested the thesis problem on the organization of the bird's egg. J. T. Patterson was then finishing his study of gastrulation in the pigeon under Whitman and was most helpful in orienting me in the field, for Whitman rarely came to the laboratory, as his large pigeon colony was kept in and about his home. When, after a year, my need for material became acute, he had 2 tiers of large cages for my birds built in the greenhouse at his own cost. After the first year he arranged for me to go to Woods Hole to study living eggs. I arrived there on a hot day early in June and was plodding up the hill with two bags and microscope when a tall impressive young man overtook me, took the bags and escorted me to my rooming house. This was the beginning of the friendship with Herbert Evans that will continue as long as I live. Three other friendships began at this time that have enriched my life: H. D. Arnold was a fellow in Physics; he became the second staff member of the Bell Laboratories and played a major role in its discoveries; J. W. E. Glattfeld was beginning his work on sugars with Nef and H. L. Wieman was pioneering in physiological cytology.

"The writing of my thesis did not begin until shortly before Whitman's untimely death so that I had only one conference on it with him. He spent 2 hours dissecting and improving the first paragraph of my introduction. That was the only help I had with the preparation of the paper."

After receiving his Ph.D. degree, Bartelmez decided that the methods of genetics had little appeal and accepted an assistantship with R. R. Bensley, which gave him the opportunity to develop a human embryological collection in the Anatomy Department of the University of Chicago, where he remained from 1910 until his retirement as Professor Emeritus in 1950. In 1912, shortly after being promoted to an instructorship at $1500, Bartelmez married Erminnie Eliza Hollis, whom he had met in Bermuda while working there with Bristol. Their marriage was a happy one, but tragically brief. In 1917, while pregnant with their third child, his wife was struck by a car, and subsequently gave birth to a premature infant. Eighteen months later she died of meningitis, probably as a result of the accident. The effect on Bartelmez was devastating, but was softened by the joining of the Bartelmez household with that of their close friends, the Glattfelds. With the help and devotion of the Glattfelds the three young Bartelmez children were brought to maturity. In commenting on the early years of his loss, Bartelmez writes: "In order to keep from brooding I worked day and night in the laboratory and the Glattfelds brought up the children." This typically generous statement does not alter the fact that Bartelmez remained a devoted father, remembered by his children for wonderful times together. One of them relates: "He took us to hunt mushrooms, on camping and biking expeditions in the mountains; he made bows and arrows and taught us archery and read aloud superbly. During later summers in Michigan he taught us to sail, which all three of us have enjoyed as adults. Two memorable summers were spent at the Scripps

Institute at La Jolla, where he taught us about sea life and helped us learn to swim in the ocean."

In 1936 Bartelmez married Mrs. Leila Beeman Arnold, the widow of his friend H. D. Arnold, and together they shared the happiness of their respective children and grandchildren. Upon his retirement in 1950, they moved to Baltimore where as a consultant in the Department of Embryology of the Carnegie Institution, under George W. Corner, Bartelmez pursued his embryological studies for seven years. In 1957 he and his wife moved to Missoula to be near Mrs. Bartelmez' children. He explained in 1958: "When I reached retiring age I was most anxious to leave the department of anatomy and Corner's offer to give me a place in the Carnegie Laboratory was a godsend. It made possible the completion of various pieces of work under ideal conditions with the stimulus of Corner and the other colleagues and the splendid technical help of Didusch, Heard and Grill. The association with the laboratory has not been terminated, fortunately for me. We now have our headquarters in Missoula where we can live in comfort in all seasons of the year and where the Department of Zoology has provided laboratory space."

Bartelmez' first major line of research, which led to important publications from 1912 to 1964, was embryological. His interest in early human embryology continued, but he made excursions into two other fields, neurohistology and reproductive biology. In each of these, as well as in the study of the development of the human central nervous system, he became an acknowledged master, and quickly identified and assailed a key problem. In neurohistology this was the precise structure of the cellular components involved in synaptic, or nerve cell to nerve cell, transmission. In reproductive biology it was the nature of the changes of the uterine mucous membrane which were responsible for menstrual bleeding. In brain development it was the determination of distinctive features of normal human embryogenesis and their relation to cerebral defects. These seemingly unrelated fields came together in Bartelmez' intense interest in the morphological basis of tissue processes at the limits of resolution of light microscopy.

By his own account, Bartelmez' curiosity about the nervous system was awakened by a neurology course with C. J. Herrick, whose behavioral approach to the analysis of nervous structure and connections was in sharp contrast to the dry accounts of neural structure he had known before. He soon came in closer contact with Herrick when, at the invitation of the pioneering cell biologist R. R. Bensley, he joined the Department of Anatomy as an assistant. At Herrick's suggestion, Bartelmez embarked upon a study of the auditory-vestibular system of fishes. He was sidetracked, however, into concentrating upon the giant Mauthner nerve cells which form a part of this system.

Mauthner cells have been of special interest to neurobiologists since the nineteenth century. These astonishing nerve cells occur as a symmetrical pair in the hindbrains of teleost fishes and of amphibian larvae, in which they represent a two-celled integrating "center" for the vigorous "startle" or escape response to strong auditory stimuli. The huge size of these cells relative to their neighbors, their unusual shape, and their connections with other nerve cells attracted Bartelmez —among others —for three reasons. First, the Mauthner cell, as the second neuron of a three-neuron reflex, is unique in revealing with conventional methods the variety and sources of many of its neural inputs. Bartelmez was able to identify at least twelve different types of nerve fibers converging upon the Mauthner cell. Second, a single large neuron takes the place of the usual neuron cluster, thus ensuring perfect synchrony of response of all muscles involved in an essential reflex. Third, the exceptionally large synaptic endings of sensory neurons upon the

Mauthner cell offered an unparalleled opportunity to examine the precise anatomical relations at the site of transmission of signals relayed from the sensory neurons to the Mauthner cell. The site of transmission, or synapse, had recently become the primary target of neurophysiological research, and reports that the giant synapses on the Mauthner cell showed continuity of protoplasm from sensory neuron to the cell challenged the generally held neuron doctrine, which proclaimed the discreteness and functional independence of nerve cells, and their separateness at places of synaptic association.

Bartelmez recognized that the exceptionally large sensory nerve-fiber endings related to this neuron could be used ideally to test the reliability of cytological methods used by investigators who disagreed on the validity of the neuron doctrine. He was aware that the eminent histologists on both sides of the continuing controversy had reached a technical impasse owing both to the small size of the synaptic structures usually studied and to the limitations of the cytological methods employed. It seems clear that Bartelmez' preparations of the large Mauthner cell synapses—first described in 1915—represented the ultimate in refinement of light-microscopic methods used to investigate this problem. In this study, and in a later one with his associate Normand Hoerr in 1933, Bartelmez demonstrated convincingly that the two protoplasms at the Mauthner cell giant synapses were separated by a sharply defined membrane. Although only a single interface line could be defined with the best available light-microscopic equipment, Bartelmez correctly anticipated J. D. Robertson's electron-microscopic findings thirty years later by inferring that two limiting plasma membranes of the two components of the synapse were so intimately apposed that only one "membrane" could be resolved. He also concluded from the morphological analysis of all of its components that the Mauthner cell system must involve an auditory reflex, in which speed and precision are very important, and not equilibratory reflexes. Many years later, electrophysiological studies of E. Furshpan and his colleagues confirmed and elaborated upon this prescient interpretation. The writer's own continuing work on the structure of the synapse was originally inspired by Bartelmez' work and was in some respects a direct continuation of it.

Although the electron microscope appears to have supplanted the light microscope by virtue of its hundredfold greater resolving power, Bartelmez' insistence on adequate preservation and on other important technical details has remained important precisely because the higher resolution of electron microscopy has revealed even more grotesquely the deficiencies of poor tissue preservation. At the close of his scientific career, when electron microscopy had fully established the generality of occurrence of appositional synaptic membranes, Bartelmez reasserted his lifelong faith in the need to judge data from preserved material by criteria based on the nature of living tissue. This point of view reflected the considerable influence of R. R. Bensley. Nor could he forget the tissue culture observation of Warren Lewis of half a century earlier, which defined an important characteristic of the limitation of the light microscope. In a letter to George W. Corner, who was completing Lewis' memoir, Bartelmez wrote: "[Lewis'] observations on connective tissue cells made it clear the processes of living cells come into contact with one another so that with the best optical equipment no boundary could be seen between them; yet they separated along the same area of contact. This was a most important finding for the interpretation of the histologic pictures at synaptic junctions in the nervous system."

During the Chicago period Bartelmez' research influenced and was influenced by not only R. R. Bensley and C. J. Herrick, but also, through intimate association, Percival Bailey, who was Bartelmez' first graduate student, Ralph W. Gerard, Stephen Polyak, Jeanette Obenchain, Heinrich Klüver, Paul Weiss, Karl Lashley, and others of the outstanding neurological group at the University. These senior investigators— along with his younger colleagues, who included A. A. Pearson, David B. Clark, and the writer—often sought his counsel on problems of the development and structure of the nervous system.

Bartelmez' enduring interest in early human embryology began with the embryological collection of the Anatomy Department at the University of Chicago. It was accentuated when he obtained a well-preserved early human embryo of the somite period in 1917. This windfall caused him to drop a two-year project on the effects of feeding endocrine glands to amphibian larvae. He took the embryo to the laboratory of Franklin Paine Mall at the Johns Hopkins University, where he established research associations with several leading figures in American embryology. Bartelmez writes: "Evans was there working on embryos of the same period and we made plans to combine our forces, and include the early somite stages in a monograph. In addition I became acquainted with Mall, Warren Lewis, Streeter and Corner. Before this work was finished I had spent a spring quarter and several successive Septembers in the Carnegie laboratory, and had seen Corner working with his monkey colony, in his pioneer studies on the menstrual cycle."

Bartelmez' studies of the development of the human brain, initiated in association with H. M. Evans, were directed toward clarifying the earliest stages of differentiation in the forward end of the nervous system, including both the otic and optic primordia and the cranial neural crest. He soon recognized the importance of finding reliable landmarks to establish an accurate sequence of events, and of adequately controlling the preservation of highly fragile young embryos. By working back from late somite stages to presomite stages, he established the importance of early-appearing and permanent landmarks such as the otic segment of the hindbrain, the cranial flexure, the optic primordium, the trigeminal neural crest, and the first somite. These classical studies, published in 1922-1926, corrected gross errors of interpretation in previous accounts of these crucial stages. Later, in the thirties, well-preserved somite human embryos obtained by the gynecologist J. I. Brewer and others, as well as rat embryonic material prepared in 1925 at Berkeley with the help of Herbert Evans, made possible a series of important studies on the cranial neural crest. These studies, begun at the University of Chicago with Mary Blount, were extended and published after his return to the Carnegie laboratory when he retired. They were instrumental in clarifying the origin and role of neural crest derived from the primary optic vesicles.

Bartelmez' early friendship with H. M. Evans, whom he had met at Woods Hole in 1908, and his subsequent association with Evans in Baltimore, probably played an important role in his initial studies of human embryonic development. In a similar manner, Bartelmez' association with George W. Corner in the unique embryological facilities of the Carnegie laboratory (where Corner was later director) stimulated Bartelmez' extensive investigations of the uterus and the uterine cycle. These researches were carried out mainly at the University of Chicago, but collaboration with Corner and with Carl G. Hartman at the Carnegie laboratory was continuously influential. Bartelmez writes of the early Chicago work on the uterus: "In the interim I had met Cary Culbertson (a Chicago gynecologist) and arranged to collect human uteri from his abundant clinical material. With the help of J. L. O'Leary and Caroline Bensley a large series of endometria was prepared for cytologic study. The need for fully controlled material in this field became increasingly more apparent and when the Rockefeller Foundation gave the University a grant for research in biology, Bensley allotted funds for a monkey colony which provided material for the work of Markee, Daron, Rossman and myself."

Thus, in the twenties, Bartelmez made a major commitment to the understanding of the events of the menstrual cycle, which led to significant contributions and publications until 1957. But even by 1937 he had become an acknowledged authority on cyclic changes in the uterus, after publishing a masterful and exhaustive review on the theories of menstruation. Subsequent collaboration with George W. Corner and Carl G. Hartman established a sound basis for defining cyclic changes in the endometrium and for relating them to stages in the development and regression of the corpus luteum. An important study of the form and function of the unusual uterine blood vessels of primates, published in 1957, concluded his experimental work on the monkey uterus.

In the period referred to above, a quantum jump was accomplished in knowledge of the cyclic changes in the uterine mucosa, the relation of these changes to the endocrine function of the corpus luteum, and their further dependence on a highly specialized vascular supply. This jump began with the pioneering experimental studies of G. W. Corner on the menstrual cycle in rhesus monkeys, and continued with major contributions by Carl G. Hartman, Edgar Allen, and George Bartelmez. Bartelmez soon became convinced of Hartman's contention that menstruation was independent of ovulation or of pre-gravid changes of the uterine mucosa, and occurred as a normal cyclical event in which bleeding was the only constant feature. He was able to confirm Hartman's work in the rhesus monkey by demonstrating with evidence from human material that menstruation may occur in the absence of a large ovarian follicle or a corpus luteum. By establishing the limits of reliability of his superb microscopic preparations, and thus separating fact from artifact, he was able to work out the sequence of regressive changes due to impaired circulation in the outer part of the endometrial lining of the uterus. The work of Bartelmez and his students, especially J. E. Markee, G. H. Daron, and I. Rossman, further established the peculiar characteristics of the spiral arteries of the uterine mucosa, their special sensitivity to general chemical or hormonal stimuli, and their variable time of rupture in different parts of the endometrium. He suggested that hemorrhage from these vessels might be induced and arrested by means of the rhythmic vascular constriction and relaxation (blushing and blanching) described by Markee in explants of endometrium in the anterior eye chamber of the monkey. Later, Bartelmez marshaled substantial evidence in favor of the view that constrictions of the spiral arteries, and consequent vascular stasis and ischemia, lead to injury and sloughing of the superficial layer of the endometrium, and to menstrual bleeding. The illustrations of elegant histological preparations in Bartelmez' paper of 1956 offer convincing evidence of the reality of the constrictions in the spiral arteries. His 1957 papers on the menstrual cycle summarize a wealth of histological and cytological observations on glandular activity, vascularization, and connective tissue components of the endometrium—observations which made possible an authoritative synthesis of events of the uterine cycle and their adaptive significance. Bartelmez' influence on gynecological practice and research was also notable, especially in the Chicago area—where he was elected an Honorary Fellow of the Chicago Gynecological Society.

Bartelmez' scientific publications are so well written that one might not suspect that their composing was generally a torment for him. He struggled for precision of thought and statement, and for a careful appraisal of previous writings, with the same insistence on technical perfection that he displayed in the laboratory. It was therefore not uncommon for a year or more to be taken in readying a manuscript for publication. It may be remarked that two older colleagues at Chicago who most influenced Bartelmez—Herrick and Bensley—were both masters of scientific writing and may have sharpened in Bartelmez those attitudes of work and thought which were already manifest in his earliest publications. At any rate, Bartelmez' writings combined the virtues of Herrick's meticulous recording of observations and interpretations with Bensley's uninhibited jousting with dogma.

Bartelmez was by nature a gentle and considerate person, but his irritation was apt to show when he was forced to deal with published data based on poorly preserved material. In discussing his strong reaction to workers who ignored the role of postmortem changes in creating artifacts and misinterpretations, he remarked that "such people need to be attacked violently or they will pay no attention whatever."

Bartelmez was so impressed with the work that was still to be done with conventional light-microscopic methods that he was somewhat reluctant to acknowledge fully the power and scope of new biochemical and electron microscopic approaches —the more so because so many of the exponents of electron microscopy showed an astonishing ignorance of the essential facts of microscopic organization and of tissue function. As a result, where he was rigorous and self-critical to a fault in dealing with microscopic problems, he was apt to be somewhat cavalier in dismissing the potentialities of new approaches, such as those in the field of histochemistry. His imagination was captured by the cloistered life advocated by Whitman and by the vision of the scholar. Anything that might interfere prompted an irritation in Bartelmez, often humorously expressed, which could only charm the listener. In practice, his barbs about nonbelievers—the unscholarly medical student or practicing physician—were often more an expression of concern than of intolerance. His widely known patience with students and his helpfulness with physicians who consulted him led to a wider appreciation of the values of the scientific approach. This, of course, was his goal; he loved to transmit learning as well as to acquire it.

Bartelmez' family background conferred on him the riches of both the scientific and the literary German classics. He was especially fond of Goethe's works, and above all loved to quote from *Faust*. In a laboratory conversation in the thirties about the unfolding of new complexities of the mechanism of blood clotting, he gleefully recalled a line from *Faust*, "Blut ist ein ganz besondrer Saft!" Or, much later at the Department of Embryology of the Carnegie Institution, when the following question was referred to him: "How many cells are there in a newborn baby?," he replied, "Weisst du wie viel Sternlein stehen an dem blauen Himmelszelt?" Bartelmez also loved Chaucer and Shakespeare and quoted them with relish.

Bartelmez embellished his scientific publications with important details from the early period of microscopic studies of tissues, often neglected by others. It is interesting that, of the pioneers whose writings he had studied in detail, the one who touched him the most was Purkinje, who himself had made major contributions to the fields of histology, embryology, and neurology, and whose findings foreshadowed the cell theory and the neuron doctrine. His interest in Purkinje led him to translate from Latin Purkinje's neglected but classical work, "Contributions to the History of the Bird's Egg Previous to

Incubation" (1830). Bartelmez' brief Foreword places Purkinje's embryological discoveries in perspective within Purkinje's life and times. Characteristically, he offered this carefully annotated translation as a tribute to one of his oldest and most esteemed scientific friends, H. M. Evans, on the occasion of his sixtieth birthday.

Bartelmez as a teacher was influenced by his department's primary concern with research and graduate training. Under R. R. Bensley, the department was an autonomous one within the University, and medical students—though numerically superior—were not distinguished from other students who came to the department for formal course work. For many years Bartelmez was responsible for and devoted to the neuroanatomy course, which he had inherited from C. J. Herrick. Like Herrick and others in the department, he was not at his best in lecturing to medical students, but developed an excellent laboratory course. He was often seen in the laboratory, urging students to examine the microscopic material provided in preference to textbook illustrations. He delighted in demonstrating special microscopic preparations to illustrate important points, and was quietly outraged when some students gave only perfunctory attention to elegant microscopic demonstrations. His emphasis on the analysis of primary materials, and on technical excellence, evoked greater response from graduate students and younger colleagues. Bartelmez demonstrated his own skill on one occasion by capping a discussion of the conditions necessary to prepare serial paraffin sections one micron thick with an awesome performance of the feat. Those medical students who pursued careers in clinical neurology were apt to recall gratefully his insistence on direct personal observations in the laboratory, long after their immediate reaction to his sometimes absent-minded lectures had faded.

Temperamentally Bartelmez was a highly sociable person, who overcame both the loneliness which followed the death of his first wife and that engendered by long hours in the laboratory. He was always at the disposal of students and colleagues who needed technical assistance or advice on how to interpret difficult points of microscopic structure. At the microscope, Bartelmez treated beginners or experts as companions in the search for knowledge, and his students remembered gratefully that they came to maturity as scientists because they were treated as professional equals once they had proved the seriousness of their purpose. The writer's friendship with Bartelmez began as a student with sessions at the microscope together, and remained close throughout Bartelmez' life. His influence upon my entire scientific career was immeasurable, and included the transmission of the spiritual as well as the methodological values of science.

For many years a few of Bartelmez' students and colleagues gathered for luncheon in his office, where current events and scientific problems vied with a curiously satisfying (though somewhat unvarying) daily menu of buttered 100 percent whole wheat toast, marmalade, Jonathan apples, and green tea. The tea was often donated by Chinese students and friends. Bartelmez especially cherished prize samples unobtainable outside China and mailed by former students. On festive occasions, often signaled by a visit from a colleague, he prepared oyster stew from a favorite recipe—probably acquired in Baltimore— and served it in cups. While working in the Hunterian Building of the Johns Hopkins School of Medicine, after retirement from the Carnegie Department of Embryology, Bartelmez enlivened the departmental luncheons in the library with his sense of humor and his still youthful enthusiasm. By this time his staples had shifted from toast and apples to crackers and imported Roquefort cheese. No derivative blue cheeses would do.

Bartelmez' lithe and springy stride was a familiar sight on the University of Chicago campus. He had been on his college gymnastic team, and continued throughout life to enjoy athletics, whether in the form of long walks, handstands, or handball. In the thirties he often repaired with his students to the handball courts "under the stands" in Stagg Field, a site to become known for the first successful nuclear chain reaction in December 1942. Handball partners learned that Bartelmez did not consider subzero weather an obstacle to the daily 5 P.M. game, even though it meant a bone-chilling run across Stagg Field from the dressing rooms in shorts and sweatshirt. Ice-skating on the Midway at the University of Chicago was another favorite sport.

Walking excursions in the Indiana sand dunes with C. J. Herrick, C. M. Child, and other biologist friends were also the occasion for vigorous and stimulating exercise, physical and mental. In his exploration through the countryside, Bartelmez cultivated his interest in mushrooms, of which he had collected and identified many species. In the summer, for many years, a farm in Chittenden, Vermont, gave further scope to his love for the outdoors, as well as relief from the dreaded hot weather in Chicago and Baltimore. In addition to facilities for visiting children and grandchildren, he had provided a small laboratory for his own use in research and writing. Later, after retirement to Missoula, he escaped the hot summer weather by taking hiking trips to high places in the Rockies.

Bartelmez was not a religious man in the ordinary sense of the word, but his lasting faith in the potentialities of human intelligence and in the power of genius was well expressed in an essay on "Man from the Point of View of His Development and Structure," published in 1926:

". . . those individuals who do more than merely acquire information, who are capable of true education, are lifted thereby above the level of inherited reflex to the heights of intellectual control. Their number can assuredly be increased as time goes on, and mankind will profit accordingly. The greatest progress, however, will probably come through the labors of the sporadic genius, the pathfinder and torchbearer who must be recognized promptly, liberated from the bondage of class and caste and disease, and left free to develop his capacities and attain his ideals. Our greatest hope lies in him." And again: "In what direction may we look for progress? There is no evidence that the upper level of intellectual attainment has risen during historic time or that the race is likely to produce a higher percentage of geniuses in the future. Our most obvious need is in the improvement of the social relations among men." This early credo fails to include what was perhaps most characteristic of Bartelmez as a man— the reverence for life expressed both in work and in the warmth of his relations with others.

During the last few years of his life Bartelmez suffered from poor health, including arthritis, partial deafness, and a terminal illness, which, with recurrent illnesses of his wife, prompted him to despair of further work after 1962. He improved so markedly with therapy that in the next five years he was able to carry on a lively correspondence with his friends, especially A. Dekaban, with whom he collaborated in studies published jointly in 1962 and 1964. Between 1965 and his last letter to Dekaban on July 6, 1967, details of their work on the development of visual and motor centers of the cerebral cortex in human embryos were the central theme of his energetic letters. His correspondence with G. W. Corner about a proposed joint paper on the coiled arteries of the uterus, and on personal matters, continued until August 15, 1967.

Bartelmez was awarded an honorary Doctor of Science degree from the University of Montana in 1966, where he had served as guest investigator in the Department of Zoology from 1957. He was elected to membership in the National Academy of Sciences in 1949. Between 1948 and 1950 he served as president of the American Association of Anatomists.

Bartelmez' devotion to science and learning, his gallant view of life, his youthful enthusiasm for new discoveries, and his lively interest in the activities of his own family and those of his associates remained keen to the end.

BIBLIOGRAPHY

KEY TO ABBREVIATIONS

Am. J. Anat. = American Journal of Anatomy
Am. J. Obstet. Gynecol. = American Journal of Obstetrics and Gynecology
Anat. Record = Anatomical Record
Carnegie Inst. Wash. Contrib. Embryol. = Carnegie Institution of Washington Contributions to Embryology
J. Comp. Neurol. = Journal of Comparative Neurology

1908

With C. L. Bristol. The poison glands of *Bufo agua.* Science, 27:455.

1912

The bilaterality of the pigeon's egg. Journal of Morphology, 23:269-329.

1915

Some effects of mammalian thyroid and thymus-glands upon the development of Amphibian larvae. Anat. Record, 9:47-49. (A)
Mauthner's cell and the nucleus motorius tegmenti. J. Comp. Neurol., 25:87-128.

1918

The relation of the embryo to the principal axis of symmetry in the bird's egg. Biological Bulletin, 35:319-61.

1920

The morphology of the synapse in vertebrates. Archives of Neurology and Psychiatry, 4:122-26.

1922

The origin of the otic and optic primordia in man. J. Comp. Neurol., 34:201-32.
With W. A. N. Dorland. Clinical and embryologic report of an

extremely early tubal pregnancy; together with a study of decidual reaction, intrauterine and ectopic. Am J. Obstet. Gynecol., 4:215-27, 372-86.

1923

The subdivisions of the neural folds in man. J. Comp. Neurol., 35:231-47.

1924

With O. Riddle. On parthenogenetic cleavage and on the role of water absorption by the ovum in the formation of the subgerminal cavity in the pigeon's egg. Am. J. Anat., 33:57-66.

Ectodermal areas of the head in young human embryos. Anat. Record, 29:109. (A)

1926

With H. M. Evans. Development of the human embryo during the period of somite formation. Carnegie Inst. Wash. Contrib. Embryol., 17:1-67.

Man from the point of view of his development and structure. Chapter 15 in: *The Nature of the World and of Man,* ed. by H. H. Newman. Chicago, University of Chicago Press.

1927

The human uterine gland cell. Anat. Record, 35:3. (A)

1928

Observations on human uterine mucosa during the flow. Anat. Record, 38:3. (A)

1929

Some factors involved in the process of menstruation. Proceedings of the Institute of Medicine of Chicago, 7:181-82.

1931

The human uterine mucous membrane during menstruation. Am. J. Obstet. Gynecol., 21:623-43.

1932

With C. M. Bensley. Human uterine gland cells. In: *Special Cytology; The Form and Functions of the Cell in Health and Disease; A Textbook for Students of Biology and Medicine,* 2d ed., ed. by E. V. Cowdry, Vol. 3, pp. 1525-63. New York, Paul B. Hoeber, Inc.

Further data on the nature of menstruation. Anat. Record, 52:4, Supplement. (A)

1933

With N. L. Hoerr. The vestibular club endings in *Ameiurus.* Further evidence on the morphology of the synapse. J. Comp. Neurol., 57:401-28.

Histological studies on the menstruating mucous membrane of the human uterus. Carnegie Inst. Wash. Contrib. Embryol., 24:143-86.

1935

The circulation in the intervillous space of the macaque placenta. Anat. Record, 61:4, Supplement. (A)

1936

With G. W. Corner and C. G. Hartman. On normal and aberrant corpora lutea of the rhesus monkey. Am. J. Anat., 59:433-57.

1937

Menstruation. Physiological Reviews, 17:28-72.

1940

With W. Bloom. Hematopoiesis in young human embryos. Am. J. Anat., 67:21-53.

Some effects of fixation and other insults on uterine epithelial cells in primates. Anat. Record, 77:509-27.

1941

Menstruation. Journal of the American Medical Association, 116: 702-4. Also in *Glandular Physiology and Therapy,* 1942, 2d ed.

Council on Pharmacy and Chemistry. Chicago, American Medical Association.

Translation.   Contributions to the history of the bird's egg previous to incubation, by Johannes Evangelista Purkinje.   In: *Essays in Biology in Honor of Herbert M. Evans, Written by His Friends*, pp. 51-58. Berkeley and Los Angeles, University of California Press.

1944

Female genital system.   Chapter 25 in: *A Textbook of Histology*, 4th ed., by Alexander A. Maximow and William Bloom, pp. 544-93. Philadelphia, W. B. Saunders Company.

1946

With I. Rossman.   Delayed ovulation, a significant factor in the variability of the menstrual cycle.   Am. J. Obstet. Gynecol., 52:28-33.

1947

With Sylvia H. Bensley.   "Acid phosphatase" reactions in peripheral nerves.   Science, 106:639-41.

The mechanism of menstruation.   Anat. Record, 96:380. (A)

1951

With H. Klüver.   Endometriosis in a rhesus monkey.   Surgery, Gynecology and Obstetrics, 92:650-60.

With G. W. Corner and C. G. Hartman.   Cyclic changes in the endometrium of the rhesus monkey.   Carnegie Inst. Wash. Contrib. Embryol., 34:99-144.

1953

Factors in the variability of the menstrual cycle.   Anat. Record, 115:101-20.

Johannes Evangelista Purkinje.   In: *Founders of Neurology*, ed. by Webb E. Haymaker, pp. 70-74. Springfield, Charles C Thomas, Publisher.

1954

With G. W. Corner. Early abnormal embryos of the rhesus monkey. Carnegie Inst. Wash. Contrib. Embryol., 35:1-9.

The formation of neural crest from the primary optic vesicle in man. Carnegie Inst. Wash. Contrib. Embryol., 35:55-72.

1956

Premenstrual and menstrual ischemia and the myth of endometrial arteriovenous anastomoses. Am. J. Anat., 98:69-95.

1957

The phases of the menstrual cycle and their interpretation in terms of the pregnancy cycle. Am. J. Obstet. Gynecol., 74: 931-55.

The form and the functions of the uterine blood vessels in the rhesus monkey. Carnegie Inst. Wash. Contrib. Embryol., 36: 153-82.

With I. Rossman. The injection of the blood vascular system of the uterus. Anat. Record, 128:223-31.

1958

Amenorrhea. In: *Encyclopaedia Britannica,* Vol. 1, p. 746. Menstruation, *ibid.,* Vol. 15, p. 252; Female reproductive system, *ibid.,* Vol. 19, pp. 177-79. Chicago, Encyclopaedia Britannica, Inc.

1960

Charles Judson Herrick, neurologist. Science, 131:1654-55.

Neural crest from the forebrain in mammals. Anat. Record, 138:269-81.

1962

The proliferation of neural crest from forebrain levels in the rat. Carnegie Inst. Wash. Contrib. Embryol., 37:1-12.

With A. S. Dekaban. The early development of the human brain. Carnegie Inst. Wash. Contrib. Embryol., 37:13-32.

1964

With A. S. Dekaban. Complete dysraphism in 14-somite human embryo. A contribution to normal and abnormal morphogenesis. Am. J. Anat., 115:27-41.

1967

Charles Judson Herrick. (Manuscript in preparation at time of death.) In: National Academy of Sciences, *Biographical Memoirs*, 43:77-108 New York and London, Columbia University Press.

Hugo Benioff

VICTOR HUGO BENIOFF

September 14, 1899–February 29, 1968

BY FRANK PRESS

VICTOR HUGO BENIOFF was born on September 14, 1899, in Los Angeles, California. His parents were both immigrants —his father from Russia and his mother from Sweden. Benioff's California roots and his origins from immigrant stock were reflected in later years in his love of nature and his sensitivity to people, particularly his sympathy for the underdog.

Benioff was drawn to science at an early age, expressing a career interest in astronomy as a boy of fourteen. He attended public schools in Los Angeles and Long Beach and took his undergraduate studies at Pomona College, where he was elected to Phi Beta Kappa in 1920 and received the A.B. degree in 1921. During his undergraduate years he served as a summer assistant working on solar astronomy at the Mount Wilson Observatory, returning to Mount Wilson each summer until his graduation from Pomona. His interest in astronomy continued following graduation and he took a position at the Lick Observatory for the year 1923-1924, observing stellar radial velocities. Were it not for his inability to tolerate the night hours and the cold, as required of an observer, Benioff would undoubtedly have become an eminent astronomer.

In 1924 he began work in Pasadena as an assistant physicist with the seismological program of the Carnegie Institution, then directed by H. O. Wood. His first assignment was to develop a drive system for the recording drums. Even at this early date Benioff's taste for sophisticated instrumental design was evidenced. By developing a new type of impulse motor driven from a fork-controlled 10 Hertz quarter-phase pulse generator, he solved the problem. This novel system was highly successful and made possible the determination of seismic-wave arrival times to the unprecedented accuracy of 0.1 second.

At about this time Benioff installed most of the original instrumentation and set up a number of the original auxiliary stations which subsequently evolved into the famous seismic network of the California Institute of Technology.

Circa 1929 he commenced design of the now world-famous variable reluctance seismograph and the linear strain seismograph. The former instrument was placed in service in 1931 and evolved to its final form in 1934. For a number of reasons, the variable reluctance seismograph was an immediate success; capable of extremely high magnification at a frequency of about 1 Hertz, it was useful for the study of near and distant earthquakes. Simplicity, reliability, sensitivity, and a judicious selection of response characteristics based upon the noise and signal spectrums are responsible for the adoption of this remarkable instrument by observatories all over the world. It made possible the precise determination of travel time, the discovery of new seismic phases, the extension of the magnitude scale to teleseismic events, and the world-wide availability of first-motion data to recover source mechanism. With minor modification this instrument was later selected for use in the World-Wide Standard Seismograph Network and formed the basis of the detection system recommended by the Geneva Conference of Experts for the monitoring of nuclear tests.

The original strain seismograph was built with water pipe and lacked the desired stability. Gradually it evolved over the years with fused quartz tubing used as the standard of length, velocity transducers with galvanometric recording, and finally variable capacitance transducers and recording oscillographs. This instrument achieved notable successes; in 1953 Benioff provided linear strain records to Frank Press and Maurice Ewing and thereby made possible the discovery of the mantle surface waves. The linear strain seismograph is now a primary source of data for the eigen-frequency spectrum of the earth.

Beginning about 1934, Benioff supervised the development of instruments for structural vibration studies in a program sponsored by the U.S. Coast and Geodetic Survey. This was followed in 1936 by a number of instrumental advances designed to improve the quality of the (Pasadena) Southern California seismograph stations, making them the most advanced network in the world. A number of resulting devices were manufactured commercially and placed in world-wide use. During this period Benioff also developed instruments for seismic prospecting—a field of rapid technological advances, keen competition, and overnight obsolescence. In these and subsequent instrumental developments Benioff led an enthusiastic staff of engineers and technicians, many of whom became well known in seismological circles: Francis Lehner, Ralph Gilman, J. L. Blayney, and William Giles.

Benioff received the Ph.D. degree from the California Institute of Technology in 1935. The Seismological Laboratory was transferred from the Carnegie Institution to Caltech in 1937 and Benioff was appointed assistant professor of seismology. In 1950 he was promoted to a full professorship at Caltech.

Although he would have made an excellent instructor, Benioff preferred research to teaching and had little contact with students either in the classroom or as thesis adviser. On the other hand, his influence via informal discussion with doctoral candidates, postdoctoral fellows, and visiting scholars was very great and more than justified the title "professor." By the mid-thirties the Seismological Laboratory of Pasadena became a world center for geophysical research owing to the originality and productivity of Benioff and his close colleagues, Beno Gutenberg and Charles Richter.

With the increasing concern for national defense connected with the outbreak of World War II in Europe, Benioff and his group undertook the development and improvement of radar and underwater listening and ranging devices mostly for the Submarine Signal Company of Boston. This work continued through the war years and terminated in 1946.

Following the war Benioff returned to geophysical research. He built an array of seismometers on Mount Palomar to study microseisms. He experimented with new types of seismograph systems involving novel concepts such as mixing strain seismograph outputs to obtain mode filtering, vectorial recording devices, mercury tube tiltmeters, tape recording and playback analysis of earthquakes. About 1957, Benioff became interested in magnetic micropulsations. He constructed an array of magnetovariographs and published one of the first papers—and still perhaps the most comprehensive—on the spectrum of geomagnetic fluctuations in the range 0.3 to 120 seconds.

Still widely used is Benioff's early definition of seismic destructiveness in which the acceleration spectrum is the important parameter in anti-seismic design. This was one manifestation of a special responsibility Benioff felt to the inhabitants of earthquake prone regions.

Benioff's curiosity was unbounded. In addition to geophysical instrumentation, he took an active interest in the fabrication of a super-lightweight bicycle and construction of exotic kites; he studied camera lenses in great detail and even delved into the workings of jet engines. The use of ultrasonic devices for cancer treatment also attracted his attention. He became intensely interested in the physics of musical instruments and worked toward the development of an electronic violin, cello, and piano. The last instrument reached fruition under sponsorship of the Baldwin Piano Company and was used in public concerts by famous artists. His motivation always was to heighten the pleasure of the listener and to lighten the task of the performer while preserving the fidelity of the instrument.

Benioff's instruments and the data which they produced were sufficient ingredients for a distinguished scientific career, However, his interests broadened, and beginning about 1950 he began working on the general problem of earthquake mechanisms and global tectonics—some fifteen years prior to the current great interest in this field. In a classic series of papers between 1951 and 1958 he introduced several of the concepts which today form the basic elements of the "new global tectonics." In attacking these problems he made good use of his broad knowledge of the engineering properties of materials. By nature he was inclined toward elegantly simple hypotheses and quantitative procedures. His approach was that of a mature scientist entering a dormant field; he was skeptical, bold, and unfettered by preexisting hypotheses.

During this period Benioff introduced the concept of instrumentally determined strain rebound. He was able to show that great earthquakes reveal a global pattern of strain accumulation and release. He outlined the relation between aftershock sequences and stress relaxation and showed that the strain rebound characteristics could be used to separate the crust and upper mantle into zones having different mechanical properties.

Benioff demonstrated that the geographic distribution of aftershocks was related to the dimension of the primary fault. He proposed that the distribution of epicenters could be used as evidence for the fault origin of ocean deeps. He cited both continental drift and continental growth as the possible causes of tectonic activity of continental margins and deep sea trenches, although he preferred the latter mechanism.

Benioff continually sought to elucidate the earthquake mechanism. He deduced source dimensions using strain energy considerations. He tried to explain the source of aftershock energy using laboratory results on creep strain. He showed how the direction of fault progression could be recovered from the asymmetric radiation pattern of seismic waves. While accepting the elastic rebound theory for shallow focus earthquakes, he proposed that certain deep focus events involved volume collapse. It is a tribute to Benioff's farsightedness that each of these contributions now represents a major field of research involving large numbers of workers.

It is fitting that the last major contribution in an already distinguished career came with Benioff's participation on one of the teams which detected the free vibrations of the earth. As early as 1952 he thought he detected these elusive planetary oscillations. Although this claim was later shown to be in error, there is no question that his efforts stimulated other geophysicists to continue the theoretical and computational work which eventually was successful, opening the new field of terrestrial spectroscopy.

Benioff's contributions to geophysics did not go unnoticed and many honors came his way. He was elected to the National Academy of Sciences in 1953, received the Arthur L. Day Award of the Geological Society of America in 1957, was elected president of the Seismological Society of America in 1958, and received the William Bowie Medal of the American Geophysical Union in 1965 "for unselfish cooperation in research." He was a fellow of the American Academy of Arts and Sciences, the Geological Society of America, the Royal Astronomical

Society, the Acoustical Society of America, the American Geophysical Union, and the American Physical Society.

Benioff was sought after for consultation by industrial firms and governmental agencies. He advised the Office of Science and Technology, the Department of State, the Department of Defense, and the Department of Water Resources of the State of California.

He married twice; in 1928 he married Alice Silverman. They had one son, Paul, in 1931 and two daughters, Dagmar (1931) and Elena (1932). His first marriage ended in divorce and in 1953 he married Mildred Lent, with whom he had a daughter, Martha, who was born in 1956.

In his middle years Benioff stood at 5 feet 10½ inches and weighed about 175 pounds, had graying, sandy-colored hair, a prominent moustache, and penetrating gray-green eyes. Typically he was sportily attired, walked with a bounce, and radiated good humor, optimism, warmth, and good will. Although he suffered from often debilitating allergic reactions, this did not show in his demeanor.

He was inclined toward liberal views, which he freely expressed, and he championed the cause of repressed minorities. He showed a rare sensitivity and concern for people as individuals, and his relationships with students, colleagues, and friends reflected his intuitive understanding of the human personality. Benioff was a proud man and he did not suffer fools or fakes very easily. However, he was humble and self-effacing as a scientist. Upon receiving the Bowie Medal he said:

"I was fortunate in coming to the Seismological Laboratory at a time when the science of seismology was in its infancy. Many of the problems then were of a simple form in which an intuitive guess now and then was a sufficient solution. I am quite sure that were I reincarnated into the world of seismology as it now is with its complex problems resolvable only with very sophisticated means, my accomplishments would approach zero, and that I would not be standing here forty years later as a recipient of the Bowie Medal."

An important factor in Benioff's life was his love of nature. He was particularly attracted to the wilderness areas of California and Nevada and lived in them for such periods as his professional life permitted. For his personal enjoyment he often bought land that he considered scenically attractive and on occasion he was a part-time rancher. Benioff had an infallible instinct for judging land values and often reaped a handsome profit when the time came to dispose of a holding. However, his primary motivation always was to share the beauties of the back country with his family and friends.

In 1964 Benioff retired from Caltech and became Professor Emeritus of Seismology. For his retirement estate he chose the wild and beautiful coast of Cape Mendocino in northern California. He spent his retirement years advising government agencies and private industry, insisting that all consultations be held in his home. In his last years he received much pleasure from his young daughter and he enjoyed clearing his land, raising animals, and growing vegetables and fruit.

Hugo Benioff died on February 29, 1968, at the age of sixty-eight in Mendocino, California. His was a monumental, multidimensional career, spanning forty years and resulting in works that will survive for a long time to come.

I am indebted to Mrs. Mildred Benioff, Robert P. Sharp, Charles Richter, Francis Lehner, Stewart Smith, and Don L. Anderson for help in preparing this memoir.

BIBLIOGRAPHY

KEY TO ABBREVIATIONS

Bull. Geol. Soc. Am. = Bulletin of the Geological Society of America
Bull. Seismol. Soc. Am. = Bulletin of the Seismological Society of America
Eng. Sci. = Engineering and Science
J. Geophys. Res. = Journal of Geophysical Research
Trans. Am. Geophys. Union = Transactions of the American Geophysical
    Union

1931

Operating frequency of regenerative oscillatory systems. Proceedings of the Institute of Radio Engineers, 19:1274-77.

1932

A new vertical seismograph. Bull. Seismol. Soc. Am., 22:155-69.

1934

A new electro-magnetic seismograph. Proceedings of the Fifth Pacific Science Congress, ed. by the General Secretary. Held under the auspices of the National Research Council of Canada and through the generosity of the Government of Canada. Victoria and Vancouver, 1933. Toronto, University of Toronto Press.
The physical evaluation of seismic destructiveness. Bull. Seismol. Soc. Am., 24:398-403.

1935

A linear strain seismograph. Bull. Seismol. Soc. Am., 25:283-309.
Preliminary report on a four-unit portable seismograph. U.S. Coast and Geodetic Survey, Special Publication No. 201.

1938

The determination of the extent of faulting with application to the Long Beach earthquake. Bull. Seismol. Soc. Am., 28:77-84.

1939

With B. Gutenberg. Atmospheric waves and currents recorded by electromagnetic barographs. Procès-Verbaux des Séances de l'Association de Meteorologie, pp. 61-62. Union Géodesique et Géophysique Internationale, 7th General Assembly, Washington, September 1939.

The instrument-development program of the seismological laboratory. Bulletin of the California Institute of Technology, 48:22-23.

With B. Gutenberg. The mammoth "earthquake fault" and related features. Bull. Seismol. Soc. Am., 29:333-40.

With B. Gutenberg. Observations with electromagnetic microbarographs. Nature, 144:478. (L)

With B. Gutenberg. Waves and currents recorded by electromagnetic barographs. Bulletin of the American Meteorological Society, 20:422-26.

1941

With B. Gutenberg. Atmospheric-pressure waves near Pasadena. Trans. Am. Geophys. Union, pp. 424-27.

1948

Seismological instruments developed at the C. I. T. Eng. Sci., 11:24-25, 31.

1949

With B. Gutenberg and C. F. Richter. Earthquake study in southern California, 1948. Trans. Am. Geophys. Union, 30:595-97.

Seismic evidence for the fault origin of oceanic deeps. Bull. Geol. Soc. Am., 60:1837-56.

1950

With B. Gutenberg and C. F. Richter. Progress Report, Seismological Laboratory, California Institute of Technology, 1949. Trans. Am. Geophys. Union, 31:463-67.

1951

Earthquakes and rock creep. Bull. Seismol. Soc. Am., 41:31-62.

Global strain accumulation and release as revealed by great earthquakes. Bull. Geol. Soc. Am., 62:331-38.

Crustal strain characteristics derived from earthquake sequences.

Colloquium on Plastic Flow and Deformation within the Earth, Hershey, Pennsylvania. Trans. Am. Geophys. Union, 32:508-14.

With B. Gutenberg. Ice. Strain characteristics of the earth's interior. Chapter XV in: *Internal Constitution of the Earth*, ed. by B. Gutenberg. (National Research Council. Physics of the Earth, Volume 7.) New York, Dover Publications.

With Maurice Ewing and Frank Press. Sound waves in the atmosphere generated by a small earthquake. Proceedings of the National Academy of Sciences, 37:600-3.

Earthquakes—recorded on tape. Eng. Sci., 15:7-11.

With B. Gutenberg and C. F. Richter. Progress Report, Seismological Laboratory, California Institute of Technology, 1950. Trans. Am. Geophys. Union, 32:749-54.

1952

With J. Buwalda, B. Gutenberg, and C. F. Richter. The Arvin Earthquake of July 21, 1952. Mineral Information Service Bulletin, 5(9):4-7. California, Department of Natural Resources, Division of Mines.

With B. Gutenberg. The response of strain and pendulum seismographs to surface waves. Bull. Seismol. Soc. Am., 42:229-37.

With B. Gutenberg. Progress Report, Seismological Laboratory, California Institute of Technology, for 1951. Trans. Am. Geophys. Union, 33:759-62.

1953

Seismographs: engineers and architects. Sphere, 1:9-11.

Earthquakes. Eng. Sci., 17:13-18.

With B. Gutenberg and C. F. Richter. Progress Report, Seismological Laboratory, California Institute of Technology, 1952. Trans. Am. Geophys. Union, 34:785-91.

1954

Orogenesis and deep crustal structure—additional evidence from seismology. Bull. Geol. Soc. Am., 65:385-400.

With B. Gutenberg and C. F. Richter. Progress Report, Seismological Laboratory, California Institute of Technology, 1953. Trans. Am. Geophys. Union, 35:979-87.

1955

Seismic evidence for crustal structure and tectonic activity. In: *Crust of the Earth,* ed. by Arie Poldervaart. Geological Society of America Special Paper No. 62, pp. 61-74. (Symposium.)

Earthquake seismographs and associated instruments. In: *Advances in Geophysics,* ed. by Helmut Eric Landsberg, Vol. II. New York, Academic Press, Inc.

With B. Gutenberg and C. F. Richter. Progress Report, Seismological Laboratory, California Institute of Technology, 1954. Trans. Am. Geophys. Union, 36:713-18.

With B. Gutenberg, C. F. Richter, and others. *Earthquakes in Kern County, California, during 1952.* Prepared under the direction of Olaf P. Jenkins, ed. by Gordon B. Oakeshott. State of California Division of Mines, Bulletin 171. (Symposium.)

Earthquakes in Kern County, California, during 1952. State of California Division of Mines, Bulletin 171. Reprint containing: General introduction to seismology, by V. H. Benioff and B. Gutenberg, pp. 131-35; Seismic development in California, by V. H. Benioff, pp. 147-51; Mechanism and strain characteristics of the White Wolf fault as indicated by the aftershock sequence, by V. H. Benioff, pp. 199-202; and Relation of the White Wolf fault to the regional tectonic pattern, by V. H. Benioff, pp. 203-4.

1956

With B. Gutenberg. *An Investigation of Microseisms.* Final report under Contract No. AF 19(122)436, Cambridge Research Center Report TR-56-257, United States Air Force. 42 pp.

With B. Gutenberg, F. Press, and C. F. Richter. Progress Report, Seismological Laboratory, California Institute of Technology, 1955. Trans. Am. Geophys. Union, 37:232-38.

1957

With B. Gutenberg, F. Press, and C. F. Richter. Progress Report, Seismological Laboratory of the California Institute of Technology, 1956. Trans. Am. Geophys. Union, 38:248-54.

1958

With Beno Gutenberg, Frank Press, and C. F. Richter. Progress Report, Seismological Laboratory of the California Institute of Technology, 1957. Trans. Am. Geophys. Union, 39:721-25.

With Markus Båth. The aftershock sequence of the Kamchatka earthquake of November 4, 1952. Bull. Seismol. Soc. Am., 48:1-15.

With F. Press. Progress report on long period seismographs. Geophysical Journal, 1:208-15.

Long period waves observed in the Kamchatka earthquake of November 4, 1952. J. Geophys. Res., 63:589-93.

Earthquakes. In: *Frontiers in Science,* ed. by Edward Hutchings, Jr., pp. 130-40. New York, Basic Books, Inc.

1959

Circum-Pacific tectonics. In: *The Mechanics of Faulting, with Special Reference to the Fault-Plane Work,* ed. by John H. Hodgson. (Symposium.) Publications of the Dominion Observatory, Vol. XX, pp. 395-402.

Fused quartz extensometer for secular tidal and seismic strains. Bull. Geol. Soc. Am., 70:1019-32.

With J. C. Harrison, L. La Coste, W. H. Munk, and L. B. Slichter. Searching for the earth's free oscillations. J. Geophys. Res., 64:1334-37.

1960

Long period seismographs. Bull. Seismol. Soc. Am., 50:1-13.

Observations of geomagnetic fluctuations in the period range 0.3 to 120 seconds. J. Geophys. Res., 65:1413-22.

1961

With R. L. Forward, S. Smith, J. Weber, and D. Zipoy. Upper limit for interstellar millicycle gravitational radiation. Nature, 189:473.

With F. Press and S. Smith. Excitation of the free oscillations of the Earth by earthquakes. J. Geophys. Res., 66:605-19.

With James N. Brune and Maurice Ewing. Long-period surface

waves from the Chilean earthquakes of May 22, 1960, recorded on linear strain seismographs.　J. Geophys. Res., 66:2895-2910.

1962

Movements on major transcurrent faults.　Chapter IV in: *Continental Drift*, ed. by S. K. Runcorn. New York, Academic Press, Inc. (Vol. 3 of the International Geophysics Series.)

1963

Source wave forms of three earthquakes.　Bull. Seismol. Soc. Am., 53:893-903.

1964

Earthquake source mechanisms.　Science, 143:1399-1406.

Edwin G. Boring

EDWIN GARRIGUES BORING

October 23, 1886–July 1, 1968

BY S. S. STEVENS

THROUGHOUT HIS LATER DECADES, Edwin Garrigues Boring had so clearly earned the title "Mr. Psychology" that it became his by popular acclaim. His death in his eighty-second year brought to a close a long and varied career as experimenter, editor, historian, administrator, and counselor to all and sundry. The immense drive that had given energy and surge to all his projects kept him going to the end, even against the ravages of myeloma, with its entailment of fragile and broken bones and its attendant pain and frustration. Seldom has a man fought to stay alive with such zest and humor, or shed such tears of heartbreak over the defeat of the spirit by the failing flesh. To those around him, it was like watching an Olympian brought down.

Boring was born in Philadelphia on October 23, 1886, missing by only twenty-four hours the anniversary he liked to call Fechner Day to commemorate the inspiration that struck the father of psychophysics as he lay abed on October 22, 1850. Boring joined a clan of ten relatives ranging from three older sisters to a great-grandfather and a maiden great-great-aunt. There were strong, vigorous women in the large household and they turned it into a matriarchy laced with high Quaker purpose. Churchgoing and the "plain language" *thee* and *thy* featured the early years of Garry Boring, as he came to be called. His father belonged to the Moravian Church, but the maternal Garrigues, of Huguenot extraction, set the Quaker tone. The large family lived above and next door to the drug store in which Father Boring compounded prescriptions in partnership with a Garrigues whose granddaughter he had married.

Was it from that family milieu that Boring acquired his high sense of fair play and his determined striving for honesty and objectivity? It is easy to credit the environment. Too easy, perhaps, for by the mere act of noting the family circumstances the biographer half implies that cause has been traced and that personality and temperament stand explained. But what would sociogenesis predict for the youngest child and only son of a druggist, raised in a God-conscious matriarchy? Meekness perhaps? Or submissiveness? Those were surely not the traits of the Boring any of us knew. The genes must have laid the template for the rugged, energetic, dynamic mesomorph whose sheer drive and stamina remained to me an awesome phenomenon throughout thirty-seven years of almost daily association.

We can readily picture the strenuous boy taxing the female household with what was called his "excitability." The women thought him too excitable to send to school until he was nine. Especially when a boy his own age came to visit would the excitement break out. The romping and childish violence would then exceed decorous bounds. He has said that he was starved for playmates, being forbidden to join the boys on the street, but no signs of the apathy of starvation showed up in him. The task of tethering such an energized, muscular youngster could not have been easy.

At last he entered the first grade, oversized and three years senior to the other beginners in the Orthodox Quaker school. He had learned few of the games and sports that most nine-year-olds have mastered, nor did he have much natural aptitude for coordinated dexterity. His movements all his life were abrupt, energetic, and impetuous. His handwriting was jerky. It was as though more energy was dammed up behind each impulsive movement than his muscles could readily control.

Young Boring's need to excel, frustrated on the playing field, found its outlet in the classroom where he quickly made up the years of schooling he had missed. The capacities of the maturing bright mind had not been dulled by the absence of teachers. Left to himself in play, he had invented his own games and conjured up his own playmates. He discovered the magic of magnetic forces acting at a distance and the mysteries of the electric current. It was a constrained and deprived environment for a spirited boy, but imagination made it rich and energy kept it active.

Winding up his schooldays in a private Quaker high school, he stood near the top of his class and had made an extra-curricular mark on the debating team and the school paper. Boring the writer was already beginning to show.

CORNELL UNIVERSITY

Engineering was what he wanted next, although later he knew it would have been physics if he had understood the difference. Anyhow, with his father's support to the tune of $50 a month, he went to Cornell for an M.E. degree, conferred in 1908, and then on to a job with the Bethlehem Steel Company at 18 cents an hour. Work for pay brought the heady feeling of independence, reinforced by a new-found social life among the young Moravian group in Bethlehem, Pennsylvania. But the threat of a promotion put the real issue into focus. He wanted something and steel-mill engineering was not it. So he quit.

He next tried teaching science in a Moravian parochial

school, but he was then in what he liked to call his 133-pound phase, and discipline broke down when some of the larger boys glued him to his chair with a coat of fresh shellac. The rigors of teaching drove him back to Cornell for an A.M. degree. He might have stayed with physics, but the siren memory of his course with E. B. Titchener, taken four years earlier, led him to the psychology laboratory, where Madison Bentley, then in charge of the animal work, gave him the push of encouragement that toppled him into psychology in the fall of 1910. By February of the next term he had won himself an assistantship at $500 a year, so he struck out for a Ph.D. degree and captured it in 1914 with a thesis on visceral sensitivity, based largely on the stimulation of his own alimentary canal by means of stomach tubes which he learned to swallow with consummate skill. As one of the required minor subjects for the Ph.D., Boring submitted his physiological study of the regeneration of a nerve in his own forearm, which he had cut in order to trace, in a four-year study, the precise course of the return of sensibility.

The brilliant, outspoken, domineering Titchener fascinated Boring almost as much as psychology itself. Boring set high appraisal on his debt to Titchener, whom he regarded as a close approximation to genius. But Titchener's debt to Boring may stand even higher, for it is Boring's accounts that have brought Titchener back to life and defined the role of his structural psychology—a psychology based on the examination of mental contents under laboratory control. Boring was pupil, Titchener was master, but the pupil with a mind of his own was not really a Titchenerian in the "school" sense, and his despair of equaling the master was no better founded than the many other insecurities that plagued him. The "uncultured engineer" became the more accomplished writer, certainly, for the pupil was brisk and gay and pointed where the master was solemn and often pedantic. The real difference lay, I think, not in their erudition or their capacities, but in their attitudes. The master wrote for himself, whereas the pupil wrote for the reader. Egoism, as Boring liked to say, is the enemy of style.

An instructorship at $1000 a year made independence sufficiently secure for marriage. The fiancée of two-and-a-half years' standing, Lucy M. Day, had started psychology at Mount Holyoke College and had taken her Ph.D. degree at Cornell in 1912. The marriage of June 18, 1914, was followed by the first of four children on January 11, 1916, which, being Titchener's birthday, was deemed a happy omen all around.

Then came World War I. The birth of a second son put Boring beyond the reach of the draft, but he wanted to be in on the action. He volunteered and was commissioned a Captain in the Medical Department of the Army, where the big thing for psychologists was the mental testing program, the vast assessment effort that startled the nation by revealing that the average recruit had a mental age of thirteen years. R. M. Yerkes was the ranking officer in charge, and after the Armistice of 1918 he invited Boring to Washington to help compile, analyze, and edit the huge report on the test results.

The war period was an active and happy one for those psychologists, for there was purpose in the air and they had a contribution to make. The days were filled with hard work and good fellowship. The Medical Department was a mounted service, and Boring added to the esprit by riding about his places of business on a horse. He also acquired a high respect for the wisdom and scientific honesty of the mental testers, a coterie held to stand outside the bounds of psychology by the Titchener in-group. In the inevitable arguments that arose concerning the nature of intelligence, Boring was later to cut through to the core with his sharp operational phrase, "Intelligence is what the tests test."

His reputation was growing—"Boring is my best student," Titchener had certified—and options for new jobs opened up. He could have gone to Minnesota at $3000, but an offer of $2500 to lecture at Harvard for a year and await the inspection of William McDougall, due from England in 1920, pleased him more. Harvard psychology, vulgarized by Hugo Münsterberg, needed to be dragged back into science and made worthy of its place in the nation's oldest university, or so it seemed. Anyhow, Boring moved his family to Cambridge, but before the lectures began there came an invitation from psychologist-president G. Stanley Hall offering $3000 a year for a three-year appointment at Clark University. It was a graduate-school appointment, not unlike that held by Titchener himself, and too good to be refused.

All went well at Clark until Hall retired, to be succeeded by a new president to whom geography, not psychology, was the favored discipline. That and the so-called Clark controversy, a brouhaha touched off by the overreaction of the new president to the postwar red scare, led to such a falling out that when Harvard beckoned once again in 1922 the call was answered, this time for keeps. He started as Associate Professor at $5500. A Stanford offer of $6500 tempted him, as later did also an offer from Princeton of $5000, and even an offer to succeed Titchener at Cornell at $6500, but Boring was determined to stick it out at difficult Harvard where the problem then was to rescue psychology from its near oblivion in the Department of Philosophy. Psychology achieved departmental status twelve years later, in 1934.

His Harvard career was almost stifled at the outset when

Boring, struck by a car on a rainy night, was made to lie in a hospital for six weeks with a fractured skull. The concussion enriched the experience of this omnivorous psychologist, for it gave him the vivid firsthand feel of amnesia. He talked with visitors, but within moments he forgot what he had said. In a book written a decade later he raised the question whether a person who converses intelligently, yet a few moments later has no memory of the substance of the conversation, can be said to be conscious. That query was part of his lifelong effort to analyze the meaning of the basic concepts of psychology.

My first encounter with Boring occurred in 1931. Having forgone my admission to the Harvard Medical School and having registered in the School of Education, I wandered over to Boring's office on the third floor of Emerson Hall to see what the author of a highly acclaimed history book might look like. His rotund bulk—he was 5 feet 7 inches tall and weighed more than 200 pounds—was wedged between desk and typewriter in one of the smallest rooms in the building. The laboratory secretary, her $1000 salary paid out of Boring's pocket in the early years, guarded the entrance from a niche in what had been a hallway.

Psychology, I learned, was a one-professor enterprise, but what a professor! You sat down and the conversation turned on. A liberal education flowed forth as Boring's erudition illuminated whatever issue arose. Talking seemed on his part as natural as breathing, perhaps the easiest form of breathing, and it was easy for a graduate student to acquire the habit of dropping in with a question or two. But that would not do. Boring was a busy man. He had to defend himself eventually by blowing up at my casual encroachment on his time. That was the first of many blow-ups—and reconciliations—that we were to share. A full head of indignation was a memorable spectacle in a personality of such intensity. But he liked the man who would have it out, apologize, shake hands, and go on again. You gained nothing with him by abandoning the field of battle.

Boring at forty-five was still giving the "systematic course" in the manner of his mentor, for Titchener, like Wundt, had conceived it the professor's duty to present a cycle of lectures that systematically reviewed the literature and gave the references for all that lay within experimental psychology.

The line of descent from Wundt to Titchener to Boring was more than direct, it resembled successive incarnations— three powerful men who dominated their respective scenes by force of will and sweep of activity. Titchener interpreted Wundt to America, translating his Teutonic volumes and finding himself engulfed in new editions that made the translating start over again. Boring, ever fascinated by the phenomenon of Titchener, interpreted him to the world through sketches and vivid anecdotes. All three men were short vigorous mesomorphs. All three found writing a congenial form of daily endeavor. All three became laboratory directors who did not themselves experiment, but who cultivated the scientific outlook and gave their students that greatest of benefactions: sound criticism of their work.

By 1932 instruction in psychology had outgrown the systematic course, or at least the ability of one man, even a Boring, to give it. For the next few years parts of it were passed around among the staff, with the inevitable uneven success, and then in 1939 the proseminar for first-year graduate students was started. Boring led off with history and systems and other members of the staff came on later. That heavy course, with assignments of about 150 pages per week, kept the incoming students highly motivated for twenty-seven years. As Edgar Pierce Professor Emeritus, Boring continued until 1966 to appear by special invitation and to charm the younger scholars with his vignettes from psychology's past.

HISTORIAN AND DIRECTOR

It was not only Boring's massive erudition, it was also his vivid and concrete style that made his *History of Experimental Psychology* the enduring classic in its field. Boring made ideas stand up and seem to walk as they contended, evolved, and faded in the inexorable march of the *Zeitgeist*. When the book was published late in 1929 it met an eager reception, for the world of psychology knew that Boring was doing a history. The book's foundations had been laid in a summer course that he gave in 1924 at the University of California at Berkeley. He had later taken sabbatical leave for a semester in order to finish the writing job, and had circulated a printed card announcing that, although he would remain in Cambridge, he would be out of reach to visitors.

With the first copies of the *History* in circulation, the mail bulged with enthusiasm. Delightful, delightful, delightful— that word recurred in letter after letter from appreciative colleagues. "Thee does express thyself well," wrote his sister Alice from her post at Yenching University. What gave delight was the reader's discovery that dull old academic history could be dressed in lively phrases with no sacrifice of erudition.

With a best-selling *History* off the press, the author could have drunk deeply of satisfaction had he not been EGB, who mistrusted his own successes, often rationalizing them as failures. Writing history was library work, not science, was one thought. Boring may now be lost to science was another. And peering out from behind his shroud of chronic insecurity he had a sharp eye for the evidences of his failure to meet his own compulsive standards. I recall that a few years later, with a volume on *Hearing* recently published, I was mulling over one of the scathing reviews it had received, when Boring sought to comfort me by showing me a review of the *History* that had quite deflated him a few years earlier. It was an enormously long and detailed review and it seemed to me generous withal. But to Boring it seemed a list of his blunders, and he found no solace in the reviewer's praise.

The 1920s and 1930s were the edgy, competitive decades. The focus of Boring's boundless drive was then on personal achievement. He hoped for a smashing success, but seemed somehow to stand half in fear of it, for how would he be sure it was genuine? Yet he chafed when the philosophers in the Department, there being no psychologist to judge him, let him remain for six years as an associate professor while his peers elsewhere were moving up. He fretted over the impossibility of knowing who was boss of the Psychological Laboratory until H. S. Langfeld moved off to Princeton in 1924 and Boring was made director. He fussed about there being only half of L. T. Troland at Harvard, while the other half was trying to put color into motion pictures at the Technicolor Company. Then Troland died in 1932. At the beginning of the Harvard period, William McDougall was on the scene, senior by some fifteen years to Boring, but McDougall seems to have kept his distance and finally to have fled to Duke University in 1927. With McDougall gone, psychology at Harvard could have hung out a sign reading "EGB, prop., 80 hours per week," for Boring was now in full charge and his work schedule equaled that of two men.

Life was not placid on the third floor of Emerson Hall with the 80-hour week setting the standard of effort, and with a compulsive need for well-planned order dictating the operation of curriculum and laboratory. Some people resisted the organized, meticulous demands of a director who filled the calendar with weekly staff meetings—woe to him who should miss one!

—and who kept elaborate accounts, balanced to the penny, both for the laboratory and for his own funds. When he was called upon in later years to verify something connected with his income tax, the men in the tax office stared in disbelief at the detail of his records. Others in the laboratory found fascination in watching a whirlwind of energy exert a breathless push to keep up with all the jobs that can pile in on a willing academic. For Boring was generous with his energy, spending it freely on students and colleagues, dispensing counsel, rewriting their paragraphs, advising them about courses, and finding them jobs and opportunities.

But over everything hung insecurity. Becoming president of the American Psychological Association in 1928, the year he became a full professor, seemed but a natural and just reward for years of service as secretary and council member. Election to the National Academy of Sciences in 1932 brought a burst of pleasure, but it did little to dampen the pervading sense of urgency, the goading and the gnawing. The gnawing was there in a literal sense, for his duodenal ulcer periodically ate its way through to hemorrhage and landed him in bed with internal bleeding. Frequent eating to quiet the ulcer had become the regimen following the unpleasantness at Clark University, and the Boring of 1930 weighed almost a hundred pounds more than the Boring of 1920. Until forbidden by medical fiat, his chain smoking had littered the laboratory with ashes and empty cans. He bought Lord Salisbury cigarettes 5000 at a time, packed 100 to a round tin. Those cigarette cans served many purposes around the laboratory, everything from ashtrays to parts bins and apparatus stands. Boring again took up smoking later on, this time in order to prove that he was master and could take it or leave it as he chose. Shortly thereafter he gave it up for good.

Book writing seldom lay for long in the background. After

the *History* came *The Physical Dimensions of Consciousness,* a treatise designed to show how psychology can get along without the traditional cleavage between mind and body—including the dualistic cleavage inherent in Titchener's psychophysical parallelism. Although the book showed that Boring in 1932 had departed far from the Titchenerian tradition, it was not so much a declaration of intellectual independence as an effort to achieve clarity for the meaning of the basic terms of psychology, terms like consciousness, sensation, and the rest. It was then, in 1932, that Boring paid me, a green graduate student, the high compliment of asking me to read the manuscript. Chapter by chapter I worked through it, a bit overeager, perhaps. We discussed many issues at his bedside, for the ulcer was acting up again. Neither of us, it seems, was wholly satisfied with some of the arguments. Boring knew whereof he sought escape, but at that stage he was too entangled in his past to effect a clean restatement. I sensed what he was driving at, but I was too inexperienced to see how the text could be made to strike closer to the target. Boring was later to call it his "immature book," one that was written a couple of years too soon, for some of the research that he was directing was soon to clarify the relation between tonal sensation and its four attributes: pitch, loudness, volume, and density. Then in 1935 a series of papers on operationism began to appear, and it now seems clear that an operational restatement of psychology's basic concepts was Boring's real aim. The papers appeared under my name, but it can be proved from page upon page of editorial criticism that large segments of those papers were generated more by Boring than by me.

CRITICISM

It is hard to portray the vigor and thoroughness with which Boring would criticize and rewrite the amateurish manuscripts of some of us beginners. Take as an example my 1935 paper on "The Operational Basis of Psychology." The final draft, the fourth, ran to 4000 words. Not counting his handwritten emendations in each revision of the text, Boring's comments and criticisms ran to 8000 words. You were not always favored with a 2-to-1 ratio, but in that instance the paper needed a double-barreled blast. Let me cite a few excerpts from those yellowing sheets of critical comment, for they show what an apprenticeship under a sharp and unstinting master could be like.

"p. 1, 2, 3. Drivel and hot air. Every psychologist knows all about this. Who wants to listen to you say it all over again.

"And condense! You write as if words were cheap. Young authors ought to have to pay $8 a page out of their own pockets for publication. Then they'd learn to make words count.

"p. 6. You must cut out the flamboyant. Example: 'One wonders why an urgent reform of this sort came through physics when psychology needed it so badly.' (a) You have no time for daydreaming and wonderment when composition costs somebody $5 a page. (b) You have to be pretty ignorant to do any sincere wondering. Psychology is a crazy little new hick science, and the idea that a general scientific reform affecting physics would come through psychology is preposterous.

"The First Person Singular. You use *I, my, me* in the part I have deleted. Let me lay down the law.

"The FPS is egoistic. There is no harm in egoism; it is one of your personal assets and it furnishes you with your personal drive. But, like the sex instinct, you have got to suppress it in public, except when you sincerely think it is wanted."

"First let me talk about the nature of the job of criticism. I have spent 10 hours on what I present to you up to here . . . in my study, behind a closed door, with the warning signal on outside, and in concentrated, rather nervous (and I am afraid you will think irritable) attention. I want you to know just what you ask for when you ask for criticism.

"Do I have to go into such detail? I do not know how else to do it. To tell you that you are verbose does no good. I told you that about your introduction and you wrote another just as bad. To say 'be succinct,' etc., means not enough. Such tricks have to be illustrated, and therefore I have to get the mood of a paragraph every now and then and write the paragraph for you. (I suppose an artist teaches painting in the same difficult way.)

"I want you to come near exhausting your own skill before you come to me for this sort of aid."

A later paper on operationism, this one aimed at the journal *Philosophy of Science,* evoked only some 2000 words of criticism. Boring finally approved the paper, but he warned about the reaction to be expected from the philosophers on the first floor of Emerson Hall. His final paragraph read:

"It is a good paper. But I have this slight reservation, because I know it is epistemology and that neither you nor I is an epistemologist. And I have observed that my brightest and best epistemological ideas meet nothing but yawns from my colleagues below decks. I never know why. I still think I'm bright, but I know they do not; and so I distrust myself. But in writing to other dumbheads (= psychologists) I am not inferior; I know I seem bright to them. So why not you too?"

That was in September 1935. In October Boring was deep in one of his recurrent tussles with Gestalt psychology. On October 8 he wrote me a brief note.

"What a time I am having with Koffka. I promised to review him [for *Psychological Bulletin*], and for the last ten days I have done nothing but read and make notes. Meanwhile I chafe because I do not get to something more important. I have just this minute finished p. 528 and am 77% done. This is dull, tedious; but I itch to write the review. I hope to say something about Gestalt psychology which is really informing, and also something general about system writing.

"I write to preempt you as chief critic. . . . You and I have a common systematic faith. (Operational definition of many of Koffka's terms would ruin him.)

"You are drafted then. Wait on me! I don't know when. But this is to work you up to the right humor."

Four days later, on Saturday, October 12, he sent me the review together with a note:

"Well I got through reading Koffka Thursday, wrote this review hot yesterday [Friday], revised it today, and now it's ready for you. I did not expect to be this far so soon. After almost three weeks struggling through the book, it did not seem possible to write the review [5300 words] in a day; but I did, finishing it at 1 AM.

"The review is not so important as I had hoped it would be. I was going to discuss the fundamental principles of system-making and apply them to Gestalt psychology, and do some other nice things of that sort. The present length of the review made me abandon that plan, and it would not be fair to take the stage from Koffka, since a review should primarily depict him. So you need not look for epoch-making paragraphs, because they are not there."

On the contrary, the review produced some great paragraphs, or so it seemed to me, especially as it subjected some of Koffka's concepts to a well-reasoned test of their operational meaning.

COLLABORATION

Despite all the rewriting and reworking of papers that we managed on each other's behalf, our names appear together on just two papers, only one of which was a scientific effort. It was a point of honor with Boring that he would put his name on a paper only if he was the major contributor. And how he scorned those senior workers who use their position to force their names onto the papers of their juniors!

Our one collaboration, in 1935, concerned the problem of the auditory attribute called tonal brightness. It was Boring's idea that with the laboratory's newly acquired miracles, a cathode-ray oscilloscope and a sharply tuned wave-analyzer, we might be able to settle a long-standing question concerning the bright and dull tones that can be produced with a siren whose holes are appropriately spaced. What we found was that tonal brightness turns out to be essentially the same as tonal density, but that is another story. The point here is that, when we came to write up the experiments, Boring disclaimed co-authorship, saying it was my expertness with the apparatus that produced the results. I argued that his were the ideas that initiated and guided the study, and I vowed to do nothing about publication if I had to do it alone. With the argument deadlocked, and both of us in a stubborn humor, several weeks passed before Boring, who could tolerate no job unfinished, dropped by again one afternoon and said, "See here, aren't we being childish?"

Boring never quite abandoned his hope that he could make a student what he called literate, meaning capable of conversing in writing. Notes, comments, observations, instructions, banter of all varieties streamed from his typewriter on small scraps of paper, or the backs of old library cards. We would find them in our pigeonholes at the top of the stairs. Boring wanted us to reciprocate, of course, but my own painfully penned missives were cramped and few. He said I should learn to type. I did. I typed several papers and the better part of a book, but whereas Boring could sit at the typewriter bolt upright, looking more than anything like the classic portrait of Brahms at the clavier, I slouched and slumped and finally slipped back into longhand. Boring, a 4-5-2 on the somatotype scales, was too low in the third component to empathize fully with introverted impediments.

If I dwell on these personal relations, it is to try to exhibit the full dimensions of the versatile, strenuous, high-principled Professor of Psychology. Graduate students or instructors could seldom gather for five minutes before the conversation turned to the latest doings or sayings of the Chief, as he was then often called. He loomed so large in the life of the laboratory that all else shrank by comparison. It seemed to me then that he could do anything, achieve anything, if only he would stop worrying about all the details. But worry is the hallmark of insecurity and frustration.

By his forty-seventh year, Boring stood ready to try any remedy that promised relief from his deep sense of defeat, even psychoanalysis, with its five sessions per week and its threat of added financial insecurity. Unsatisfied with the first analyst he tried, he turned to Hanns Sachs, a kindly soul who reminded him of Titchener. Boring was never sure that psycho-analysis gave him his money's worth (cost: $1680, at half price), but the harm done was at least no more than pecuniary. Watching from the sidelines, I could detect no obvious changes as he threw himself into one job after another with his full frantic vigor. Some years later, in a published symposium, both he and his analyst undertook to analyze the analysis. Both analyst and patient acknowledged that the personality emerged unchanged.

PSYCHOLOGY ONE

Prominent among the annual chores was the introductory psychology course. "Psychology One" it was destined to be called when television taped it in 1956 in order to charm and instruct its audiences. As course assistant in the 1930s, I witnessed the careful planning and the intense concern that went into each lecture. There were many great moments in the course. Boring's mimicking of the expressions of emotion as outlined by Darwin was one highlight, and no one could outperform his portrayal of the complete shrug. The renowned indifference of the Harvard undergraduate disintegrated under the gay onslaught of a short, bear-shaped man bubbling with facts and ideas, the whole of it spiced by demonstrations. The large lecture room known as Emerson D was usually full to overflowing, and the batting average ran around .500 for a burst of applause at the end of the hour.

Solid stuff went into Boring's lectures: the basic physics of light and sound, the structure and physiology of the sense organs, the principles of perceptual constancy, the illusions, the facts of learning, the nature of reflex action, the physiology of emotion, and many other topics that taxed the understanding of the undergraduate.

Although he had small regard for the writing of elementary texts, a distraction from the main business of science, he collaborated with H. S. Langfeld and H. P. Weld in the editing of a series of textbooks, widely known as the BLW texts. They were pitched at a level that challenged undergraduates in the Ivy League and the other colleges that have relatively high standards of admission, and they sold well in those places. But they represented no newsstand psychology. The first volume, appearing in 1935 and called *Psychology: A Factual Textbook,* gave no quarter in its attempt to marshal what psychology knows, as opposed to its opinions and its conversational theories. A new text, much rearranged, appeared in 1939, and a final one, greatly enlarged, appeared in 1948. Although the separate chapters of the various BLW's were contributed by specialists, their drafts went through the homogenizing process of a Boring-type editing, so that the final text had a uniformity of style seldom achieved in a collaboration.

During World War II Boring turned his skills to another group endeavor—the production of a popular book on military psychology, one that might speak to the common soldier. Now, a man of Boring's perspicacity could see that no level of "academic" writing, no toning down or talking down, would capture attention and keep the soldier reading if he picked up the book in a Post Exchange. It had to be done in a popular style, in the true meaning of that term. It demanded short sentences, concrete examples, brisk paragraphs, all of it talking straight to the reader. Few academics can switch from one style to another, but through two editions of *Psychology for the Fighting Man* Boring teamed up with a science writer and proved his ability to command a style that peddled the facts of psychology through the sale of some 380,000 copies. The royalties accrued to the sponsor, the National Research Council.

At the other end of the audience spectrum stands the specialist in a scientific discipline. When you write history for his eye, the style may safely move up the scale of difficulty, for the expert will pounce on the fact rather than the expression. Boring's often-expressed diffidence about tackling the history of the experimental specialties in psychology rested on his conviction that his knowledge could not equal that of the devotee. Nevertheless he resolved to try his hand at the history of sensation and perception. The book was delivered in 1942 to a world at war and little concerned with scholarship. Never very popular by market standards, the book has nevertheless proved its usefulness. The specialist rejoices to have it at hand.

NEW VENTURES

In 1949, having completed twenty-five years as director of the Psychological Laboratory, first in the top floors of Emerson

Hall and, after 1946, in the basement of Memorial Hall, Boring persuaded the Dean to accept his resignation. Thereupon began what by his own judgment were to become the best years of his life. The tasks ahead were the things he liked best and did best. In his sixties and seventies his successes finally caught up with his aspirations, but without seeming in the slightest to diminish his drive or to blunt the edge of his ever-probing curiosity.

In 1950 there appeared a new and much enlarged edition of the *History of Experimental Psychology,* whose first edition had appeared in 1929. The new volume became a classic, replacing a classic, for in the new edition Boring showed even more clearly how the *Zeitgeist* operates on Great Men, and how they in turn lend their names to the forward steps of science, providing the tags with which we learn to sort out and remember history.

The purchase in 1951 of an old farmstead at Harborside, Maine, where the Borings had for some two decades been regular summer visitors, was the beginning of a happy, active rustication that filled the summers with the challenge of endless projects indoors and out, and provided a study where Boring's indispensable typewriter and dictation machine could be kept busy at least half the day. Children and grandchildren enlivened Harborside, and Frank Boring, like his father also a psychologist, became the sailor of the family.

Another challenge that spiced his seventies was the founding and editing of *Contemporary Psychology,* a journal devoted solely to book reviews. Seldom has a fresh venture started life under such competent ministrations. Certainly, few new publications could boast a greater accumulation of editorial experience—or sagacious good sense. For in addition to all his other "editings," Boring had for thirty years served in one or another capacity as an editor of the *American Journal of Psy-*

chology, the world's oldest journal in the field. But the challenge of the new publication lay not so much in editing per se as in molding a new medium to a high criterion of urbanity and interest. The tone was set on the editorial page, "CP Speaks," where psychologists were treated to editorial pronouncements that blended Boring's brand of wit and wisdom. Boring found it great fun, so much fun that he suffered keen disappointment at the end of his six-year term when his age of seventy-five was judged too great for appointment to another term. As it turned out, he would have made it through, just barely. Instead, he turned to other business, mostly writing, editing, and lecturing.

And of course there were honors to be received. Clark University, whose president had rebuffed him in 1922 as a supposed subversive during a red scare, invited him to return thirty-four years later for an honorary degree. The next year, 1957, the small, select Society of Experimental Psychologists, of which Boring was a charter member, held a special dinner in his honor, an occasion on which contributions from many students and colleagues were presented to Harvard to start the Boring Library Fund. "Thank you all," he wrote, "not only for what you have done, but also for not waiting until I was dead!" That was the year of his retirement, but only in the sense that he dropped from the regular payroll. Activity did not falter, and when the psychologists moved into the new William James Hall in 1964-1965 he was given space and facilities with which to carry on.

A grand occasion for him and all his many friends was the American Psychological Association meeting of 1959 when the Gold Medal was bestowed upon him as a "psychologist whose lifetime career has made a truly distinguished contribution."

PERSPECTIVE

Boring managed to be all things to psychology, perhaps the last great universalist of the profession, beloved by biotrope and sociotrope alike. "Mr. Psychology" he was indeed, with energy and interest to lavish on every aspect of his calling. He performed its humblest chores and held its highest offices. He excelled as teacher, historian, critic, editor, expositor, and statesman. It was he who in 1943 chaired the committee that put the American Psychological Association together in its present unified form. And his effectiveness extended beyond psychology, to such things as the chairmanship of the Publications Committee of the American Philosophical Society, to which Boring was elected in 1945.

"A hodgepodge of a life" was his modest phrase for it, and such it might seem if we focus only on the catalogue of his pursuits. Why, his letter writing alone would fill the working day of any ordinary man, for he conversed with psychologists the world over—a stream of correspondence that ran to about a thousand letters a year, with seldom a letter of only one page. Many of those letters contain masterful discussions of a principle or an idea. Many glow with warmth and gay humor. All are literate.

A hodgepodge indeed! Many facets perhaps, but a constellation of polished facets is what makes a gem.

Take any facet of Boring and it shines. His prodigious output touched so many people in such varied ways that his public enjoyed no single consensus regarding the true nature of the man. There was Boring the incisive biographer, Boring the champion of women in psychology, Boring the maker of aphorisms, Boring the resolver of the moon illusion, Boring the defender of justice, Boring the advocate of scientific controls, Boring the philosopher of science. The list goes on and on. Where is the unity in all this? What structure held the facets of the gem in place?

A tremendous human being stood behind those many manifestations, the kind of human being that nature does not often contrive as it sorts the genes into the configurations that determine the shape of life. It seems most unlikely that a person like Boring could have begun as an empty organism (to use his phrase) waiting for experience to wire it up for action. His was a constitution highly endowed with muscle and brain, and with a vast capacity for intense feeling and deep emotion. Credit the environment for the content (but not the quality) of his thought. Credit Bentley for enticing him out of physics and into psychology. Credit Harvard's need of rescue for his many years in Cambridge. Such are the accidents that shape the content, but the happenstance of existence provides no explanation for the enduring invariance of energy and action that we witness in Edwin Garrigues Boring.

BIBLIOGRAPHY

KEY TO ABBREVIATIONS

Am. J. Phys. = American Journal of Physics
Am. J. Psychol. = American Journal of Psychology
Am. Psychol. = American Psychologist
Am. Scientist = American Scientist
Contemp. Psychol. = Contemporary Psychology
J. Abnormal Social Psychol. = Journal of Abnormal and Social Psychology
J. Hist. Behav. Sci. = Journal of the History of the Behavioral Sciences
Proc. Am. Phil. Soc. = Proceedings of the American Philosophical Society
Proc. ——— Internat. Congr. Psychol. = Proceedings of the ——— International Congress of Psychology
Psychol. Bull. = Psychological Bulletin
Psychol. Rev. = Psychological Review

1912

With M. Bentley and C. A. Ruckmick. New apparatus for acoustical experiments. Am. J. Psychol., 23:509-16.
Note on the negative reaction under light-adaptation in the planarian. Journal of Animal Behavior, 2:229-48.

1913

Introspection in dementia precox. Am. J. Psychol., 24:145-70.
The course and character of learning in dementia precox. Bulletin of the Government Hospital for the Insane, 5:51-79.
Learning in Dementia Precox: A Study from the Psychological Laboratory of the Government Hospital for the Insane, Washington, D.C. (Psychological Monographs, Vol. 15, No. 2.) Princeton, Psychological Review Co. iv + 101 pp.

1914

Method in the investigation of sensibility after the section of a cutaneous nerve: preliminary communication. Proceedings of the Society for Experimental Biology and Medicine, 11:69-71.
The marking system in theory. Pedagogical Seminary, 21:269-77.

1915

The sensations of the alimentary canal. Am. J. Psychol., 26:1-57.

The thermal sensitivity of the stomach. Am. J. Psychol., 26:485-94.

Processes referred to the alimentary tract: a qualitative analysis. Psychol. Rev., 22:306-31.

1916

The number of observations upon which a limen may be based. Am. J. Psychol., 27:315-19.

Cutaneous sensation after nerve-division. Quarterly Journal of Experimental Physiology, 10:1-95.

Capacity to report upon moving pictures as conditioned by sex and age: a contribution to the psychology of testimony. Journal of Criminal Law and Criminology, 6:820-34.

1917

Urban's tables and the method of constant stimuli. Am. J. Psychol., 28:280-93.

On the computation of the probable correctness of differences. Am. J. Psychol., 28:454-59.

A chart of the psychometric function. Am. J. Psychol., 28:465-70.

With Amy Luce. The psychological basis of appetite. Am. J. Psychol., 28:443-53.

With Lucy D. Boring. Temporal judgments after sleep. In: *Studies in Psychology, Contributed by Colleagues and Former Students of Edward Bradford Titchener,* pp. 255-79. Worcester, Mass., Louis N. Wilson.

1919

Mathematical vs. scientific significance. Psychol. Bull., 16:335-38.

Psychology. In: *Nelson's Loose-Leaf Encyclopedia.* New York, Thomas Nelson & Sons.

1920

The logic of the normal law of error in mental measurement. Am. J. Psychol., 31:1-33.

With E. B. Titchener. Sir Thomas Wrightson's theory of hearing. Am. J. Psychol., 31:101-13.

The control of attitude in psychophysical experiments. Psychol. Rev., 27:440-52.

Statistics of the American Psychological Association in 1920. Psychol. Bull., 17:271-78.

A priori use of the Gaussian law. Science, 52:129-30.

Predilection and sampling of human heights. Science, 52:464-66.

Intelligence. In: *Nelson's Loose-Leaf Encyclopedia*. New York, Thomas Nelson & Sons.

1921

The stimulus-error. Am. J. Psychol., 32:449-71.

Joint editor and author. *Psychological Examining in the United States Army*. Memoirs of the National Academy of Sciences, Vol. 15. Washington, U.S. Govt. Print. Off. v + 890 pp.

1922

Urban's tables again. Am. J. Psychol., 33:303-4, 450.

1923

With E. B. Titchener. A model for the demonstration of facial expression. Am. J. Psychol., 45:471-85.

Intelligence as the tests test it. New Republic, 34:34-37.

1924

Is there a generalized psychometric function? Am. J. Psychol., 35:75-78.

Attribute and sensation. Am. J. Psychol., 35:301-4.

Relation of the limen of dual impression to Head's theory of cutaneous sensibility. Proc. VIIth Internat. Congr. Psychol., pp. 57-62. Oxford, England. Cambridge, Cambridge University Press.

1926

Auditory theory with special reference to intensity, volume and localization. Am. J. Psychol., 37:157-88.

Scientific induction and statistics. Am. J. Psychol., 37:303-7.

With Helen Peak. The factor of speed in intelligence. Journal of Experimental Psychology, 9:71-94.

The paradox of psychic research. Atlantic Monthly, 137:81-87.

Anger. In: *Nelson's Loose-Leaf Encyclopedia*. New York, Thomas Nelson & Sons.

1927

Construction and calibration of Koenig cylinders. Am. J. Psychol., 38:125-27.

Empirical psychology. Am. J. Psychol., 38:475-77.

Edward Bradford Titchener. Am. J. Psychol., 38:489-506.

Problem of originality in science. Am. J. Psychol., 39:70-90.

The intensity of sensation. Proc. VIIIth Internat. Congr. Psychol., pp. 71-78. Groningen, Holland. Groningen, P. Noordhoff.

1928

A new system for the classification of odors. Am. J. Psychol., 40:345-49.

Demonstrational experiments in memory. Am. J. Psychol., 40:513-14.

Do American psychologists read European psychology? Am. J. Psychol., 40:674-75.

Did Fechner measure sensation? Psychol. Rev., 35:443-45.

Psychological necrology (1903-1927). Psychol. Bull., 25:302-5, 621-25.

1929

The psychology of controversy. Psychol. Rev., 36:97-121.

History of Experimental Psychology. New York, Century Company. xvi + 699 pp.

Discrimination. In: *Encyclopaedia Britannica,* 14th ed., Vol. 7, p. 420. Chicago, Encyclopaedia Britannica, Inc. Organic sensations, *ibid.,* Vol. 16, p. 897; Psychophysics, *ibid.,* Vol. 18, pp. 720-21; Edward Bradford Titchener, *ibid.,* Vol. 22, p. 252; Visceral sensations, *ibid.,* Vol. 23, p. 192.

1930

The *Gestalt* psychology and the *Gestalt* movement. Am. J. Psychol., 42:308-15.

A new ambiguous figure. Am. J. Psychol., 42:444-45.

The two-point limen and the error of localization. Am. J. Psychol., 42:446-49.

Psychology for eclectics. In: *Psychologies of 1930,* by Alfred Adler *et al.,* pp. 115-17. Worcester, Mass., Clark University Press.

1931

The psychologist's circle. Psychol. Rev., 38:177-82.

Behaviorism. In: *Nelson's Loose-Leaf Encyclopedia*. New York, Thomas Nelson & Sons.

1932

Max von Frey, 1852-1932. Am. J. Psychol., 44:584-86.

The physiology of consciousness. Science, 75:32-39.

Gestalt psychology. In: *Nelson's Loose-Leaf Encyclopedia*. New York, Thomas Nelson & Sons.

1933

The Physical Dimensions of Consciousness. New York, D. Appleton-Century Company, Inc. xii + 251 pp.

1934

With A. G. Ekdahl. The pitch of tonal masses. Am. J. Psychol., 46:452-55.

Edward Bradford Titchener. In: *Encyclopedia of the Social Sciences,* Vol. 7, pp. 639-40. New York, The Macmillan Company.

1935

Georg Elias Müller, 1850-1934. Am. J. Psychol., 47:344-48.

The relation of the attributes of sensation to the dimensions of the stimulus. Philosophy of Science, 2:236-45.

With H. S. Langfeld and H. P. Weld. *Psychology: A Factual Textbook.* New York, John Wiley & Sons, Inc. xviii + 555 pp.

1936

Temporal perception and operationism. Am. J. Psychol., 48:519-22.

Psychophysiological systems and isomorphic relations. Psychol. Rev., 43:565-87.

Another note on scientific writing. Science, 84:457-59.

With S. S. Stevens. The nature of tonal brightness. Proceedings of the National Academy of Sciences, 22:514-21.

Georg Elias Müller (1850-1934). Proceedings of the American Academy of Arts and Sciences, 70:558-59.

1937

Isochromatic contours.   Am. J. Psychol., 49:130-34.

The lag of publication in journals of psychology.   Am. J. Psychol., 49:137-39.

Titchener and the existential.   Am. J. Psychol., 50:470-83.

A psychological function is the relation of successive differentiations of events in the organism.   Psychol. Rev., 44:445-61.

With H. S. Langfeld and H. P. Weld. *Manual of Psychological Experiments.* New York, John Wiley & Sons, Inc. ix + 198 pp.

1938

The society of experimental psychologists: 1904-1938.   Am. J. Psychol., 51:410-23.

Titchener on meaning.   Psychol. Rev., 45:92-96.

1939

The psychophysics of color tolerance.   Am. J. Psychol., 52:384-94.

Editor, with H. S. Langfeld and H. P. Weld. *Introduction to Psychology.* New York, John Wiley & Sons, Inc. xxii + 652 pp.

1940

With A. H. Holway.   The moon illusion and the angle of regard.   Am. J. Psychol., 53:109-16.

Size constancy and Emmert's law.   Am. J. Psychol., 53:293-95.

The size of the differential limen for pitch.   Am. J. Psychol., 53:450-55.

With A. H. Holway.   The apparent size of the moon as a function of the angle of regard: further experiments.   Am. J. Psychol., 53:537-53.

With A. H. Holway.   The dependence of apparent visual size upon illumination.   Am. J. Psychol., 53:587-89.

With H. Sachs.   Was this analysis a success?   J. Abnormal Social Psychol., 35:3-16.

1941

With A. H. Holway.   Determinants of apparent visual size with distance variant.   Am. J. Psychol., 54:21-37.

Communality in relation to proaction and retroaction. Am. J. Psychol., 54:280-83.

With M. Scheerer and K. Goldstein.   A demonstration of insight: the horse-and-rider puzzle.   Am. J. Psychol., 54:437-38.

Statistical frequencies as dynamic equilibria. Psychol. Rev., 48: 279-300.

An operational restatement of G. E. Müller's psychophysical axioms.   Psychol. Rev., 48:459-64.

1942

With D. W. Taylor.   Apparent visual size as a function of distance for monocular observers.   Am. J. Psychol., 55:102-5.

With D. W. Taylor.   The moon illusion as a function of binocular regard.   Am. J. Psychol., 55:189-201.

Sensation and Perception in the History of Experimental Psychology. New York, D. Appleton-Century Company, Inc. xv + 644 pp.

With M. Bentley and K. M. Dallenbach. William James, 1842-1910.   Am. J. Psychol., 55:309.

Human nature vs. sensation: William James and the psychology of the present.   Am. J. Psychol., 55:310-27.

The psychology of perception: its importance in the war effort. Am. J. Psychol., 55:423-35.

1943

The celebrations of the American Psychological Association. Psychol. Rev., 50:1-4.

The growth of psychological journals in America. Psychol. Rev., 50:80.

Psychology for the fighting man: report of the subcommittee on a textbook of military psychology.   Psychol. Bull., 40:591-94.

The moon illusion.   Am. J. Phys., 11:55-60.

With M. Van de Water *et al. Psychology for the Fighting Man.* Washington, D.C., Infantry Journal Press. 456 pp.

1944

The use of operational definitions in science. Psychol. Rev., 52:243-45, 278-81.

With A. I. Bryan. Women in American psychology: prolegomenon. Psychol. Bull., 41:447-54.

With T. G. Alper. Intelligence test scores of northern and southern white and Negro recruits in 1918. J. Abnormal Social Psychol., 39:471-74.

Editor. *Psychology for the Armed Services*. Prepared by a committee of the National Research Council with the collaboration of many specialists. Washington, Infantry Journal Press. xvii + 533 pp.

1946

Mind and mechanism. Am. J. Psychol., 59:173-92.

With A. I. Bryan. Women in American psychology: statistics from the OPP questionnaire. Am. Psychol., 1:71-79.

With G. W. Allport. Psychology and social relations at Harvard University. Am. Psychol., 1:119-22.

Perception of objects. Am. J. Phys., 14:99-107.

With A. I. Bryan. Women in American psychology: factors affecting their careers. Transactions of the New York Academy of Sciences, Series II, 9:19-23; Pi Lambda Theta Journal, 25:92-95.

1947

With A. I. Bryan. Women in American psychology: factors affecting their professional careers. Am. Psychol., 2:3-20.

With S. S. Stevens. The new Harvard psychological laboratories. Am. Psychol., 2:239-43.

1948

Current trends in psychology: a special review. Psychol. Bull., 45:75-84.

Editor, with H. S. Langfeld and H. P. Weld. *Foundations of Psychology*. New York, John Wiley & Sons, Inc. xv + 632 pp.

With R. S. Harper. Cues. Am. J. Psychol., 61:119-23.

With M. D. Boring. Masters and pupils among the American psychologists. Am. J. Psychol., 61:527-34.

1950

A History of Experimental Psychology. 2d ed. New York, Appleton-Century-Crofts, Inc. xxi + 777 pp.

Learning vs. training for graduate students.   Am. Psychol., 5:162-63.

Great men and scientific progress.   Proc. Am. Phil. Soc., 94:339-51.

The influence of evolutionary theory upon American psychological thought.   In: *Evolutionary Thought in America,* ed. by Stow Persons, pp. 268-98. New Haven, Yale University Press.

1951

A color solid in four dimensions.   L'Année Psychologique, 50: 293-304.

The book review.   Am. J. Psychol., 64:281-83.

With Ward Edwards.   What is Emmert's law?   Am. J. Psychol., 64:416-22.

Consciousness.   In: *Encyclopaedia Britannica,* Vol. 6, p. 282. Chicago, Encyclopaedia Britannica, Inc. Psychology (general article), *ibid.,* Vol. 18, pp. 675-80; History of psychology, *ibid.,* Vol. 18, pp. 708-14.

The woman problem.   Am. Psychol., 6:679-82.

1952

With Wayne Dennis.   The founding of the APA.   Am. Psychol., 7:95-97.

Visual perception as invariance.   Psychol. Rev., 59:141-48.

The Gibsonian visual field.   Psychol. Rev., 59:246.

Organic sensations.   In: *Encyclopaedia Britannica,* Vol. 16, p. 897. Chicago, Encyclopaedia Britannica, Inc. Psychophysics, *ibid.,* Vol. 18, pp. 720-21; Visceral sensations, *ibid.,* Vol. 23, p. 192.

The validation of scientific belief: a conspectus of the symposium. Proc. Am. Phil. Soc., 96:535-39.

Foreword.   In: *Pain Sensations and Reactions,* by J. D. Hardy, H. G. Wolff, and H. Goodell, pp. v-x. Baltimore, The Williams & Wilkins Company.

Editor, with Heinz Werner, Robert M. Yerkes, and Herbert S.

Langfeld. Preface: *A History of Psychology in Autobiography,* Vol. IV, pp. v-vi. Worcester, Mass., Clark University Press.

Edwin Garrigues Boring. *A History of Psychology in Autobiography,* Vol. IV, pp. 27-52. Worcester, Mass., Clark University Press.

Life membership. Am. Psychol., 8:86-88.

Psychological museum. Am. Psychol., 8:166.

John Dewey, 1859-1952. Am. J. Psychol., 66:145-47.

A history of introspection. Psychol. Bull., 50:169-89.

The role theory in experimental psychology. Am. J. Psychol., 66:169-84.

1954

With Suzanne Bennett. Psychological necrology (1928-1952). Psychol. Bull., 51:75-81.

Science and faith: a foreword. In: *Catholics in Psychology: A Historical Survey,* by H. Misiak and V. M. Staudt, pp. ix-xi. New York, McGraw-Hill Book Co., Inc.

Psychological factors in the scientific process. Am. Scientist, 42: 624, 639-45.

The nature and history of experimental control. Am. J. Psychol., 67:573-89.

1955

The present status of parapsychology. Am. Scientist, 43:108-17.

Introspection. In: *Encyclopaedia Britannica,* Vol. 12, p. 542. Chicago, Encyclopaedia Britannica, Inc.

Dual role of the Zeitgeist in scientific creativity. Scientific Monthly, 80:101-6.

Psychology. In: *What Is Science?* ed. by James Roy Newman, pp. 291-314. New York, Simon & Schuster, Inc.

1956

CP speaks: modern language theory. Contemp. Psychol., 1:13, 22.

1957

Robert Mearns Yerkes (1876-1956). Yearbook of the American Philosophical Society, 1956, pp. 133-40.

1958

Karl M. Dallenbach.   Am. J. Psychol., 71:1-40.

Introductory statement.   In: *International Directory of Psychologists*, ed. by E. H. Jacobson and H. C. J. Duijker, pp. ix-x. Assen, The Netherlands, Royal Van Gorcum & Co., N.V.

1959

On eschewing teleology.   Science, 129:608-10.

Lewis Madison Terman, 1877-1956.   In: National Academy of Sciences, *Biographical Memoirs*, 33:413-61. New York, Columbia University Press.

John Gilbert Beebe-Center, 1897-1958.   Am. J. Psychol., 72:311-15.

Science and the meaning of its history.   Key Reporter, 24(4):2-3.

1960

The pattern of modern psychology: the psychodynamics of the history of discovery.   Bulletin of the British Psychological Society, No. 40, pp. 16-19.

Lashley and cortical integration.   In: *Neurophysiology of Lashley: Selected Papers*, ed. by Frank A. Beach *et al*, pp. xi-xvi. New York, McGraw-Hill Book Co., Inc.

The psychologists' concept of mind.   Journal of Psychological Researches (Madras), 4(3), 7 pp.

1961

Fechner: inadvertent founder of psychophysics.   Psychometrika, 26:3-8.

The beginning and growth of measurement in psychology.   Isis, 52:238-57.

Psychologist at Large: An Autobiography and Selected Essays. New York, Basic Books. 371 pp.

1962

Newton and the spectral lines.   Science, 136:600.

On the moon illusion.   Science, 137:902-6.

Comments to reviewers.   Contemp. Psychol., 7:324.

Boring on Titchener.   In: *A History of Cornell,* by M. G. Bishop, pp. 621-23. Ithaca, Cornell University Press.

1963

Science reporting in journals and newspapers.   Science, 139:1100. (L)

History, Psychology, and Science: Selected Papers, ed. by Robert I. Watson and Donald T. Campbell. New York, John Wiley & Sons, Inc. 372 pp.

The social stimulus to creativity.   Science, 142:622.

Gustav Theodor Fechner.   In: *Colliers Encyclopedia,* Vol. 9, pp. 628-29. New York, Crowell-Collier Publishing Company.

1964

Cognitive dissonance: its place in science.   Science, 145:680-85.

Size-constancy in a picture.   Am. J. Psychol., 77:494-98.

Eponym as placebo.   Proc. 17th Internat. Congr. Psychol., pp. 9-23. Washington, 1963. Amsterdam, North-Holland Publishing Company.

Psychology: a behavioral reinterpretation; the trend toward mechanism.   Proc. Am. Phil. Soc., 108:451-54.

1965

On the subjectivity of important historical dates: Leipzig 1879. J. Hist. Behav. Sci., 1:5-9.

Edward Wheeler Scripture, 1864-1945.   Am. J. Psychol., 78:314-17.

Editor (with R. J. Herrnstein).   *A Source Book in the History of Psychology.* Cambridge, Harvard University Press. xvii + 636 pp.

Extrasensory induction of brain waves.   Science, 150:1244.

1966

Editor's introduction: Gustav Theodor Fechner, 1801-1887.   In: *Elements of Psychophysics,* by Gustav Fechner, pp. lx-xvii.   New York, Holt, Rinehart & Winston, Inc.

Sociotropes, biotropes, and teaching.   Am. Psychol., 21:80-83.

A note on the origin of the word psychology.   J. Hist. Behav. Sci., 2:167.

Discussion (bidimensional history).   International Journal of Psychiatry, 2:357-61.

Paranormal phenomena: evidence, specification, and chance.   Introduction to *ESP: A Scientific Evaluation*, by C. E. M. Hansel, pp. xiii-xxi. New York, Charles Scribner's Sons.

1967

Psychology.   In: *The New Book of Knowledge*, Vol. 15, pp. 488-501. New York, Grolier, Inc.

Preface.   *History of Psychology in Autobiography*, ed. by Edwin G. Boring and Gardner Lindzey, Vol. V, pp. v-ix.   New York, Appleton-Century-Crofts, Inc.

Titchener's experimentalists.   J. Hist. Behav. Sci., 4:315-25.

Psychologists' letters and papers. Isis, 58:103-7.

1968

Whither CP?   Contemp. Psychol., 13:8.

With Edith L. Annin and Robert I. Watson.   Important psychologists, 1600-1967.   J. Hist. Behav. Sci., 4:303-15.

Foreword.   *A Study of Franz Brentano: His Psychological Standpoint and His Significance in the History of Psychology*, by Antos C. Rancurello, pp. vii-ix. New York, Academic Press, Inc.

Judson Herrick

CHARLES JUDSON HERRICK

October 6, 1868–January 29, 1960

BY GEORGE W. BARTELMEZ*

THE AMERICAN HERRICKS are descended from Heneri Herrick, who came to Massachusetts from the Midlands of England in 1628. In 1854 Nathan Herrick migrated with his family from Stowe, Vermont, to the West and four years later settled in the growing town of Minneapolis. His eldest son, Henry Nathan, had married Anna Strickler, a girl of Swiss descent who had been intrigued by the prospect of spending her life in the wide open spaces of the West. Charles Judson was the youngest of her four sons. Their father had become pastor of a frontier Baptist church, but the chief support of the family came from the small farm on which they lived and labored.

Charles began his formal education in a one-room schoolhouse, but he had already been introduced to Nature by his elder brother Clarence.[1] His interest in collecting and identifying plants continued through his college days. His schooling was originally directed toward the ministry, but after two years in the "classical" course at college he decided that he was not "called to be a minister of the Gospel." He prepared

---

* Manuscript transmitted to the Academy by Dr. Heinrich Klüver after the death of Dr. Bartelmez.

[1] See C. J. Herrick, "Clarence Luther Herrick, Pioneer Naturalist, Teacher, and Psychobiologist," *Trans. Amer. Philos. Soc.*, 45, part 1 (March 1955):85 pp.

himself for majoring in science and took his B.S. degree at
the University of Cincinnati in 1891. In the following year
he married Mary Elizabeth Talbot, daughter of the retired
president of Denison University, and obtained what he called
"a settee of sciences" at a small college in Kansas. When he
found that the president of the college was offering a course
in psychology he ventured to suggest that his own course on
the nervous system be coordinated with it. "Young man," said
the president, "the brain has no more to do with the operations
of the mind than have the cabbages out there in my garden."

In the succeeding academic year he enrolled as a graduate
student at Denison University under his brother Clarence, who
had become Professor of Biology there. At the end of the
year his brother was stricken with acute pulmonary tuberculosis
and had to resign his professorship. C.J.H., at the age of
twenty-five years, took over the bulk of the teaching and the
administration of the department. In addition, he refused to
suspend the publication of the *Journal of Comparative
Neurology,* which his brother had founded two years previously, in 1891, "because its suspension would break my
brother's heart and jeopardize his recovery." It was a purely
personal enterprise and he became editor, business manager
without secretary, proofreader, supervisor of engravings, and,
on occasion, typesetter. These labors continued until 1907
except for the academic year of 1896. Many a robust man
would have been overwhelmed, but C.J.H. was inspired and
his research program was not interrupted. From 1902 to 1907
he served as secretary of Section F of the American Association
for the Advancement of Science.

In 1896 he obtained leave of absence from Denison University and worked at Columbia University and Woods Hole
for his Ph.D. degree. In 1898 he was appointed Professor of

Zoology at Denison, where he was quite content with his opportunities. When, in 1907, he was offered the professorship of Neurology at the University of Chicago he hesitated to accept, because of his health and the example of his brother's early death due primarily to overwork. The opportunity of abundant time and support for research, the incentive of inspiring colleagues like R. R. Bensley working on the relations of structure to function, the presence of graduate students, the freedom from tedious and annoying executive duties, and a salary almost twice what he had been making were all powerful inducements. His wife's question, "Would you sooner go to Chicago and burn out or stay here and rust out?" settled the matter. Mary was an ideal wife; without her help he could not have accomplished what he did. He continued to work at the University of Chicago for thirty years. During his stay there, the Indiana Dunes country became a refuge from the foul air of the city. In 1910 "Bubbly Creek" at the stockyards still periodically filled much of the city with its stench, supplemented by the steel mills at Gary.

In 1918 Herrick was elected to membership in the National Academy of Sciences.

After his mother's death in 1934 (she was 104 years old) the Herricks went to live with their daughter, "Doctor Ruth," in Grand Rapids, Michigan. He kept in touch with the neurologists at the University of Michigan where the most distinguished of his students, Professor Elizabeth C. Crosby,[2] arranged to preserve his large library. Its unique reprint collection includes many significant papers not available elsewhere in this country. He continued his exacting histological studies for thirteen years thereafter.

[2] See Elizabeth C. Crosby, "Charles Judson Herrick (October 6, 1866 [sic]–January 29, 1960)," *J. Comp. Neurol.*, 115 (1960):3–8.

RESEARCH

The leitmotiv of Herrick's scientific career was to contribute to the "psychobiology" envisioned by his brother Clarence in 1891. This was to be a coordinated attack on the "mind-body" problem by comparative anatomists, physiologists, psychologists, and psychiatrists in correlation with the advances in other fields of science. In 1956 he summarized the progress in this field in his *The Evolution of Human Nature*.

He began his research career while still an undergraduate at Cincinnati, working on the nervous system of locally available bony fishes. In the course of the next seventeen years he established his reputation as a comparative neurologist with a series of studies on this group. He made a detailed study of structure as related to function by selecting species highly adapted to particular modes of life in which the peripheral and central nervous systems had hypertrophied. Thus in the carps and their allies there is a large organ in the mouth adapted to separating the edible from the inedible material scooped up from the bottom of ponds and streams. The nerves which supply this palatal organ and also their centers in the brain are so prominent that they can be identified in normal animals. This "natural experiment" made it possible to recognize the previously unknown gustatory centers and their functional connections with other regions of the brain and spinal cord.

His studies on the feeding habits of catfish demonstrated another gustatory system present in the outer skin of trunk, fins, and head including the barbels. All are supplied by a large branch of a cranial nerve (the facial). It had been known that there were two kinds of sense organs in the skin of some groups of fishes: the lateral line organs supplied by several cranial nerves and the "terminal buds" supplied by the facial nerve. It was common knowledge that catfish are carnivorous bottom feeders, particularly active at night or when the water is muddy. The resemblance of the microscopic structure of the terminal buds of the skin to human taste buds as well as those in the mouths of other vertebrates led Herrick to train a group of catfish to distinguish between meat or meat juice (which they could accurately localize and snap up) and a bit of cotton wool brought into contact with the tail fin under conditions in which vision was excluded. The fish were living happily in an aquarium and the trauma of surgical interference was avoided.

His doctoral thesis was the first complete functional analysis of every nerve of the head and adjacent spinal cord. It was stimulated by Henry Fairfield Osborn's (1889) discovery that the cranial nerves are made up of groups ("components") of fibers which differ in size and structure from those of other groups as well as in their endings in the brain. In the same year E. P. Allis showed in another fish that the fibers which supply the organs of the lateral line of head and trunk can be distinguished from other components and traced by gross dissection. In 1895 O. S. Strong followed the various components of certain cranial nerves of the frog tadpole to their peripheral and central endings, using all the staining methods known at the time. Herrick went to Columbia University in 1896 to work under Osborn and Strong, choosing the unspecialized minnow, Menidia, for his analysis. The technique of preparing a complete series of sections of the head of a bony fish for microscopic study had to be worked out before the analysis could begin. The importance of this complete analysis impressed Ira Van Gieson, then director of the Pathological Institute of New York State Hospitals, and he made it possible to prepare adequate illustrations and publish Herrick's 300-page monograph with its seven large lithographic plates. A sufficient number of copies of the plates were printed so that they could be published in the *Journal of Comparative Neurology* as well as in the *Archives of Neurology and Psychopathology*. No such sumptuous work has appeared in the *Journal* since then. The monograph is now recognized as the cornerstone of the "American School of Neurology." It has provided evidence for a fundamental analysis of the brain stem applicable to all vertebrates, namely the presence of four longitudinal columns, dorsally two formed by a series of centers that receive impulses from the environment and adjoining centers for visceral stimuli, and ventrally a column of centers concerned with visceral reactions adjoining which are the cell groups that control the skeletal musculature.

At the University of Chicago Herrick had abundant leisure time and financial support for research, readily available material, and technical help. He began at once an intensive study of the brains of salamanders. This group of amphibians has survived through the ages since the Devonian period with relatively few skeletal changes. The brains of living urodeles have little more than the basic equipment present in all vertebrate brains for total reactions of the body as a whole. They can be assumed to be similar to the brains of the earliest vertebrates that acquired the ability to breathe air and crawl over dry land with four legs. They are not distorted by any highly developed systems such as are present in many fishes nor are they masked by the hypertrophy of centers and conduction systems such as evolved in reptiles and mammals. The urodele brain is primitive but by no means simply organized. It was more than forty years before Herrick decided that he had found all the details that his methods could reveal. In 1948 he published his monograph on *The Brain of the Tiger Salamander*.

Part I of this work is a profound discussion of the mode of functioning of the brain of vertebrates as interpreted by their overt behavior. His close friend, G. E. Coghill, had in the interim worked out the genesis of behavior and its mechanisms in the salamanders. Herrick carried on the analysis to the adult stage and on through the series to the most elaborately organized neural mechanism known, the human cerebral cortex. This analysis involved his studies on the groups in the line of descent, that is, reptiles and primitive mammals, as well as a review of the extensive literature inspired by the "American School."

In Part II of the monograph he presents the details of his microscopic analyses on more than 500 amphibian brains. He recognized some 57 cell groups and more than 120 fiber bundles, in many of which he could determine the beginning and endings. Few conduction systems have been described so completely in any vertebrate brain. It could only be done after an exhaustive study of complete series of sections of over 250 brains prepared by the Golgi method. Such preparations are unique in that they differ widely in the regions stained in different brains and in various parts of the same brain. Thus one area or one element of an area may be revealed in great detail leaving the surrounding region clear. Dense thickets of interwoven cell processes and endings of fibers may be present, the "neuropil" of the pioneer histologists, which are valuable landmarks and presumably important centers of integration. In other brains the centers of integration can be analyzed because only a few of the nerve cells and all of their branches are stained, while in still others only a few fibers with their endings have been picked out from the surrounding bundles of fibers. Sometimes in these small brains a few fibers of a conduction system can be followed through the whole brain and not only their beginnings and endings but also their connections en route can be demonstrated. Such preparations can be interpreted only by an investigator who is familiar with every detail revealed by other histologic methods and is able to prepare drawings of the essential features. Like S. Ramón y Cajal, Herrick drew all of his detailed illustrations. Of the 113 figures of this work, 110 are from his pen and half of them were made from Golgi preparations.

His unraveling of the structure and connections of the interpeduncular nucleus was a notable achievement. This center has long been known, for it is present in every vertebrate brain, but his was the first adequate analysis. The center is characterized by certain synaptic fields, "glomeruli," highly vascularized, unusually dense areas of neuropil, with connections from many regions of the brain. In some glomeruli only the cells with their processes were stained, in others one or another of the fiber tracts from other regions with their endings appeared. In some, the cells lining the cavity of the brain showed elaborately branched processes extending into the neuropil. He suggested that these "ependymal" cells may contribute a secretion to the synaptic neuropil. This would be adding a new and unexpected factor to a synapse. There are many such suggestions for further investigation.

The *Tiger Salamander* is the most complete account of the structure of any vertebrate brain that has ever been made; its functional interpretations will serve as the basis for future work. After it had been completed he decided to give up the long hours of labor at the microscope. He devoted himself to cultivating his associations with his surviving philosophically-minded friends, to reading, meditating, and writing *The Evolution of Human Nature.*

HERRICK AND THE JOURNAL OF COMPARATIVE NEUROLOGY

In 1891 Clarence Herrick founded a periodical, the *Journal of Comparative Neurology,* that was prepared to publish, as he said, "anything from any source, bearing on a broad comparative study of the brain and mind." He had no outside support, no collaborators, no subscribers, and only the hope of contributors. When he was totally incapacitated three years later, he resigned his professorship at Denison University and recommended that the publication of the *Journal* be suspended. Brother Charles J. undertook to assume his academic duties and also to save the *Journal*. He succeeded in both projects and the *Journal* is now one of the outstanding biological periodicals in America. Except for small subsidies from Denison and Cincinnati universities at the time and some help from friends, notably H. H. Donaldson and O. S. Strong, the deficits from the publication of the *Journal* were paid out of his own meagre salary (Volumes 6 to 14). His sense of responsibility for the *Journal* is illustrated by his action when in 1905 his laboratory went up in flames. His "fireproof" safe contained the manuscript of the doctoral dissertation of Ariëns Kappers of Amsterdam, who had personally provided the plates for his illustrations. When the door of the safe was pried open, the manuscript appeared to be a large black cinder. After learning that no copy of it had been made, Herrick began a dissection of the cinder and found that only the end of every line was completely black. The manuscript had been handwritten in an iron-tannin ink and he found that it could be deciphered with difficulty under oblique illumination. The footnotes were totally destroyed and so he filled them in "by the judicious use of scientific imagination." It took the summer's vacation to prepare a typescript which was sent to the author and returned with but few changes! In later years he repeatedly felt obliged to rewrite manuscripts that had been written in dictionary English by foreign contributors and students who came to work in his laboratory.

In 1904 the largely morphological character of the papers

submitted to the *Journal* led Herrick to join forces with R. M. Yerkes, who brought in contributions on animal behavior. The Founder lived long enough in that year to commend enthusiastically this addition to his plan for the development of a psychobiology and to see the first number of the *Journal of Comparative Neurology and Psychology*. The association of Herrick and Yerkes continued to the great satisfaction of the editors until 1910, when the *Journal of Animal Behavior* was founded in order to provide additional space for the rapid increase of work in this field.

In 1908 Herrick deeded the *Journal of Comparative Neurology and Psychology* to the Wistar Institute as a gift and the Institute undertook to print and publish it in the same format as the *American Journal of Anatomy*, the *Anatomical Record,* and the *Journal of Morphology*. In 1914 the American Association of Anatomists voted to increase the dues of its members so as to be able to subsidize the publication program of the Wistar Institute. The members of the Association became subscribers to the four journals, which saved the lives of all of them and contributed to their prestige. This arrangement was continued until 1923, when the sequelae of the Great War had begun to subside. Then the Wistar Institute gave the members the privilege of subscribing to its journals at 25 percent less than the published rate.

Herrick continued as Managing Editor of the *Journal of Comparative Neurology* until 1927, when he induced G. E. Coghill to take his place while he remained chairman of the Editorial Board. In 1948 he assumed an "emeritus" status but the Board continued to consult him on major issues and on occasion he did not hesitate to veto its decisions.

TEACHING

At Denison University, from 1893 until 1898 when he was appointed Professor of Zoology, Herrick was the entire Department of Biology although continuing with his research program at the same time.

During his first two quarters at Chicago in 1907 he delivered a brilliant series of lectures on comparative neurology to a group of students attracted to the University by his coming. To those of us whose knowledge of the nervous system was confined to its gross anatomy, the course was a revelation and an inspiration.

In the following spring quarter he introduced a new method of approach to the presentation of neuroanatomy to medical students. P. S. Roofe (his biographer) has published a series of letters[3] between Herrick and Adolf Meyer in 1909. They compared and criticized their respective programs for such a course. Both presented the subject by interpreting structure in terms of function; Herrick from the comparative aspect, Meyer from the clinical. This led to improvements in both courses.

After the publication of his *Introduction to Neurology* in 1915, many teachers of neuroanatomy were alerted to the value of presenting function with structure, and after the appearance in 1920 of S. W. Ranson's *The Anatomy of the Nervous System,* which adopted Herrick's analysis of the brain, a whole flock of textbooks for medical students was published based on the functional approach to the subject.

In 1916, at the request of the Department of Psychology, Herrick offered a course on "Elementary Neurology" for graduate students. There were no prerequisites, all the rules and regulations of the pedagogues were disregarded, attendance was voluntary both for laboratory and for conferences, the content of the latter being usually determined by questions raised by the students. There were only two requirements for credit: a term paper that critically discussed a subject chosen by the student and a statement of such contents of the course

[3] See P. S. Roofe, "Neurology Comes of Age," *J. Kansas Med. Soc.,* 66 (1963): 124–29.

as were most pertinent to the student's interest and program. For twenty years the course was filled to capacity by students not only from the Department of Psychology but from other scientific departments and from the divinity school and the faculty of philosophy as well. Herrick regarded the course as the most satisfactory and stimulating work of his teaching career.

Another achievement at the University of Chicago was the organization of the "Neurology Club." This was purely a feast of reason needing no gastronomic allure. It was the first approach toward the development of a psychobiology. Members of most biological departments and eventually clinical neurologists, psychiatrists, and other clinicians of Billings Hospital found it instructive and stimulating. Some of the men generally participating in the meetings of this interdisciplinary group were Percival Bailey, Paul C. Bucy, Stephen Polyak, David Bodian, A. Earl Walker, Karl S. Lashley, Heinrich Klüver, Anton J. Carlson, Arno B. Luckhardt, Ralph S. Lillie, Ralph W. Gerard, Nathaniel Kleitman, Edmund Jacobson, Peter C. Kronfeld, Carl R. Moore, Paul Weiss, and B. H. Willier.

Many experienced investigators as well as graduate students were attracted to his laboratory at the University of Chicago. They came from Norway, Holland, Germany, Yugoslavia, Australia, New Zealand, Japan, and China.

In 1917 he collaborated in planning a course for neurosurgeons who had volunteered for service in World War I; and then he volunteered also. He was commissioned a major in the Sanitary Corps of the Army and put to work performing autopsies on the animals used in the physiological laboratory. Before long he was transferred to the Army Medical Museum and ordered to become a pathologist. A group of draftees, all candidates for the Ph.D. in biology, were placed under his command. They set up a histological laboratory and eventually prepared a vast amount of microscopic material as well as a large collection of normal and injured brains. Not long after his discharge in 1919 all of this material had disappeared from the Museum, leaving no trace.

THE FINAL SUMMARY

The breadth and depth of Herrick's thinking are revealed in *The Evolution of Human Nature,* which was published four years before his death. In the introduction he wrote, "I did not devote sixty years to intensive study of the comparative anatomy of the nervous system merely to collect dead facts or to add to the store of 'accumulative knowledge.'[4] I wanted to find out what these animals do with the organs they have and what they do it for, with the expectation that this knowledge would help us to unravel the intricate texture of the human nervous system and show us how to use it more efficiently." He presents a variety of scientific evidences for the understanding of mind, defining psychobiology as "the study of the experience of living bodies, its method of operation, the apparatus employed and its significance as vital process, all from the standpoint of the individual having the experience." It calls for the cooperative efforts of specialists. "The first task is to discover by objective inquiry the properties of the living mechanisms that execute all animal behavior and the laws of their operation. The second group of studies must be concerned with the investigation of all kinds of mental processes by scientifically controlled introspection. . . . Introspective psychology gives us scientific knowledge of the spiritual life and the psychological factors of behavior."

"The laws of the physiological factors and those of the psychological factors are not directly comparable, for no com-

---

[4] He might have added, "helpful as this addition has been to the understanding of the subject."

mon units of measurement for them have as yet been found. The third task of psychobiology, then, is to define as exactly as possible the relations between the physiological processes and the colligated mental processes. This is the province of physiological psychology. When these relationships are adequately known we shall be able to formulate the principles of the mechanics of mental processes. . . . We have reason to believe that this goal is not unattainable."

His survey of the evolution of behavior in living creatures provides objective evidence of the basis for the attack on the problem. It can be summarized as follows:

In all animals that have a nervous system it controls the adaptation of the species to its environment. When its behavior is adequate the species survives. The evolutionary history of adaptive behavior parallels that of bodily structure; the more complex the behavior, the more elaborate is the structure of the nervous system.

All vertebrates have a forebrain primitively dominated by smell, a midbrain associated largely with vision and hearing, a hindbrain, the primary center for the cranial nerves, and a spinal cord for the nerves of the trunk and limbs. The polarized neural mechanism for analyzing incoming impulses and for integrating responses is the same in all vertebrates. Primitive species have little more than this fundamental neural equipment.

As sense modalities become more refined and behavior is adapted to a wider range of environmental conditions, certain parts of the brain become relatively larger, more intricate in structure and connections. The cerebral hemispheres of the forebrain especially are larger when more sense modalities are carried into them.

From the outset of mammalian evolution in the tertiary period the brain case was relatively larger than in any reptile.

Among living mammals there is a progressive increase in the size of the cerebral hemispheres as we pass from the simpler to the more highly organized groups. The outer layers of cells of the hemispheres ("cortex") are as distinctive mammalian characters as are the mammary glands.

In all primates, including man, the pattern of arrangement of centers in the cortex is the same. Those primates that became more manlike (anthropoid apes) have developed behaviors more like the conscious cerebral activities of man.

The series of fossil "hominids" that arose after the liberation of the hands from locomotion show a relatively rapid increase in the capacity of the brain case. The brain became progressively larger presumably in association with the use of tools and the development of speech. There is no evidence of so rapid an increase in any anthropoid strain.

The average brain of Homo sapiens weighs twice as much as that of any great ape; its association centers, which are independent of direct connections with afferent and efferent impulses, are relatively much larger.

The activities of the human mind are not merely greater quantitatively than those of any other animal; the acquisition of language through social inheritance has stimulated the development of cerebral activities that are qualitatively different from those of any animal.

This is but one of the series of topics presented in the book. The book itself is a scrupulously documented and annotated compendium of a long and active life. There are discussions of the fundamental differences between the analytic (discriminatory) and integrative (perceptive) functions of the cerebral cortex. "All thinking is now and here: but in this present act of thinking, memories of things past in time and remote in space and predictions of the future are tied into the mental process, so that in thought the perceptual data of time and space lose some of their specific qualities and limitations. When symbolized in the mental processes they may emerge, lose their sharply defined boundaries, and re-appear in a radically different setup of relationships. . . . Some of our abstract ideas may be totally devoid of any temporal or spatial quality." He stresses subjective experience and its control of behavior, and the inadequacy of a purely objective psychology. He considers "psi" phenomena and discusses values: "science has a code of moral values that are inherent in the organic structure of science and essential for its existence." "Science is a way of life in quest of truth for life's sake." He attacks dogmas in science as in other fields. There are chapters on sociology from the biological point of view. The totalitarian societies are compared with insect colonies where the individual is sacrificed for the benefit of the colony. "The ideal society is based on the voluntary cooperation of intelligent and altruistic individuals."

BIBLIOGRAPHY

KEY TO ABBREVIATIONS

Anat. Anz. = Anatomischer Anzeiger
Anat. Record = Anatomical Record
Ann. Rep. Ohio State Acad. Sci. = Annual Report of the Ohio State
    Academy of Science
Denison Univ. Bull., J. Sci. Lab. = Denison University Bulletin, Journal
    of the Scientific Laboratories
J. Comp. Neurol. = Journal of Comparative Neurology
J. Nerv. Ment. Dis. = Journal of Nervous and Mental Disease
J. Philos. = Journal of Philosophy
J. Philos., Psychol., Sci. Methods = Journal of Philosophy, Psychology
    and Scientific Methods
Proc. Nat. Acad. Sci. = Proceedings of the National Academy of Sciences
Psychol. Rev. = Psychological Review
Sci. Monthly = Scientific Monthly
U.S. Fish Comm. Bull. = United States Fish Commission Bulletin

The following list does not include newspaper articles or reviews, except a few regarded as of permanent scientific interest.
Some autoabstracts are selected from a large number, particularly
those of papers not otherwise published.

1891

With C. L. Herrick. Biological notes upon *Fiber, Geomys* and
    Erethizon. Denison Univ. Bull., J. Sci. Lab., 6:15-25.
Studies in the topography of the rodent brain: Erethizon dorsatus
    and Geomys bursarius. Denison Univ. Bull., J. Sci. Lab.,
    6:26-46.
With C. L. Herrick. Contributions to the morphology of the
    brain of bony fishes. I. Siluridae. J. Comp. Neurol., 1:211-28.

1892

Recent views with reference to the structure of the nervous system,
    by Professor Heinrich Obersteiner. J. Comp. Neurol., 2:73-
    83. Translation.

1893

Recent advances in the study of the nervous system. Transactions
    of the Kansas Academy of Science, 13:7-73.

Current views of the structure of olfactory organs and taste-bulbs.
    J. Comp. Neurol., 3:xcv-cii.
Laboratory notes from Denison University. VI. Illustrations of the
    surface anatomy of the brain of certain birds. J. Comp.
    Neurol., 3:171-76, with Plate XXVI.

1894

The evolution of Huxley.   Dension Collegian, 27:60-62.
Leonowa's recent observations on the anencephalic and amyelic
    nervous system.   J. Comp. Neurol., 4:1-6.
The cranial nerves of Amblystoma punctatum.   J. Comp. Neurol.,
    4:193-207, with Plates XIX-XX.

1895

The correlation between specific diversity and individual vari-
    ability, as illustrated by the eye-muscle nerves of the Amphibia.
    In: *Proceedings of the 7th Annual Session of the Association of
    American Anatomists,* New York, 1894, pp. 27-28. Washington,
    Beresford, Printer.

1897

Nature studies as a preparation for advanced work in science.
    Ohio Educational Monthly, 46:150-59.
The cranial nerve components of teleosts.   Anat. Anz., 13:425-31.

1898

With C. L. Herrick.   Inquiries regarding current tendencies in
    neurological nomenclature.   J. Comp. Neurol., 7:162-68.
Report upon a series of experiments with the Weigert methods
    with special reference for use in lower brain morphology.   New
    York State Hospital Bulletin, October, 1897. 31 pp. (Issued
    1898.)
The cranial nerves of bony fishes.   J. Comp. Neurol., 8:162-70.

1899

The metameric value of the sensory components of the cranial
    nerves.   Science, 9:312-13. (A)
The peripheral nervous system of the bony fishes. U.S. Fish
    Comm. Bull. for 1898, 18:315-20.

The cranial and first spinal nerves of Menidia: a contribution upon the nerve components of the bony fishes. J. Comp. Neurol., 9:153-455; Archives of Neurology and Psychopathology, 2:21-319.

1900

The trigemino-facial ganglionic complex of Gadus and Amiurus. Science, 11:168-69. (A)

A contribution upon the cranial nerves of codfish. J. Comp. Neurol., 10:265-316.

Auditory nerve and its end-organs. Comparative anatomy and phylogeny. In: *Reference Handbook of the Medical Sciences,* 2d ed., ed. by Albert H. Buck, Vol. 1, pp. 627-33. New York, William Wood and Company.

1901

Cranial nerves. The doctrine of nerve components. In: *Reference Handbook of the Medical Sciences,* 2d ed., ed. by Albert H. Buck, Vol. 3, pp. 312-26. New York, William Wood and Company.

The cranial nerves and cutaneous sense organs of the North American siluroid fishes. J. Comp. Neurol., 11:177-249.

With C. L. Herrick. Various entries in Vol. 2 of: *Dictionary of Philosophy and Psychology,* ed. by J. Baldwin. New York, The Macmillan Company. (Note: In the 1928 edition of this Dictionary, Vol. 2, entries by Herrick and Herrick are to be found on pp. 150-66 and 172-76.)

1902

The feeding habits of fishes. School Science, 2:324-27. (Periodical title is now School Science and Mathematics.)

A note on the significance of the size of nerve fibers in fishes. J. Comp. Neurol., 12:329-34; Denison Univ. Bull., J. Sci. Lab., 12:33-38; 11th Ann. Rep. Ohio State Acad. Sci., p. 27. (A)

An illustration of the value of the functional system of neurones as a morphological unit in the nervous system. American Journal of Anatomy, 1:517.

The sense of taste in fishes. Science, 16:400. (A)

1903

On the morphological and physiological classification of the cutaneous sense organs of fishes. American Naturalist, 37:313-18; Science, 17:251-52. (A)

Olfactory nerve. I. Anatomical part. In: *Reference Handbook of the Medical Sciences*, 2d ed., ed. by Albert H. Buck, Vol. 6, pp. 349-55. New York, William Wood and Company.

The summer laboratory as an instrument of biological research. Science, 18:263-68.

The organ and sense of taste in fishes. U.S. Fish Comm. Bull. for 1902, 22:237-72; Denison Univ. Bull., J. Sci. Lab., 12:39-96.

The doctrine of nerve components and some of its applications. J. Comp. Neurol., 13:301-12; 12th Ann. Rep. Ohio State Acad. Sci.

On the phylogeny and morphological position of the terminal buds of fishes. J. Comp. Neurol., 13:121-38.

1904

Convocation week. Science, 19:385-87.

Editorial. J. Comp. Neurol., 14:165-70.

The dynamic character of morphology. *Congress of Arts and Science*, ed. by Howard J. Rogers, Vol. 5, p. 283. Universal Exposition, St. Louis. Boston and New York, Houghton, Mifflin, and Company; Cambridge, The Riverside Press. (By error attributed to C. S. Herrick.)

1905

A functional view of nature as seen by a biologist. J. Philos., Psychol., Sci. Methods, 2:428-38.

The central gustatory paths in the brains of bony fishes. J. Comp. Neurol., 15:375-456; Denison Univ. Bull., J. Sci. Lab., 13:35-116.

1906

What medical subjects can be taught efficiently in the literary college? Proceedings of the 16th Annual Meeting of the Association of American Medical Colleges, Pittsburgh, pp. 34-38. Chicago, American Medical Association.

The relation between the nerves of taste and touch in fishes. Science, 23:260. (A)

On the connections of the funicular nuclei in the brains of fishes. Science, 24:297. (A)

On the centers for taste and touch in the medulla oblongata of fishes. J. Comp. Neurol., 16:403-39; Science, 25:31. (A)

Editorial. Human and comparative neurology. J. Comp. Neurol., 16:464-66.

Discussion of what medical subjects can and what cannot be properly and efficiently taught in the literary college. Transactions of the 36th Annual Meeting of the Ohio College Association, Columbus, pp. 16-18.

1907

Comparative psychology. Popular Science Monthly, 70:76-78.

A study of the vagal lobes and funicular nuclei of the brain of the codfish. J. Comp. Neurol., 17:67-87.

The central reflex connections of cutaneous taste buds in the codfish and the catfish: an illustration of functional adaptation in the nervous system. Science, 25:736-37. (A)

Editorial. *Concilium bibliographicum.* J. Comp. Neurol., 17: 360-63.

Editorial. Professor Golgi on the doctrine of the neurone. J. Comp. Neurol., 17:519-22.

Editorial. Neurological terminology. J. Comp. Neurol., 17:522-23.

On the *commissura infirma* of the brains of fishes. Anat. Record, 1:88. (A)

The tactile centers in the spinal cord and brain of the sea robin, Prionotus carolinus L. J. Comp. Neurol., 17:307-27.

On the phylogenetic differentiation of the organs of smell and taste. J. Comp. Neurol., 18:157-66.

The morphological subdivision of the brain. J. Comp. Neurol., 18:393-408.

On the *commissura infirma* and its nuclei in the brains of fishes. J. Comp. Neurol., 18:409-31.

Editorial. Two recent tendencies in cerebral morphology. J. Comp. Neurol., 18:663-70.

1909

The nervus terminalis (nerve of Pinkus) in the frog. J. Comp.
Neurol., 19:175-90; Anat. Record, 3:259. (A)
The criteria of homology in the peripheral nervous system. J.
Comp. Neurol., 19:203-9; Science, 29:437. (A)

1910

The evolution of intelligence and its organs. Science, 31:7-18.
The relations of the central and peripheral nervous systems in
phylogeny. Anat. Record, 4:59-69.
The morphology of the cerebral hemispheres in Amphibia. Anat.
Anz., 36:645-52.
The morphology of the forebrain in Amphibia and Reptilia. J.
Comp. Neurol., 20:413-547.

1911

An educational ideal for the small college. Denison Alumni Bulletin, 2:2,18.
Notes on the association centers. J. Nerv. Ment. Dis., 38:750-53.

1912

Instinct and intelligence. Psychological Bulletin, 9:50. (A)

1913

Some reflections on the origin and significance of the cerebral
cortex. J. Animal Behavior, 3:222-36.
The foundations of culture. Denison Univ. Bull., J. Sci. Lab.,
17:205-18.
Anatomy of the brain. In: *Reference Handbook of the Medical
Sciences,* 3d ed., ed. by Thomas Lathrop Stedman, Vol. 2, pp.
273-342. New York, William Wood and Company.
Table of cranial nerve components. Chicago, privately printed.
With Jeannette B. Obenchain. Notes on the anatomy of the cy-
clostome brain: Ichthyomyzon concolor. J. Comp. Neurol.,
23:635-75.

1914

The cerebellum of Necturus and other urodele Amphibia. J.
Comp. Neurol., 24:1-29; Folia Neurobiologica, 8:431-33. (A)

The medulla oblongata of larval Amblystoma. J. Comp. Neurol., 24:343-427.

Articles on: Cranial nerves (Vol. 3, pp. 321-39); Ear: anatomy of the auditory (acoustic) nerve and its end-organs (Vol. 3, pp. 719-25); and End organs, nervous (Vol. 4, pp. 20-27), in: *Reference Handbook of the Medical Sciences*, 3d ed., ed. by Thomas Lathrop Stedman. New York, William Wood and Company.

1915

With G. E. Coghill. The development of reflex mechanisms in Amblystoma. J. Comp. Neurol., 25:65-85.

Introspection as a biological method. J. Philos., Psychol., Sci. Methods, 12:543-51.

An Introduction to Neurology. Philadelphia, W. B. Saunders Co. xi + 355 pp. 2d ed., 1918; 3d rev. ed., 1922; 4th ed., 1927; 5th ed., 1931.

1916

Olfactory nerve. In: *Reference Handbook of the Medical Sciences*, 3d ed., ed. by Thomas Lathrop Stedman, Vol. 6, pp. 865-70. New York, William Wood and Company.

1917

The internal structure of the midbrain and thalamus of Necturus. J. Comp. Neurol., 28:215-348.

Articles on: Phrenic nerve (pp. 187-88); Spinal cord and spinal nerves (pp. 828-55), in: *Reference Handbook of the Medical Sciences*, 3d ed., ed. by Thomas Lathrop Stedman, Vol. 7.

1918

With Elizabeth C. Crosby. *A Laboratory Outline of Neurology.* Philadelphia, W. B. Saunders Co. Pp. 5-120. 2d ed., 1920.

1919

The sense of fishes. Natural History, 19:322-24; Aquatic Life, 4:163-66.

1920

Irreversible differentiation and orthogenesis. Science, 51:621-25; Anat. Record, 17:348. (A)

1921

A sketch of the origin of the cerebral hemispheres. J. Comp. Neurol., 32:429-54.

The brain of *Caenolestes obscurus*. Field Museum of Natural History, Publication No. 207, Zoological Series, 14:157-62. Chicago, The Museum.

The connections of the vomeronasal nerve, accessory olfactory bulb and amygdala in Amphibia. J. Comp. Neurol., 33:213-80.

1922

Some factors in the development of the amphibian nervous system. Anat. Record, 23:291-305.

What are viscera? Journal of Anatomy, 56:167-76.

Functional factors in the morphology of the forebrain in fishes. Libro en honor de D. Santiago Ramón y Cajal, Vol. 1, pp. 143-204. Madrid.

1923

Sketch of the evolution of the cerebellum. Anat. Record, 25:132. (A)

1924

Origin and evolution of the cerebellum. Archives of Neurology and Psychiatry, 11:621-52.

The nucleus olfactorius anterior of the opossum. J. Comp. Neurol., 37:317-59.

Neurological Foundations of Animal Behavior. New York, Henry Holt & Company. xii + 334 pp.

The nature of life. Chapter VI in: *Contributions of Sciences to Religion,* by S. M. Mathews *et al.* New York, D. Appleton & Co.

The amphibian forebrain. I. Amblystoma, external form. J. Comp. Neurol., 37:361-71.

The amphibian forebrain. II. The olfactory bulb of amblystoma. J. Comp. Neurol., 37:373-96.

1925

Morphogenetic factors in the differentiation of the nervous system. Physiological Reviews, 5:112-30.

Some relationships of the visceral nervous system. International Clinics (Philadelphia), 1:36-45.

The innervation of palatal taste buds and teeth of Amblystoma. J. Comp. Neurol., 38:389-97.

Self-control and social control. In: *The Child, the Clinic, and the Court,* pp. 156-77. New York, New Republic, Inc.

The natural history of purpose. Psychol. Rev., 32:417-30.

The amphibian forebrain. III. The optic tracts and centers of Amblystoma and the frog. J. Comp. Neurol., 39:433-89.

The problem of the cerebral cortex. Science, 62:523. (A)

1926

Brains of Rats and Men: A Survey of the Origin and Biological Significance of the Cerebral Cortex. Chicago, University of Chicago Press. xiii + 382 pp.

Biological determinism and human freedom. International Journal of Ethics, 37:36-52.

Fatalism or Freedom: A Biologist's Answer. New York, W. W. Norton & Company, Inc.; London, Kegan Paul, Trench, Truebner & Co., Ltd., 1927.

1927

The amphibian forebrain. IV. The cerebral hemispheres of Amblystoma. J. Comp. Neurol., 43:231-325.

The beginnings of the cerebral cortex. Science, 66:404. (A)

Science and living. Denison Univ. Bull., J. Sci. Lab., 22:172-80.

1928

Behavior and mechanism. Social Forces, 7:1-11.

The spiritual life. Journal of Religion, 8:505-23.

1929

The medulla oblongata of Necturus.   Anat. Record, 42:50. (A)

Heredity, environment—and ethics.   Child Study, 6:143-45.

The limitations of science.   J. Philos., 26:186-88.

The Thinking Machine. Chicago, University of Chicago Press. 374 pp. 2d ed., 1932.

Behavior and mechanism.   In: *Mind and Behavior,* Vol. 3, pp. 9-44, of *Man and His World,* ed. by Baker Brownell. New York, D. Van Nostrand Company, Inc.

Mechanism and organism.   J. Philos., 26:589-97.

Anatomical patterns and behavior patterns.   Physiological Zoology, 2:439-48.

1930

The order of nature.   Monist, 40:182-92.

The medulla oblongata of Necturus.   J. Comp. Neurol., 50:1-96.

The scientific study of man and the humanities.   In: *The New Social Science,* ed. by Leonard D. White, pp. 112-22. Chicago, University of Chicago Press.

Localization of function in the nervous system.   Proc. Nat. Acad. Sci., 16:643-50; Science, 71:514. (A)

The nervous tissue.   Chapters IX-XIX in: *A Text-book of Histology,* by Alexander A. Maximow, completed and edited by William Bloom, pp. 225-330. Philadelphia, W. B. Saunders Co.

1931

The amphibian forebrain. V. The olfactory bulb of Necturus. J. Comp. Neurol., 53:55-69.

1932

Henry Herbert Donaldson: an appreciation.   J. Comp. Neurol., 55:3-5.

1933

The functions of the olfactory parts of the cerebral cortex.   Proc. Nat. Acad. Sci., 19:7-14; Science, 76:522. (A)

Morphogenesis of the brain.   Journal of Morphology, 54:233-58.

The amphibian forebrain. VI. Necturus. J. Comp. Neurol., 58:1-288.

The amphibian forebrain. VII. The architectural plan of the brain. J. Comp. Neurol., 58:481-505.

The amphibian forebrain. VIII. Cerebral hemispheres and pallial primordia. J. Comp. Neurol., 58:737-59.

The evolution of cerebral localization patterns. Science, 78:439-44.

Francis Leroy Landacre. J. Comp. Neurol., 58:543-51.

1934

The amphibian forebrain. IX. Neuropil and other interstitial nervous tissue. J. Comp. Neurol., 59:93-116.

The amphibian forebrain. X. Localized functions and integrating functions. J. Comp. Neurol., 59:239-66.

What a naturalist means by nature. New Humanist, 7:1-6.

The hypothalamus of Necturus. J. Comp. Neurol., 59:375-429.

Neurobiotaxis in the corpus striatum. Psychiatrische en Neurologische Bladen, 1934, pp. 419-25. (Festbündel C. U. Ariëns Kappers, pp. 155-61.)

The interpeduncular nucleus of the brain of Necturus. J. Comp. Neurol., 60:111-35.

Nervous tissue. Chapters IX to XIII in: *A Text-book of Histology*, by Alexander A. Maximow and William Bloom, pp. 166-243. 2d rev. ed. Philadelphia, W. B. Saunders Co.

Factors of neural integration and neural disorder. In: *The Problem of Mental Disorder*, ed. by Madison Bentley, pp. 197-215. New York, McGraw-Hill Book Co., Inc.

The endocranial blood vascular system of Amblystoma. Zeitschrift für mikroskopisch-anatomische forschung, 36:540-44.

1935

The membraneous parts of the brain, meninges and their blood vessels in Amblystoma. J. Comp. Neurol., 61:297-346.

A topographic analysis of the thalamus and midbrain of Amblystoma. J. Comp. Neurol., 62:239-61.

Is the cerebral cortex equipotential? Journal of General Psychology, 13:398-400.

The motor tegmentum of Amblystoma. Anat. Record, 61:23, Supplement. (A)

1936

Conduction pathways in the cerebral peduncle of Amblystoma. J. Comp. Neurol., 63:293-352.

Is truth a value? J. Philos., 33:169-75.

Neurobiological foundations of modern humanism. Proceedings of the Institute of Medicine of Chicago, 11:86-99.

Control of behavior, its mechanism and evolution. American Journal of Psychiatry, 93:249-61.

Error in neurophysiology. Chapter VIII in: *The Story of Human Error*, ed. by Joseph Jastrow, pp. 251-67. New York, D. Appleton-Century Company, Inc.

Mechanisms of nervous adjustment. Jubilee symposium on Problems of Nervous Physiology and of Behavior. Dedicated to J. S. Beritoff, published by the Georgian Branch of the Academy of Sciences of USSR, Tiflis. Pp. 51-56 in English, pp. 57-62 in Russian.

1937

Development of the brain of Amblystoma in early functional stages. J. Comp. Neurol., 67:381-422.

Our endowment. Denison Univ. Bull., J. Sci. Lab., 32:145-53.

1938

Development of the cerebrum of Amblystoma during early swimming stages. J. Comp. Neurol., 68:203-41.

A biologist looks at the profit motive. Social Forces, 16:320-27.

Cerebral development of Amblystoma. Anat. Record, 70:36, Supplement. (A)

A biological survey of learning. Educational Trends, 6:5-13.

Development of the brain of Amblystoma punctatum from early swimming to feeding stages. J. Comp. Neurol., 69:13-30.

The brains of Amblystoma punctatum and A. tigrinum in early feeding stages. J. Comp. Neurol., 69:391-426.

The moral life. Hyde Park Baptist News, 3(6). Published by Hyde Park Baptist Church, Chicago.

1939

Internal structure of the thalamus and midbrain of early feeding larvae of Amblystoma. J. Comp. Neurol., 70:89-135.

The cerebrum of Amblystoma tigrinum in midlarval stages. J. Comp. Neurol., 70:249-66.

A neurologist makes up his mind. (Mellon lecture.) Sci. Monthly, 49:99-110.

Cerebral fiber tracts of Amblystoma tigrinum in midlarval stages. J. Comp. Neurol., 71:511-612.

1940

With A. T. Rasmussen and O. Larsell. John Black Johnston, 1868-1939. Anat. Record, 76:1-3.

1941

The founder and the early history of the Journal. J. Comp. Neurol., 74:25-38.

The optic system of fibers in brains of urodele amphibians. Anat. Record, 79:31-32, Supplement No. 2. (A)

Development of the optic nerves of Amblystoma. J. Comp. Neurol., 74:473-534.

Little academies I have known. Sci. Monthly, 53:133-41.

The eyes and optic paths of the catfish, Ameiurus. J. Comp. Neurol., 75:255-86.

George Ellett Coghill. Science, 94:202-4.

Naturalistic ethics. Humanist, 1:73-79.

Optic and postoptic systems of fibers in the brain of Necturus. J. Comp. Neurol., 75:487-544.

1942

Scientific pioneering in the middle west. Sci. Monthly, 54:49-56.

The young naturalists' society. Sci. Monthly, 54:251-58.

Incubation stages of scientific investigation. Sci. Monthly, 54:361-69.

Optic and postoptic systems in the brain of Amblystoma tigrinum. J. Comp. Neurol., 77:191-353.

What churches are for. Humanist, 2:132-36.

George Ellett Coghill, 1872-1941. In memoriam. Anat. Record, 83:1-7.
The meaning of science in human affairs. Denison Univ. Bull., J. Sci. Lab., 37:140-52.
George Ellett Coghill (1872-1941). Year Book of the American Philosophical Society, 1941, pp. 364-67.

1943

George Ellett Coghill. In: National Academy of Sciences, *Biographical Memoirs*, 22:251-73. New York and London, Columbia University Press.
The cranial nerves. A review of fifty years. Denison Univ. Bull., J. Sci. Lab., 38:41-51.

1944

Apparatus of optic and visceral correlation in the brain of Amblystoma. Journal of Comparative Psychology, 37:97-105.
The incentives of science. Sci. Monthly, 58:462-66.
The fasciculus solitarius and its connections in amphibians and fishes. J. Comp. Neurol., 81:307-31.

1945

The natural history of experience. Philosophy of Science, 12:57-71.
A liberal education. Bulletin of the American Association of University Professors, 31:348-56.

1946

Editorial. Cornelius Ubbo Ariëns Kappers. J. Comp. Neurol., 85:308-11.
Scientific method and human values. American Scientist, 34:239-45.
World federation in embryo. Humanist, 6:40-42.
Progressive evolution. Science, 104:469.
The natural history collections of Denison University. Denison Univ. Bull., J. Sci. Lab., 39:175-82.

1947

Seeing and believing. Sci. Monthly, 64:253-60.
The proprioceptive nervous system. J. Nerv. Ment. Dis., 106:355-58.

1948

The Brain of the Tiger Salamander, Ambystoma tigrinum. Chicago, University of Chicago Press. viii + 409 pp.
Mabel Bishop. (Memorial Resolution.) Anat. Record, 100:397-98.
With O. Larsell. The proprius system. Anat. Record, 100:673. (A)
Evolution and mind. In: *Encyclopaedia Britannica,* Vol. 8, pp. 929-31. Chicago, Encyclopaedia Britannica, Inc.
George Ellett Coghill, Naturalist and Philosopher. Chicago, University of Chicago Press. xxi + 280 pp.

1949

A biological survey of integrative levels. In: *Philosophy for the Future,* ed. by Roy Wood Sellars *et al.,* pp. 222-42. New York, The Macmillan Co.

1950

Mechanisms of nervous adjustment. Dialectica (Neuchâtel), 4:243-47.
Adolph Meyer, 1886-1950. J. Comp. Neurol., 92:129-32.

1951

Introduction. In: *The Attitude Theory of Emotion,* by Nina Bull. Nervous and Mental Disease Monographs No. 81, pp. ix-xiii. New York, Nervous and Mental Disease Monographs.
Oliver S. Strong, 1864-1951. J. Comp. Neurol., 94:177-80.

1955

Clarence Luther Herrick, pioneer naturalist, teacher and psychobiologist. Transactions of the American Philosophical Society, 45:1-85.
Psychology from a biologist's point of view. Psychol. Rev., 62:333-40.

1956

Analytic and integrative nervous functions. Dedicated to J. Beritoff, published by the Georgian Branch of the Academy of Sciences of USSR, Tiflis. Pp. 335-39 in English, pp. 339-42 in Russian.

Humanism of today and tomorrow.   Humanist, 16:111-13.

Machines and men.   Humanist, 16:210-16.

The Evolution of Human Nature. Austin, University of Texas Press. 506 pp.

1957

Medical teaching by a non-medical specialist.   Perspectives in Biology and Medicine, 1:17-32.

1958

With George H. Bishop.   A comparative survey of the spinal lemniscus system.   In: *Reticular Formation of the Brain,* pp. 353-60. International Symposium Henry Ford Hospital, Detroit. Boston, Little, Brown and Company.

1961

The nature and origins of human mentation. (Introduced and edited by Paul G. Roofe after Dr. Herrick's death.) World Neurology, 2:1027-45.

H. H. Hess

HARRY HAMMOND HESS

May 24, 1906–August 25, 1969

BY HAROLD L. JAMES

HARRY HAMMOND HESS was one of the truly remarkable earth scientists of this century; indeed it would be difficult to name another of comparable depth, breadth, and impact. His was a rare, perhaps unique talent. It combined far-ranging interests and a brilliant intuiton with a capability and willingness to carry out work calling for extreme detail and precision. His career was an extraordinary one: a mineralogist of world repute who became even better known for introduction of new concepts on the origin of continents and oceans and for his leadership in space science affairs; a quiet and unassuming scientist of puckish disposition who became a wartime Navy commander and rose ultimately to the rank of Rear Admiral.

Harry Hess was born in New York City, the son of Elizabeth Engel Hess and Julian S. Hess, who was a member of the New York Stock Exchange. His paternal grandfather, Simon Hess, was a leader in construction work in New York, first in harbor dredging and later in dam construction. Harry's middle name, Hammond, derives from the town of Hammond, Indiana, where his maternal grandfather, Julius Engel, operated a liquor distillery. Harry had one brother, Frank, who graduated from Yale in 1931 and is now in real estate and retailing in Huntington, New York. Harry's heritage was Germanic, yet there was so little in his personality and career that whould fit the supposed Germanic mold that one must again conclude that this stereotype, like that of the humorless Englishman, should be abandoned for all time.

Harry Hess entered Yale University in 1923 from Asbury Park High School in New Jersey, where he had specialized— with no great distinction—in foreign languages. At Yale he began with a major in electrical engineering but soon shifted to geology, where he came into contact with a distinguished faculty, including the outstanding mineralogist and petrologist Adolf Knopf. Possibly apocryphal—though related by Harry himself—is the story that he failed his first course in mineralogy, and that Knopf, a hard taskmaster, predicted no future for him in a field in which he subsequently was to become a world leader.

After award of the B.S. degree from Yale in 1927, Harry then spent two strenuous and memorable years as an exploration geologist in northern Rhodesia, working in the bush most of the time with a native African crew. Harry loved to recount tales of this venture; obviously, despite hardship and danger, he enjoyed it hugely and in all likelihood it strengthened those innate traits of humor, tolerance, quiet competence, and coolness under stress that were to be his hallmarks in later life. In 1929 he returned to the United States to begin graduate studies at Princeton University. A persistent story is that his original intent was to enter Harvard, but that as an inveterate smoker he was turned away by the No Smoking signs that dotted the buildings there.

At Princeton, Harry was a member of an extraordinary and diversified group of graduate students working principally under A. F. Buddington, A. H. Phillips, R. M. Field, and Edward Sampson. Each of these major professors left a mark on Harry's subsequent career: Buddington in petrology, Phillips in mineralogy, Field in oceanic structure, and Sampson in mineral deposits, particularly those of the stratiform complexes. In a curious, yet absolutely typical way, Harry's future research was to combine and extend concepts and approaches drawn from all these sources. His debt to all, but particularly to "Bud," his teacher and close friend, was freely acknowledged. He became a classic example of one who stood on the shoulders of giants to reach further, just as we who follow will stand on his. His doctoral dissertation was a field and laboratory study of an altered peridotite body at Schuyler, Virginia, and he was awarded the Ph.D. degree by Princeton in 1932.

After completion of his graduate studies at Princeton, Harry taught at Rutgers (1932-1933) and was a Research Associate at the Geophysical Laboratory in Washington, D.C. (1933-1934). In 1934 he joined the Princeton faculty and married Annette Burns, daughter of George Plumer Burns, professor of botany at the University of Vermont. Annette was to be his strong support for the rest of his life, and in later years was to be his constant companion at scientific meetings and conferences. Harry is survived by two sons: George, who is a physicist at the University of Virginia; and Frank, who is with a publishing firm at Whitehorse, Yukon Territory.

It is not easy to summarize Harry's career, because only superficially does it fall into neat categories of time. Buddington has written elsewhere that Harry Hess lived five lives contemporaneously. This is true, yet these separate activities intermeshed and complemented each other, in ways often unknown to his associates in any one area. The distinctive aspect, in fact, is one in which every thread of activity and research interest, beginning with those of student days, becomes imperceptively interwoven with time into a pattern of increasing breadth, color, and complexity.

In 1931, while still a graduate student, Harry participated in a submarine gravity study of the West Indies under F. A. Vening Meinesz. This work was extended in the next few years to the Lesser Antilles, using a U.S. Navy submarine obtained through the persuasion of R. M. Field, and Harry acquired a reserve officer rating of Lieutenant (J.G.) in order to facilitate operations. These studies resulted in Harry's first major paper (1938) on island arcs and their origin. Still a reserve officer at the time of the attack on Pearl Harbor, December 7, 1941, Harry took the 7:42 train the next morning to report for active duty and served for the remainder of World War II. His first assignment was in New York with responsibility for detection of enemy submarines in the North Atlantic. His leadership and incredible intuitive ability to perceive patterns of operation led ultimately to a very high "kill" rate and within two years to virtual elimination of the submarine threat. Harry then maneuvered affairs so that he was assigned to the decoy vessel *U.S.S. Big Horn,* which provided him with a firsthand test of the effectiveness of the detection program, and thereafter he managed to remain on sea duty. Ultimately he became Commander of the attack transport *U.S.S. Cape Johnson* in the Pacific and participated in the landings on the Marianas, Leyte, Linguayan Gulf, and Iwo Jima.

Typically, Harry's strenuous wartime activities did not halt his scientific curiosity. The *Cape Johnson,* like most ships of its class in World War II, was fitted with sounding gear, and by discrete choices of travel routes —perhaps not always in strict accord with orders—and continuous use of the equipment, bathymetric knowledge of the Pacific was vastly extended and the submerged flat-topped mounts now known as guyots (in honor of the first professor of geology at Princeton) were first found. The results of these investigations were published shortly after the end of the war (1946, 1947, 1948), but publication of these papers was by no means to be the end of his involvement with marine affairs. His continued interest led him in the fifties to take leadership in a proposal to drill through the thin oceanic crust into the earth's mantle, an idea originating with oceanographer Walter Munk. Project Mohole was launched by the spontaneously generated American Miscellaneous Society (AMSOC), and funds were allocated by the National Science Foundation in 1958 for preliminary work. The project came to an inglorious end in 1966, in part because of escalation of costs and the entry of partisan political factors, in part because of disagreement among scientists and engineers as to the need for intermediate steps, and in part because of failure to recognize that the lighthearted origins of AMSOC were only a thin cover for deeply serious intent and commitment. The project did, however, establish feasibility of dynamic positioning for deep water drilling, and the experience was invaluable to the present highly successful ocean drilling program being sponsored by The National Science Foundation.

Harry's detailed mineralogic studies began in the laboratory under A. H. Phillips at Princeton and in the field under Arthur Buddington and Edward Sampson. These studies resulted in many papers, two of which are classic: "Pyroxenes of Common Mafic Magmas," published in 1941, and *Stillwater Igneous Complex, Montana,* published in 1960. The pyroxene paper remains the foundation for all modern studies. Few people who knew Harry for his broader speculations on the crust and mantle of the earth realized that throughout the years he was a major contributor to an understanding of this important group of rock-forming minerals. In 1938, he and Phillips showed that the fine-scale lamellae of calcium-poor orthopyroxene were due to subsolidus exsolution of calcic pyroxene, rather than to twinning; in 1952 he produced a definitive paper on unit cell dimensions. It is significant that at the time of his death Harry was a designated NASA Principal Investigator for the pyroxenes of the returned lunar samples. The long-delayed monograph on the Stillwater complex stemmed in large part from work with fellow graduate students Arthur L. Howland and Joe Webb Peoples in the early thirties. Though now supplemented and enlarged by more detailed studies, it remains a marvellous example of sound conclusions drawn by brilliant intuition from limited data. The same ability that led Harry to detect patterns in enemy submarine activity in World War II was the despair of those students of crystal-settled complexes who saw him reach the right answers with only a skimpy amount of data.

Peridotite—its origin and significance—probably was the object of Harry's deepest scientific devotion. Almost from the beginning of his involvement with the subject in his doctoral thesis, he realized that this mantle-derived rock was a key to the understanding of the deeper crustal structure of the earth and to the recognition of older orogenic belts. His 1939 paper presented to the 17th International Geological Congress was his first exposition of the relation between island arcs, gravity anomalies, and peridotite. Many of his initial ideas later were abandoned —Harry was never hesitant to discard an earlier view if the evidence called for it—but the role of this unusual rock was to be the critical factor in his later theories of the nature and behavior of oceanic crust. His last field study, like the first, was on peridotite. In July 1969, only a month before his death, he went to Barberton Mountain Land, in South Africa, to examine the evidence for extrusive lavas of peridotite composition, which had been reported to him by his former student, A. E. J. Engel.

Harry Hess was a pioneer in development of the now widely accepted theory of ocean-floor spreading. In 1960, in a widely circulated report to the Office of Naval Research, Harry proposed that the mid-oceanic ridges were the loci of upwelling mantle convection cells that progressively moved mantle material outward and eventually under the continents, a brilliant concept that now appears to be confirmed by the symmetrical distribution of magnetic anomalies on both sides of the ridges. His paper was published formally in 1962, and a study made in 1969 indicates that it was the most referenced work in solid-earth geophysics in the years 1966-1968. Whether his concept of a serpentinized peridotite under the ocean floors proves valid or not, this paper stimulated intense research and is part of what is the major advance in geologic science of this century.

In 1947, after returning from the wars, Harry rejuvenated the Princeton activity in the Caribbean. The Princeton Caribbean Research Project, supported by Princeton University, the National Science Foundation, the Office of Naval Research, several oil companies, and the governments of Puerto Rico, Venezuela, and Colombia, explored every aspect of Caribbean geology. It still continues, and it already has resulted in the publication of thirty-four Ph.D. dissertations and has been the graduate training ground for a host of students from many parts of the world. Special tribute was paid to Harry during the Venezuelan Geological Congress in November 1969, in recognition of his great contributions to geologic understanding of the region.

As a reserve officer in the Navy after World War II, Harry spent several weeks on active duty in Washington each year, and was on call for advice on emergency issues such as the Cuban missile crisis, the loss of the submarine *Thresher*, and the Pueblo affair.

Following his election to the National Academy of Sciences in 1952, Harry increasingly was called upon to serve as an adviser to federal scientific organizations. In succession he was chairman of the Committee for Disposal of Radioactive Wastes, chairman of the Earth Sciences Division of the National Research Council, and, until his death, chairman of the Space Science Board. In this last role, he was highly influential in design of space exploration of the earth's moon and of the planets.

Harry was chairman of the Department of Geology at Princeton from 1950 to 1966 and served on many important University committees. He was, despite a quiet, low-keyed approach, extremely effective here as in other affairs; one dean was heard to remark of Harry that his bite was worse than his bark. He was an outstanding teacher—but in a highly unorthodox way. Though an excellent lecturer when the spirit moved him, basically he believed that students "learned by doing," not by being talked to. Any student, graduate or undergraduate, who showed the spark of scientific curiosity could depend on personal attention; Harry would supply him with ideas and references to the key literature that would spur him on.

Many honors were awarded Harry Hess. He was elected to the National Academy of Sciences in 1952, to the American Philosophical Society in 1960, and to the American Academy of Arts and Sciences in 1968. He was President of the Geodesy Section of the American Geophysical Union, 1951-1953, and of the Tectonophysics Section, 1956-1958. He was President of the Mineralogical Society of America in 1955 and of the Geological Society of America in 1963. He was an honorary Foreign Member of the Geological Society of London, the Geological Society of South Africa, and the Sociedad Venezolana de Geologos. In 1966, the same year he received the Penrose

Medal Award of the Geological Society of America, he was elected Foreign Member of the Accademia Nazionale dei Lincei and was awarded the $32,000 Feltrinelli Prize. In 1969, Yale University awarded him an honorary doctorate degree. Posthumously, he was awarded the Distinguished Public Service Award by the National Aeronautics and Space Administration. The Navy awarded him the Victory Ribbon, World War II; the American and European Theater Ribbons; the Asiatic-Pacific Ribbon (four stars); the Philippine Liberation Ribbon (one star); and the Naval Reserve Medal.

Harry's trademark, always evident in his doodles, was the rabbit. But, as many found, this slightly built, quiet, unobtrusive man was no rabbit in fact; he was a fierce fighter for science, a dedicated and steadfast defender of any cause he thought to be just. Yet withal he was a gentle and kindly person, tolerant of the foibles and weaknesses of mankind— including his own. Those of us who knew him lost a great friend, and the world lost a great scientist and a scientist-statesman.

In compiling this biographical memoir of Harry Hess I have received aid from a number of people, notably from Annette Hess and Frank Hess on family matters, and from Arthur Buddington, John Maxwell, Benjamin Morgan, and William Thurston on Harry's professional career. I am particularly indebted to Dr. Buddington, who made available to me his extensive files and drafts of a memoir to be published elsewhere, and to Mrs. Guenever P. Knapp for the bibliographic compilation and other materials.

BIBLIOGRAPHY

KEY TO ABBREVIATIONS

Am. J. Sci. = American Journal of Science
Am. Mineralogist = American Mineralogist
Bull. Geol. Soc. Am. = Bulletin of the Geological Society of America
Econ. Geol. = Economic Geology
J. Geol. = Journal of Geology
Proc. Geol. Soc. Am. = Proceedings of the Geological Society of America
Trans. Am. Geophys. Union = Transactions of the American Geophysical
    Union

1932

Interpretation of gravity-anomalies and sounding-profiles obtained in the West Indies by the International Expedition to the West Indies in 1932. Trans. Am. Geophys. Union, 13th annual meeting, pp. 26-33.

1933

With R. M. Field. A bore-hole in the Bahamas. Trans. Am. Geophys. Union, 14th annual meeting, pp. 234-35. Bull. Geol. Soc. Am., 44(1):85. (A)
Hydrothermal metamorphism of an ultrabasic intrusive at Schuyler, Virginia. Am. J. Sci., 26(154):377-408.
Interpretation of geological and geophysical observations. In: *The Navy-Princeton Gravity Expedition to the West Indies in 1932,* pp. 27-54. Washington, U.S. Hydrographic Office.
The problem of serpentinization and the origin of certain chrysotile asbestos, talc, and soapstone deposits. Econ. Geol., 28(7):634-57.
Submerged river valleys of the Bahamas. Trans. Am. Geophys. Union, 14th annual meeting, pp. 168-70.

1935

With A. H. Phillips. Metamorphic differentiation at serpentine-country rock contacts. Proc. Geol. Soc. Am., 1934, pp. 425-26. (A)
The problem of serpentinization (discussion). Econ. Geol., 30(3): 320-25.

1936

With A. H. Phillips. Chemical composition and optical properties of some calcic plagioclases. Am. Mineralogist, 21(3):194. (A)

Plagioclase, pyroxene and olivine variations in the Stillwater Complex. Am. Mineralogist, 21(3):198-99. (A)

With A. H. Phillips. Metamorphic differentiation at contacts between serpentinite and siliceous country rocks. Am. Mineralogist, 21(6):333-62.

With P. MacClintock. Submerged valleys on continental slopes and changes of sea level. Science, 83:332-34.

1937

Further discussion on submerged canyons. Science, 85:593.

Geological interpretation of data collected on cruise of USS *Barracuda* in the West Indies—preliminary report. Trans. Am. Geophys. Union, 18th annual meeting, pp. 69-77.

A primary ultramafic magma. Trans. Am. Geophys. Union, 18th annual meeting, pp. 247-49.

With A. F. Buddington. Layered peridotite laccoliths in the Trout River area, Newfoundland. A discussion. Am. J. Sci., 33:380-88. (Princeton University Contribution to the Geology of Newfoundland, No. 17.)

With A. H. Phillips. Orthopyroxenes of the Bushveld type. Am. Mineralogist, 22(12):6. (A)

With J. T. Rouse, F. Foote, J. S. Vhay, and K. P. Wilson. Petrology, structure, and relation to tectonics of porphyry intrusions in the Beartooth Mountains, Montana. J. Geol., 45:717-40.

1938

Gravity anomalies and island arc structure with particular reference to the West Indies. Proceedings of the American Philosophical Society, 79:71-96. Bull. Geol. Soc. Am., 49:1885 (A), and Mines Magazine, 29:135 (A).

Orthopyroxenes of the Bushveld type. Am. Mineralogist, 23:450-56.

Primary banding in norite and gabbro. Trans. Am. Geopnys. Union, 19th annual meeting, pp. 264-68.

A primary peridotite magma. Am. J. Sci., 35:321-44.

1939

Extreme fractional crystallization of a basaltic magma; the Stillwater igneous complex. Trans. Am. Geophys. Union, 20th annual meeting, pp. 430-32. (A)

Island arcs, gravity anomalies, and serpentinite intrusions. A contribution to the ophiolite problem. 17th International Geological Congress, USSR, 1937, Report, Vol. 2, pp. 263-83. Moscow.

A new bathymetric chart of the Caribbean area. Trans. Am. Geophys. Union, 20th annual meeting, p. 422. (A)

Recent advances in interpretation of gravity anomalies and island arc structure. International Union of Geodesy and Geophysics, 7th General Assembly, Document A, pp. 46-48. Washington, International Union of Geodesy and Geophysics.

World distribution of serpentinized peridotites and its geologic significance. Am. Mineralogist, 24:275-76. (A)

1940

Appalachian peridotite belt, its significance in the sequence of events in mountain building. Bull. Geol. Soc. Am., 51:1996. (A)

Crystallization of pyroxenes and the pigeonite problem. Trans. Am. Geophys. Union, 21st annual meeting, pp. 358-59. (A)

Peridotite intrusions, gravity anomalies and island arcs. Pan-American Geologist, 73:312. (A)

The petrology of the Skaergaard intrusion, Kangerdlugesuaq, East Greenland, by L. R. Wager and W. A. Deer (1939). An essay review. Am. J. Sci., 238:372-78.

Recent advances in interpretation of gravity anomalies and island-arc structure (West Indies). Union Géodesique et Géophysique Internationale. Association de Géodesie, Travaux, tome 16, rept. 5-b, Annexe, pp. 25-28.

With W. M. Ewing. Continuation of a gravity survey of the Caribbean region and the correlation of gravity field with geological structure. Yearbook of the American Philosophical Society, 1939, pp. 236-38. (A)

With F. Betz, Jr. The floor of the north Pacific ocean. Trans. Am. Geophys. Union, 21st annual meeting, pp. 348-49. (A)

With A. H. Phillips. Optical properties and chemical composition of magnesian orthopyroxenes. Am. Mineralogist, 25:271-85.

1941

Pyroxenes of common mafic magmas. Am. Mineralogist, 26:515-35, Part I; 573-94, Part II.

1942

Structure and gravity field of the Caribbean region. In: *Proceedings of the 8th American Scientific Congress,* Vol. 4, Geological Sciences, p. 399. Washington, Department of State.

With F. Betz. The floor of the north Pacific ocean. Geographical Review, 32:99-116.

1944

Augite in Hawaiian basalt. Am. J. Sci., 242:625.

Report of special committee on geophysical and geological study of ocean basins, 1943-44. Trans. Am. Geophys. Union, 25th annual meeting, appendix H, pp. 365-66.

1946

Report of special committee on geophysical and geological study of ocean basins. Trans. Am. Geophys. Union, 27(4):594-95.

Bathymetry and geologic structure of the western north Pacific. Bull. Geol. Soc. Am., 57:1202-3, Part II. (A)

Drowned ancient islands of the Pacific basin. Am. J. Sci., 244: 772-91. Also in: International Hydrographic Review, 24:81-91, 1947; and Smithsonian Institution, Annual Report for 1947, pp. 281-300, 1948.

1947

New bathymetric map H. O. 5485. Excavating Engineer, 39:434-35.

Optical properties of common clinopyroxenes. Bull. Geol. Soc. Am., 58:1192. (A)

Report of special committee on geophysical and geological study of ocean basins. Trans. Am. Geophys. Union, 28:502-3.

Major structural trends of the western north Pacific. Transactions of the New York Academy of Sciences, Ser. 3, 9:245-46. (A)

1948

Major structural features of the western north Pacific, an interpretation of H. O. 5485, bathymetric chart, Korea to New Guinea. Bull. Geol. Soc. Am., 59:417-45.

Optical property curves for common clinopyroxenes. Am. Mineralogist, 33:199. (A)

Report of the chairman of the special committee on geophysical and geological study of ocean basins, 1947-48. Trans. Am. Geophys. Union, 29:913-14.

With E. P. Henderson. Moore County (N.C.) meteorite: a further study with comment on its primordial environment. Mineralogical Society of America, 29th annual meeting, program and abstracts, p. 8. Bull. Geol. Soc. Am., 59:1330. (A)

1949

Chemical composition and optical properties of common clinopyroxenes, Part I. Am. Mineralogist, 34:621-66.

With J. C. Maxwell. Geological reconnaissance of the Island of Margarita, Venezuela, Part I. Bull. Geol. Soc. Am., 60:1857-68.

With E. P. Henderson. The Moore County (N.C.) meteorite: a further study with comment on its primordial environment. Am. Mineralogist, 34:494-507.

With G. L. Davis. Radium content of ultramafic igneous rocks. II. Geological and chemical implications. Am. J. Sci., 247:856-82.

1950

Catastrophe in the Caribbean. Research Reviews, February, pp. 1-5.

Investigaciones geofisicas y geologicas en la region del Caribe. Associacion Venezolana de Geologia, Mineria y Petroleo, Boletin, tomo II, num. 1, pp. 5-22.

Vertical mineral variation in the Great Dyke of Southern Rhodesia (with discussion). Transactions of the Geological Society of South Africa, 53:159-66.

With M. W. Buell, Jr. The greatest depth in the oceans. Trans. Am. Geophys. Union, 31:401-5.

1951

Comment on mountain building. In: Colloquium on plastic flow deformation within the earth, B. Gutenberg, chm. Trans. Am. Geophys. Union, 32:528-31.

With A. Poldervaart. Pyroxenes in the crystallization of basaltic magma. J. Geol., 54:472-89.

1952

Orthopyroxenes of the Bushveld type, ion substitutions and changes in unit cell dimensions. Am. J. Sci., Bowen Volume, pp. 173-87.

With G. Dengo and R. J. Smith. Antigorite from the vicinity of Caracas, Venezuela. Am. Mineralogist, 37:68-75.

Presentation of the Day medal of the Geological Society of America to Martin J. Buerger. Proc. Geol. Soc. Am., 1951, p. 55.

1953

With J. C. Maxwell. Caribbean research project. Bull. Geol. Soc. Am., 64:1-6.

With J. C. Maxwell. Major structural features of the south-west Pacific: a preliminary interpretation of H. O. 5484, bathymetric chart, New Guinea to New Zealand. In: *Proceedings of the 7th Pacific Science Congress*, Vol. 2, pp. 14-17. Held at Auckland and Christchurch, New Zealand, 1949. Wellington, Harry H. Tombs, Ltd.

With H. Kuno. Unit cell dimensions of clinoenstatite and pigeonite in relation to other common clinopyroxenes. Am. J. Sci., 251:741-52.

1954

Changes in the Earth's crust with time. (From "Symposium on geophysics and geophysical geodesy," March 1954.) Bulletin Géodésique, 31:78-79.

Geological hypotheses and the Earth's crust under the oceans. In: *A Discussion on the Floor of the Atlantic Ocean*, pp. 341-48. Proceedings of the Royal Society of London, Series A, Vol. 222, No. 1150.

Sixteenth award of the William Bowie medal; citation. Trans. Am. Geophys. Union, 35:389-90.

1955

The oceanic crust. Journal of Marine Research, 14:423-39.

Serpentines, orogeny and epeirogeny. In: *Crust of the Earth*, ed. by A. W. Poldervaart, pp. 391-407. Geological Society of America, Special Paper No. 62. New York, The Society. (Symposium)

1956

Discussion (of "The magnetic properties and differentiation of dolerite sills—a critical discussion," by Frederick Walker). Am. J. Sci., 254:446-51.

1957

Presentation of the Roebling medal of the Mineralogical Society of America to Arthur F. Buddington. Am. Mineralogist, 42:256-61.

The Vening Meinesz negative gravity anomaly belt of island arcs (1926-1956). Koninklijk Nederlandsch Geologisch-Mijnbouw-kundig Genootschap, Verhandelingen, Geologisch Serie, deel 18, pp. 183-88.

1958

With W. R. Thurston. Disposal of radioactive waste on land. Trans. Am. Geophys. Union, 39:467-68.

1959

The AMSOC hole to the Earth's mantle. Trans. Am. Geophys. Union, 40:340-45.

Nature of great oceanic ridges. Preprints of the 1st International Oceanographic Congress (New York, August 31–September 12, 1959), pp. 33-34. Washington, American Association for the Advancement of Science. (A)

Presentation of Arthur L. Day medal to John Verhoogen. Proc. Geol. Soc. Am., 1958, pp. 75-76.

Obituary of Reginald A. Daly. Proceedings of the Fall Meeting of the Geological Society of London (1959), No. 1572, pp. 135-36.

Outstanding problems of Caribbean geology. Second Caribbean Geological Conference, January 4-9, Mayagüez. Mayagüez, University of Puerto Rico. (A)

1960

The AMSOC hole to the Earth's mantle. American Scientist, 48:254-63.

Caribbean research project: progress report. Bull. Geol. Soc. Am., 71:235-40.

Evolution of ocean basins. Report to Office of Naval Research. Contract No. 1858(10), NR 081-067. 38 pp.

Stillwater Igneous Complex, Montana, a Quantitative Mineralogical Study. With an appendix on optical properties of low temperature plagioclase, by J. R. Smith. Geological Society of America, Memoir No. 80. New York, The Society. 230 pp.

With J. C. MacLachlan and R. Shagam. Geology of the La Victoria area, Aragua, Venezuela. Bull. Geol. Soc. Am., 71:241-47.

1962

History of ocean basins. In: *Petrologic Studies: A Volume in Honor of A. F. Buddington*, ed. by A. E. J. Engel, Harold L. James, and B. F. Leonard, pp. 599-620. New York, Geological Society of America.

Obituary of Richard Montgomery Field. Trans. Am. Geophys. Union, 43:1-3.

1963

With R. L. Fisher. Trenches. In: *The Earth Beneath the Sea: History*, Vol. 1 of *The Sea: Ideas and Observations on Progress in the Study of the Seas*, ed. by M. N. Hill, pp. 411-36. New York, Interscience Publishers.

1964

Seismic anisotropy of the uppermost mantle under oceans. Nature, 203:629-31.

Histoire des bassins de l'océan. Nucleus, 5:380-92.

The oceanic crust, the upper mantle and the Mayagüez serpentinized peridotite. In: *A Study of Serpentinite: The AMSOC Core Hole Near Mayagüez, Puerto Rico*, ed. by C. A. Burk, pp. 169-75. NAS-NRC Publication 1188.

With G. Otalora. Mineralogical and chemical composition of the Mayagüez serpentinite cores. In: *A Study of Serpentinite: The AMSOC Core Hole Near Mayagüez, Puerto Rico*, ed. by C. A. Burk, pp. 152-68. NAS-NRC Publication 1188.

1965

Mid-oceanic ridges and tetonics of the sea-floor. In: *Submarine Geology and Geophysics*, 17th Colston Symposium, ed. by W. F. Whittard and R. Bradshaw. London, Butterworth & Co. 464 pp.

1966

With H. S. Ladd. Mohole: preliminary drilling. Science, 152:544-45.

With J. D. Sides and W. H. Tonking. The mohole project, phase II. Geological Survey of Canada (Ottawa), Paper 66-13, pp. 146-78.

Caribbean research project, 1965, and bathymetric chart. In: *Caribbean Geological Investigations,* ed. by H. H. Hess, pp. 1-10. Geological Society of America, Memoir 98. 310 pp.

1967

Drowned ancient islands of the Pacific basin. In: *Source Book in Geology 1900-1950,* ed. by Kirtley F. Mather, pp. 371-74. Cambridge, Harvard University Press. (Reprint, in part, of the article in Am. J. Sci., 244:772-91, 1946.)

Our next space goals; what should they be? Scientific Research, 2:42b-d. (Reprinted, under the title "On satisfying human curiosity." In: University; a Princeton Quarterly, No. 35, pp. 31-32, Winter 1967-1968.)

With J. C. Maxwell and E. Moores. Peridotites and related ultramafic rocks. In: *Upper Mantle Project, U.S. Progress Report to ICSU,* p. 166. Washington, NAS-NRC.

The space program—goal or no goal during the 1970's? Astronautics & Aeronautics, 5:17-18.

Editor. *Basalts: The Poldervaart Treatise on Rocks of Basaltic Composition.* New York, Interscience Publishers, Inc. 2 vols., 862 pp. 1967, 1968.

1968

The ocean floor and a dynamic earth. Accademia Nazionale dei Lincei, Adunanze Straordinaire per il Conferimento dei Premi della Fondazione A. Feltrinelli, vol. 1, fasc. 4, pp. 81-87. (Above paper also printed in: Antonio Feltrinelli, Celebrazione del XXV Anniversario della Morte: Accademia Nazionale dei Lincei, Celebrazioni Lincee, 16, pp. 51-57.)

Reply. Journal of Geophysical Research, 73:6569. (Reply to: "Arthur Holmes: originator of spreading ocean floor hypothesis," by A. A. Meyerhoff.)

Review. *Ultramafic and Related Rocks,* ed. by Peter J. Wyllie. Geotimes, 13:34-36.

1969

Toward a balanced space program.   American Astronautical Society Newsletter, 8(3):4-5.

With G. Otalora (and with a chemical analysis by Eugene Jarosewich).   Modal analysis of igneous rocks by x-ray diffraction methods with examples from St. Paul's rock and an olivine nodule.   Am. J. Sci., 267:822-40.

1970

With F. J. Vine.   Sea-floor spreading.   In: *The Sea*, Vol. 4, Part II, ed. by Arthur E. Maxwell, pp. 587-622. New York, Wiley-Interscience.

George E. Kimball

GEORGE ELBERT KIMBALL

July 12, 1906–December 6, 1967

BY PHILIP M. MORSE

G EORGE KIMBALL was a generalist, capable of achieving outstanding recognition in two fields of science and of
leaving his mark on other fields of human endeavor. Perhaps
his greatest contribution was the education and inspiration he
gave to many younger men, now working in various fields of
science and technology.

Kimball was born in Chicago, in 1906. None of his immediate family evidenced an interest in science. His father started
as an office boy in the Chicago office of a New Britain, Connecticut, cutlery firm and worked his way up to be president
of the firm, selling many things beside cutlery. Kimball's
mother was a grade-school teacher in Illinois before she married. His only sister had a career in radio and the theater and
his only brother was a Rhodes scholar who became a professor
of journalism at Columbia. When Kimball was three years
old his family moved to New Britain, the home office of the
firm his father eventually was to head, thus reversing a family
migration. Kimball's grandfather had moved from Salem, Massachusetts, to Chicago early in this century.

Kimball grew up in New Britain, displaying few remembered signs of precocity and no marked preference for science.
He took all the Latin his local high school could provide but

his chemistry teacher was the one who caught his interest. After a year at Exeter Academy, he went on to Princeton, in 1924, urged there by his father, who felt that there were too many Yale graduates in Connecticut.

George was a fairly typical undergraduate at Princeton—he was on the water-polo team—though not a typical chemistry student of the time. He later claimed he chose the chemistry program because it allowed him to take as much physics and mathematics as chemistry, and he wanted to learn all three subjects. It was a fruitful time at Princeton in those subjects: Hugh S. Taylor was breaking new ground in chemistry; E. U. Condon and H. P. Robertson arrived there in 1927, fresh from Göttingen and filled with the new quantum mechanics; Veblen and Eisenhart were still teaching; E. P. Adams was still giving his gemlike lectures on analytic dynamics; the next wave was about to break. By the time Kimball received his bachelor's degree, in 1928, his interest had centered on quantum chemistry.

His abilities were such that the Chemistry Department offered him one of its best graduate fellowships, so he returned to Princeton, to work under Hugh Taylor, to soak up more physics and mathematics and, though yet a graduate student, to give a private course in quantum mechanics to the faculty of the Chemistry Department. E. Bright Wilson, who was two years behind Kimball, remembers that "I had an enormous respect for his knowledge and his ability to explain things. He seemed to know everything, and I think he really did. It was not at all that he was boastful or a show-off—I used to seek him out for enlightenment, and he always provided it."

His first research in quantum chemistry was forestalled by Henry Eyring, at that time in Berkeley. This did not matter much, for Eyring came on to Princeton the next year, 1931, and the two began a fruitful ten-year collaboration that resulted in their well-known treatise on quantum chemistry. Kimball's thesis for the doctoral degree, granted in 1932, was on the quantum mechanics of the recombination of hydrogen atoms.

Meantime John Slater, new head of the Physics Department at M.I.T., had been making progress in the quantum mechanics of molecular and crystal structure, and Kimball was desirous of extending his knowledge in this direction. He applied for a National Research Fellowship in physics for 1932-1933 but missed out because he was not well known to the physics fraternity. He stayed on at Princeton as instructor and next year applied for a National Research Fellowship in chemistry and won, coming to M.I.T. for the two years 1933-1935. Though he was officially assigned to the Chemistry Department, he spent much of his time working with Slater and others in the newly reconstituted Physics Department at the Institute.

These were heady times. The new faculty was augmented by a galaxy of postdoctoral fellows, and a new generation of graduate students enlivened the scene. Among this aerie of eaglets Kimball more than held his own. In 1965 he wrote a reminiscence of those times for the *International Journal of Quantum Chemistry*, which says, in part:

"The group which inhabited the third floor of the Eastman Laboratory sat at the feet of an academic trinity. John Slater (then 33 years of age) was the Old Man, with a long and illustrious career behind him. Philip Morse was the junior member of the trinity (he and I had been graduate students together at Princeton). The third, and most spiritual member was Julius Stratton, another old man (only a year younger than Slater), who mystified everyone (except Bill Hanson) by being more interested in Maxwell's equations than in the Schroedinger equation.

"These were exciting days, for in spite of Dirac's brave claim that the principles of quantum mechanics as then understood (1928) were sufficient to explain the whole of chemistry and most of physics, it was clear that the demonstration was far from complete. The great interest in Slater's group was in what is now called solid-state physics, and in the attempt to derive the properties of solids from the principles of quantum mechanics.

"The great Depression was at its height (my first job after I earned my Ph.D. paid the magnificent salary of $900 a year). As a result the group of graduate students and postdoctoral fellows with whom I worked lived a sort of Vie de Boheme. The center of this life was the third floor of the Eastman Laboratory, where we shared office space. We spent our evenings as well as our days there, but not always at our work. There was a ping-pong table, and someone discovered that the long, long corridors of M.I.T. made a wonderful place to roller skate.

"Every afternoon we had tea, served by Alice Hunter, student in chemistry, who has since done me the honor of becoming my wife. Those teas became a sort of discussion group, led by Norbert Wiener, who would argue violently on any subject, such as Chinese grammar, or whether or not the number of palindromic primes is infinite.

"From time to time we would have a party. The most famous of these was a theater party at which we all had seats in the second balcony to see a D'Oyly-Carte performance of the Gondoliers. Alice Hunter brought her knitting, including a large ball of bright orange yarn. During an intermission Ralph Johnson, sitting beside her, picked up the yarn and Satan (in the person of Bill Shockley) whispered 'Throw it.' Ralph did, all the way to the orchestra pit. Someone tried to throw it back, but it only got as far as the first balcony. From there it was thrown back and forth until the whole theater was festooned with orange yarn. Finally an ingenious usher broke the yarn and carried the remains of the ball up to the second balcony.

"My office mate was George Shortley. He was putting the finishing touches on Condon and Shortley's *Theory of Atomic Structure*. It is interesting to note that out of this rather small group, three of us, Philip Morse, George Shortley and myself have since served as presidents of the Operations Research Society of America.

"As far as I know John Slater is the only member of this group still working in quantum mechanics. The rest of us were diverted by World War II into other fields. Quantum mechanics is seldom mentioned as a way of training students to be business managers, but more of us seem to have landed in that spot than any other; Ralph Johnson became vice president of Thomson-Ramo-Wooldridge Inc.; Harry Krutter is chief scientist of the Naval Air Development Center; and George Shortley became director of the Washington operations of Booz, Allen Applied Research."

In addition to writing two papers with Shortley on quantum theory and one on the electronic structure of diamond, Kimball lectured on quantum chemistry in the Chemistry Department during his stay at M.I.T., helped organize a graduate course in methods of theoretical physics, and continued work on the text on quantum chemistry he and Eyring had begun. During the summer of 1935 he returned to Princeton, to work with Eyring. After a year spent teaching physics at Hunter College, he entered the Chemistry Department of Columbia University as an assistant professor. With a few intermissions he remained there until 1956, becoming Professor of Chemistry in 1947.

The five years 1936-1941 were productive ones. He published nine papers on reaction rates and electrochemical surface effects, he introduced and taught courses in quantum chemistry, and he supervised graduate student research. Some reminiscences by his colleagues will indicate his continuing interest in the educational process. For example, Professor Louis P. Hammett writes: "George was outstanding for his ability to understand, rearrange, and restate a mathematical development in a way to make it relatively intelligible. I have heard that he was successful in this respect with admirals, I have again and again seen him successful with chemists, including especially myself. He was a highly effective teacher with graduates and advanced undergraduates; I don't remember that he had much experience with elementary students. He was always extremely generous with his learning and his time, perhaps even too generous."

Professor Joseph E. Mayer writes: "During the time I was at Columbia George concerned himself considerably with our examinations, grading, and advising of graduate students. This was something that he felt we were not doing well, as we were not (but then I have never been at a department where I felt it was well done). He was, at the time, on the College Entrance Board Advisory Committee. I remember that he was a strong adherent of the short answer (multiple choice) type of question. This was partly because of necessity on an examination given to a very large population, but he had other arguments for its value; one that the grading could be absolutely quantitative and impersonal, and secondly that by having many questions one reduced the statistical fluctuation occasioned by hitting a student's 'blind spot' in an examination with few questions. He was, however, very aware, as few faculty members seem to be, of the necessity of very careful choice and wording in the questions.

"All this may sound as if George wanted to reduce education to a mechanical system, which was far from the case. He was very interested and concerned with the students and he had a considerable intuitive understanding of them. Above all, he was tolerant! I know he had a very critical appraisal of his friends' and colleagues' intelligence, but he was far too kindly to show obvious disapproval. I always felt he liked people. George and Alice had a home in Leonia, N.J., a few blocks from ours. We played bridge with them and some four other couples quite often. George was probably the best player of the group."

As to the effect of his interest in examinations, one of his students, Dr. Isaac Asimov, writes: "I had a lab course from Kimball in physical chemistry and at one time was asked one question out of a number of possible questions and drew a complete blank. I got a zero. I came to him afterward and said that the question I was asked was the *only* one of the alternatives I couldn't answer perfectly and that a mark of zero was not a true measure of the state of my knowledge. He said, 'The time will come when you will be asked a question, and it will be the *only* one of a number of alternatives which you *can* answer perfectly. You will then get a mark of one hundred and that will not be a true measure of the state of your knowledge either. But you will not complain then, will you?' Very much against my will, I saw the justice of that and subsided. I kept my zero—but I passed the course."

In 1942, when I was asked by the Navy to organize a group to analyze antisubmarine tactics, Kimball was one of the first persons I recruited. I remembered his breadth of interest, his analytic ability, and the clarity of his exposition, all of them important for the task ahead. He joined the group within a month. Almost immediately he showed his worth. Together we worked out the basis of the theory of search, and then wrote it up, all in less than two months. The writing was, if anything, more difficult than the theory, for we were addressing naval officers, who were to use the results to work out search plans and convoy escort patterns. Kimball toured the naval bases along the east coast, explaining the ideas, working out applications, and learning the practical difficulties.

Within the year he became Deputy Director of the group, called the Operations Research Group (ORG) during the war, later called the Operations Evaluation Group, U.S.N. It grew to number seventy-odd analysts by 1945. Kimball's abilities were in daily use as an educator, as a universal scientific encyclopedia, and as a deviser of simple algorithms to solve tough problems quickly. His colleague then and later, Arthur A. Brown, comments: "In the ORG the initial work dealt with search and with the optimum geometirc patterns for the depth-charge bombing of German U-boats. In a very short space of time the group was working on tactical patterns for destroyer attacks, on the question of reliability of aircraft sightings, and the related question of whether or not to send out a destroyer force.

"This brought us into the question of convoy protection and convoy size, and into liaison with the Coastal Command of the R.A.F. The work spread into the South Atlantic and into the Pacific, in relation to our own submarine offensive against the Japanese supply lines; to our combat air patrols against attacks on the Third and Fifth Fleet operations; and to defensive tactics against Kamikaze attacks. By the end of the war the group had a network of field operations and a solid place in Washington's strategic councils. George Kimball was in the midst of all this and he contributed largely to it.

"Many of his contributions were simple and also ingenious. In 1943, before the present digital computers had been developed, he set up and ran a Monte-Carlo experiment on an IBM sorter. What he did was to draw the silhouette of a submarine on a punch card, punch out the inside of the submarine, take another card and move the silhouette according to a random draw from a two-dimensional normal distribution, do it again, and so on, until he had a respectable deck of randomized submarines. Then, using the sorter, he dropped a number of different depth-charge patterns onto the cloud of submarines and counted the hits. He was apologetic whenever he had to talk about it, saying that anyone would have thought of it. Nevertheless *he* was the one who did think of it, and do it, and it resulted in valuable conclusions when they were needed."

The day after Hiroshima, I, as Director of ORG, obtained one of the first copies of the "Smythe Report" to arrive in Washington. Within twenty-four hours my Deputy, Kimball, and I briefed Admiral King and his staff on the naval implications of the A-bomb; a day later we briefed Secretary of the Navy Forrestal and the joint Senate-House Naval Affairs Committee.

In the midst of all this, Kimball's work with Eyring and John Walter, started ten years earlier, was completed and the book *Quantum Chemistry* was published in 1944. At the end of the war some of the Operations Research Group decided to delay returning to their peacetime positions long enough to record what had been learned. Kimball and I wrote the volume *Methods of Operations Research;* Bernard Koopman, who had joined the group in 1943 wrote *Search and Screening;* and Charles Sternhell and Alan Thorndike wrote a technical history of *Anti-Submarine Warfare in World War II.* All three volumes were initially classified. It was not till 1951 that the first volume was declassified and turned over to a commercial publisher; the other two volumes were never declassified. The *Methods* still is used as an introduction to the subject, and is still referred to in the literature.

After this, Kimball returned to the Chemistry Department

at Columbia, to resume his research and teaching in theoretical chemistry. That he was successful is evidenced by the dozen papers he published on chemical kinetics and on other subjects in chemical physics. Honors began to come his way. He received the Presidential Citation of Merit for his war work; he was elected to the National Academy of Sciences in 1954. He also retained his interest in the new field he had helped pioneer during the war, operations research. He continued his contacts with the Navy, acting as consultant with the Operations Evaluation Group and serving on various advisory panels on underwater ordnance. When the Weapons Systems Evaluation Group (WSEG) was formed in 1949, to carry out operations analysis for the Joint Chiefs of Staff and the Secretary of Defense, he contributed to its work, for a time as consultant and then for a while as a full-time member of the group. He also assisted in organizing the NATO Advisory Panel on Operations Research.

Even during the war Kimball had become convinced that operations research could be effectively applied in industry and in the public sector. He was interested in enlarging public awareness of its potentialities and was active in organizing the Operations Research Society of America, which was founded in 1952, with Kimball as a member of the society's first council. By 1964, when he was elected the society's president, the society had about 5000 members.

In the 1950s Kimball began to spend some time with the operations research division of Arthur D. Little, Inc., assisting in its consulting work for industry and for the Navy. This work increasingly engrossed his attention until, in 1956, he left Columbia and came full time to A. D. Little, first as Science Advisor and then, in 1961, as Vice President. When asked, later, whether he missed teaching, he replied that he was still teaching and that it was a greater challenge to teach people who didn't want to learn or didn't know they were learning.

Much of his work with A. D. Little dealt with applications of theory to the specific problems of the client. Most of this has of course not been published. A partial list of his internal reports and notes indicates that he initiated developments in dynamic programming, decision theory, inventory, and reliability theory, which others fed into the open literature later. Kimball was never particularly interested in publication. He would spend a great deal of time solving specific problems of immediate importance, or in making clear the underlying theory to clients or to classes, but to establish priority by publication, with all its drudgery of typescript, galley and page proof, had less attraction for him than some new problem. He always maintained that there was too much publication anyway.

Arthur Brown reports Kimball's comment when Brown said that someone should have pointed out that the theory of search anticipated the basic principles of information theory; that the probability of target detection is just the entropy of the target distribution. Kimball remarked that this was of course true, but everyone had known about entropy for decades. In his view all he had done was to apply known theory in a context which needed theoretical clarification.

Kimball also did his part as citizen and parent. John B. Lathrop, a neighbor and colleague at A. D. Little, reports: "George had a strong sense of responsibility to the community and gave it as much time as he could. He spent many years as officer, committeeman, or consultant for church, Boy Scouts, and community. An example is his study of the growth of the school population of his home town of Winchester, Mass., done for the local School Committee. His classification of the people of Winchester as 'old families,' 'new families in old houses,' and 'new families in new houses' and his tracing of the different patterns of change and incidence of school-age children in these groups was a model of useful statistical analysis, forecasting, and clear understanding of the phenomenon he studied. He concluded the report with a basis for decision— the earliest, expected, and latest dates when various school additions would be overcrowded.

"George had strong interests—and really was expert—in many fields; languages, naval history, bridge, music, cooking. For years he made almost all the family's gravy, and taught his children how (he was convinced it took a chemist to make a good gravy). There was a blackboard in the family kitchen and frequently he would sit there over a cocktail while dinner was under way, discussing calculus or chemistry or physics with one or another of the children. Three of the four children have definite scientific leanings. Prudence, the oldest, has a Ph.D. in chemistry; Thomas will probably pursue applied mathematics when he gets out of the Air Force; Martha, the youngest, is a chemistry major; Susanna, alone, did not have a scientific bent."

For his last several years, Kimball suffered from serious cardiac illness. For the final year, at least, he was in constant pain. Those who saw him daily knew that this was so, but none were made aware of it by his manner, his actions, or his words. He continued to work actively on all projects and in all the fields that interested him. His death, in fact, came in the midst of his duties; when he died, on December 6, 1967, he was in Pittsburgh as a member of the Visiting Committee of the Carnegie-Mellon University's Chemistry Department. At the time of his death he was chairman of the Northeastern Section of the American Chemical Society.

Kimball was a generalist—which doesn't seem to rate the acclaim the specialist gets nowadays—but his value to operations research, indeed to science, lay in his universal interests.

He could bring concepts from chemistry to bear on inventory and marketing problems; he could devise an abstruse mathematical algorithm to make a digital computer produce random numbers as fast as was needed. Everything he did had to be done well; if he couldn't do it well he didn't do it. In fact, his uncompromising standards kept him from publishing much good work, because it wasn't in final, polished form. Many of us wished that more of his lectures could have reached a wider audience, but that was not his way. He preferred to work directly with people, not via the printed word. And this was in line with his concentration on immediate problems, rather than on abstract theory.

Many of us would agree with Joseph Mayer's comment: "George and Alice were delightful friends to have and we enjoyed them immensely. I have always thought that George was one of the most pleasant companions of an evening, with whiskey and soda after a good dinner. He was not particularly a person who sparkled; he was just comfortably tolerant and *very* intelligent and informative."

Kimball's style of work was rooted in his personality. It was characterized by simplicity of thought and method. Another characteristic was theoretical power and depth. A third was a permanent adherence to reality. He never liked the spinning of elaborate webs of mathematics and he never liked to be too far from actual data. He was sensitive to problems of wording, emphasis, and timing in the presentation of research results, but he was wholly uncompromising in matters of principle. He set an example worth following.

BIBLIOGRAPHY

KEY TO ABBREVIATIONS

J. Am. Chem. Soc. = Journal of the American Chemical Society
J. Chem. Phys. = Journal of Chemical Physics
J. Colloid Sci. = Journal of Colloid Science

1932

The recombination of hydrogen atoms. J. Am. Chem. Soc., 54:2396.

With Henry Eyring. The five-electron problem in quantum mechanics and its application to the hydrogen-chlorine reaction. J. Am. Chem. Soc., 54:3876.

1933

With Henry Eyring. The quantum mechanics of seven and eight electrons with spin degeneracy. J. Chem. Phys., 1:239.

With Henry Eyring and Albert Sherman. The quantum mechanics of chemical reactions involving conjugate double bonds. J. Chem. Phys., 1:586.

1934

With G. H. Shortley. Analysis of non-commuting vectors with application to quantum mechanics and vector analysis. Proceedings of the National Academy of Sciences, 20:82.

With G. H. Shortley. The numerical solution of Schrodinger's equation. Physical Review, 45:815.

1935

The electronic structure of diamond. J. Chem. Phys., 3:9.

1937

With Irving Roberts. The halogenation of ethylenes. J. Am. Chem. Soc., 59:948.

Bimolecular association reactions. J. Chem. Phys., 5:310.

1938

The absolute rates of heterogeneous reactions. I. The general theory of adsorption. J. Chem. Phys., 6:447.

1940

The absolute rates of heterogeneous reactions. II. Electrode reactions. J. Chem. Phys., 8:199.

Directed valence. J. Chem. Phys., 8:188.

Recent developments in the theory of chemical bonds and reaction rates. Chapter 1 in: *Twelfth Catalysis Report,* pp. 1-17. National Research Council. New York, John Wiley & Sons, Inc.

With Alvin Glasner. The rate of solution of metals in acids as a function of overvoltage. I. The diffusion potential. J. Chem. Phys., 8:815.

With Alvin Glasner. The rate of solution of metals in acids as a function of overvoltage. II. The solution of cadmium in sulfuric acid. J. Chem. Phys., 8:820.

1941

Overvoltage and the structure of the electrical double layer at a hydrogen electrode. J. Chem. Phys., 9:91.

1944

The kinetics of the electroreduction of acetone. J. Chem. Phys., 12:415.

With Henry Eyring and John Walter. *Quantum Chemistry.* New York, John Wiley & Sons, Inc. vi + 394 pp.

1945

Hydrogen overvoltage in concentrated sulfuric and phosphoric acid solutions.   J. Chem. Phys., 13:53.

1948

The vapor pressure of some alkali halides.   J. Chem. Phys., 16: 220.

1949

Diffusion-controlled reaction rates.   J. Colloid Sci., 4:425.
Punched card calculation of resonance energies.   J. Chem. Phys., 17:706.
Diffusion-controlled reactions in liquid solutions.   Industrial and Engineering Chemistry, 41:2551.

1950

The effect of salts on the viscosity of solutions of polyacrilic acid. J. Colloid Sci., 5:115.
The determination of energy levels from thermodynamic data.   J. Chem. Phys., 18:626.

1951

Application of a modified quantum-mechanical cellular method to the hydrogen molecule.   J. Chem. Phys., 19:690.
Quantum theory.   Annual Review of Physical Chemistry, 2:1-22.
With Philip M. Morse. *Methods of Operations Research.* New York, John Wiley & Sons, Inc. vii + 158 pp.

1952

Industrial operations research.   Manufacturing Management Series, No. 200.

1954

Decision theory: operations research in management. Advanced Management, 19(12):5.

1956

Nature of operations research. A. D. Little Report.
Note on the free cloud method for ground states of molecules. A. D. Little Report.

1957

Some industrial applications of military operations research methods. Operations Research, 5:201.
Use of Gaussian wave functions in molecular calculations. J. Chem. Phys., 26:1285.
Notes on model testing. A. D. Little Report.
Dynamic programming and project scheduling. A. D. Little Report.
General principles of inventory control. A. D. Little Report.

1958

A critique of operations research. Journal of the Washington Academy of Sciences, 48:123.
The hyperexponential distribution. A. D. Little Report.
Reliability analysis. A. D. Little Report.
Reconciliation of profit and public welfare. A. D. Little Report.

1959

With Ernest M. Loebl. A quantum mechanical theory of complex ion formation. Journal of Chemical Education, 36:233.
Notes on dynamic programming. A. D. Little Report.
With James C. Hetrick. A model for the discovery and application of knowledge. A. D. Little Report.

1961

With Vincent E. Giuliano, Paul E. Jones, Richard F. Meyer, and Barry A. Stein. Automatic pattern recognition by a Gestalt method. Information and Control, 4:332.

1963

Quantum mechanics. In: *Proceedings of the Conference on Desalination Research*, pp. 173-77. NRC Publication 942. Washington, National Academy of Sciences–National Research Council.

Walter D Lambert

WALTER DAVIS LAMBERT

January 12, 1879–October 27, 1968

BY CHARLES A. WHITTEN

WALTER DAVIS LAMBERT was born January 12, 1879, in New Brighton, New York. He died October 27, 1968, at the Washington Hospital Center after a brief illness. Funeral services were held in Salisbury, Connecticut.

His ancestry was English, with records indicating descendancy from William the Conqueror on the Lambert side of the family as well as on the maternal side. His paternal grandfather, Henry Lambert (1812-1909), who came to America in 1836, was the son of an English colonel, Luke Lambert (about 1780-1824). Henry led a varied career of keeping store, studying theology, joining the Gold Rush of the 1850s to California, and later returning to New England and the ministry. Dr. Lambert's father, Walter Lambert (1849-1930), was a banker associated with firms engaged in international finance. He has been described as a quiet man except on the golf course when his game was not good. He had several hobbies including philately, astronomy (he built a telescope for himself), and designing and building hull models of small sailing craft for his friends. Also, he was an ardent small-craft sailor and a capable deep-water navigator, having sailed in the Bermuda races. Dr. Lambert's mother, Elizabeth Bigelow Davis (1853-1932), was born in Northboro, Massachusetts.

The Davis line in New England has been traced to Dolor Davis, who came from England in 1634. For the most part, the Davis family descendants were successful farmers and businessmen.

Dr. Lambert had three sisters and a brother. One sister died young and another, Mary, died a month before Dr. Lambert. His brother, Richard D. Lambert, lives in Orleans, Massachusetts, and his youngest sister, Marjorie (Mrs. Horace Groff), lives in Sheffield, Massachusetts. Dr. Lambert was married to Bertha Brown on June 18, 1917; she died October 15, 1959.

Lambert received his early education at a public school on Staten Island and at Friends' Seminary, Rutherford Place, in New York City. He attended Harvard University, graduating with highest honors in mathematics, magna cum laude, in 1900. He had been elected to Phi Beta Kappa in January 1900. He continued his study of mathematics at Harvard, and the following year received a Master of Arts degree.

In 1901-1902 Lambert was an instructor of mathematics at Purdue University in Lafayette, Indiana. The next two years he taught mathematics and astronomy at the University of Maine in Orono. In 1904 he accepted a position as mathematician with the U.S. Coast and Geodetic Survey.

In 1907 the University of Pennsylvania in Philadelphia awarded him a special scholarship for graduate study, designating him a Harrison Fellow. In addition to his advanced study, he also taught mathematics. He was elected to Sigma Xi in 1909. His Government Service Record indicates that he continued an association with the Survey on a part-time basis while in Philadelphia, assisting in the measurement of magnetic variations and obtaining tidal height records. In 1911 he returned to Washington and resumed his full-time duties with the Survey.

In 1917 Lambert was commissioned a First Lieutenant in the U.S. Army and was later assigned to the 101st Engineering Regiment in France. In some of his correspondence relating to his military service, he wrote: "I headed a detachment of young Americans who helped run a cement factory at Mantes-sur-Seine, otherwise Mantis-Gassicourt, a suburb of Paris. Presumably this was because I had a good command of French." In 1919, after the war, he was reassigned to the Coast and Geodetic Survey.

Lambert's talents had been recognized by John F. Hayford and William Bowie at the time of his initial appointment. They encouraged him to investigate all of the mathematical and physical aspects of the geodetic problems being considered at that time. He was an ardent student and clear writer. Throughout his life, his advice and knowledge were frequently requested by young geodesists. Lambert took great pains to encourage their inquisitiveness and their interest in geodesy. He published more than sixty articles dealing with geodesy. There are as many unpublished articles and reports in the archives of the Coast and Geodetic Survey which are referred to frequently by scientists in the Washington area. A mere scanning of the titles in this collection of papers reveals the breadth of his interests. By referring to the chronological order, one can trace the development of geodetic science during the first half of the twentieth century.

Lambert took an active part in the affairs of the International Association of Geodesy (IAG). In the years immediately after World War I, Hayford and Bowie had been the principal U.S. delegates to international conferences. In Bowie's later years, Lambert often accompanied him to such meetings. After Bowie's retirement in 1937, Lambert was recognized as the chief delegate officially representing the United States. He was the "International Reporter on Earth

Tides" for IAG for a period of thirty years (1924-1954). The Proceedings of the Fifth International Symposium on Earth Tides, held in Brussels in 1964, were published in his honor.

Much more significant is the support he gave IAG during and immediately after World War II. In 1936, at the Edinburgh General Assembly, Lambert had been elected 2d Vice President of IAG, a position uniquely assigned to a representative from the country to be the host for the next General Assembly. The following assembly was held in Washington in September 1939. Dr. A. Vening Meinesz, of the Netherlands, was the President of IAG. General Georges Perrier from France was the Secretary General. Perrier had arrived in the United States for the General Assembly, but had to return to Paris before the meeting actually opened. Many other delegates from Europe had to return under similar orders because of the outbreak of what was to become World War II. In addition to other responsibilities, Lambert filled the role of Secretary General, forwarding to the Central Bureau in Paris complete reports on each day's meetings. It was not feasible to make administrative decisions and there were no elections because of the lack of a representative delegation.

During the following seven years, Lambert and Perrier continued to correspond in spite of the difficulties imposed by wartime censorship. They carried out the work of the Association in a very remarkable manner. Many of the officers and key personnel engaged in the work of the Association were in places where travel and communication were restricted. News of some was utterly lacking, and only in later years was it learned that a few had died.

In 1946, after the International Union of Geodesy and Geophysics (IUGG) had held an Extraordinary General Assembly in Cambridge, the International Association of Geodesy met in Special General Assembly in Paris. Lambert was elected President of IAG to serve until the Oslo Assembly in 1948. At Oslo he was reelected and served until the Brussels Assembly in 1951. At that time, the Association honored him by electing him Honorary President for the rest of his life.

Lambert also contributed to the work of the International Astronomical Union (IAU). He assisted in the solution of many problems, scientific and administrative, associated with the international program for determining the variation of latitude. The International Latitude Service, so named at that time, received its direction from the two scientific unions most interested in the results —IAU and IUGG through IAG. The chapter on the variation of latitude in the National Research Council Bulletin No. 78, "Physics of the Earth-II, The Figure of the Earth," was written chiefly by Lambert. That chapter is still accepted as the clearest explanation and definition of this aspect of polar motion ever published.

Because of his knowledge of all fields of geodesy and his talent for clarity of expression, Lambert was asked by the publishers of the *Encyclopaedia Britannica,* 14th edition, to prepare the section on Geodesy. Portions of that original statement have appeared in subsequent editions and were still being published in 1969.

For the major part of Lambert's career in the Coast and Geodetic Survey, he had not been assigned administrative tasks, but was permitted to conduct research and have the support and assistance of his colleagues and associates within the Division of Geodesy. However, he did not completely escape the management role, and during the last few years of his service he was Chief of the Gravity and Astronomy Branch in the Geodesy Division. He was not inclined to permit the administrative details to interfere with his real interests, and he easily disposed of the governmental trivia through assignment to his assistants.

The regulations for retirement at the age of seventy became a mere formality for Lambert. In 1949, the year of his retirement, he received three significant honors. He was uniquely honored by election to the National Academy of Sciences. He was also honored by the American Geophysical Union through the award of the William Bowie Medal. As the Bowie medalist, he was cited for his unselfish cooperation in the broad field of earth sciences. In his modest way, he humbly expressed his appreciation by thanking his many colleagues and by referring to his outstanding superiors of former years, one of whom had been Bowie. The third honor in that year was his recognition by the Department of Commerce with the award of the Gold Medal for Exceptional Service.

Soon after his retirement, the Lamberts left their home in suburban Washington and returned to New England. The quiet, comfortable living in the northwestern corner of Connecticut in the town of Canaan had far more appeal than the heat and humidity of Washington. He visited Washington for scientific meetings, making his headquarters at the Cosmos Club where he could entertain his friends and relax in familiar surroundings.

The files of the Coast and Geodetic Survey contain personal notes of instruction or requests from Lambert indicating a postretirement activity almost equal to that of earlier years. Those files also contain a literary gem—a description of his visit to the Babson Gravity Research Foundation in southern New Hampshire—which sparkles with his wit and keen observance of surroundings, and which he mailed to the office without any specific instruction for publication.

Even though Lambert preferred to continue his postretirement career by study in his home in Connecticut, he was sought frequently as a special consultant. He became an active participant in the research programs of the Institute of Geodesy at Ohio State University. In 1950, Dr. Weikko A. Heiskanen, of Finland, had been asked to serve as Director of that Institute at Columbus, and in the same year Lambert joined him. This was a very fortunate arrangement. These two world leaders of geodesy had been closely associated for many years through their cooperative work in physical geodesy, Heiskanen as Director of the Finnish Geodetic Institute and also Director of the International Isostatic Institute at Helsinki, and Lambert through his work with the Coast and Geodetic Survey and the International Association of Geodesy. Ohio State University honored Lambert in 1957 by conferring on him the degree of Doctor of Science in recognition of his many contributions to the science of geodesy. His association with Ohio State University continued for many years. In the Preface of Heiskanen and Moritz's *Physical Geodesy,* published in 1967, one finds an expression of thanks to Lambert for his assistance in the review of the manuscript.

In reviewing Lambert's contributions to geodesy, there is hardly any branch of the science in which he did not make some type of investigation. Throughout his life, though, there was a continuing effort which may be described as the study of the physical properties of the earth's gravity field and their geodetic application, with particular emphasis on mathematical methods. Even in his eighty-fifth year, while participating in the symposium "Extension of Gravity Anomalies to Unsurveyed Areas," he presented a paper, "The Isostatic Reduction of Gravity Data and Its Indirect Effect," in which he made positive recommendations for future study.

Lambert was interested in many local, national, and international scientific societies and organizations to which he contributed much of his time and energy in support of their programs. The following list of his active and honorary memberships gives some indication of the breadth of these activities:

National Academy of Sciences (1949)
Paris Academy of Sciences
Royal Astronomical Society (elected "Associate," 1963)
International Astronomical Union
International Association of Geodesy (Vice President, 1936-1946; President, 1946-1951; Honorary President, 1951-1968)
American Geophysical Union (President, Section of Geodesy, 1929-1932)
American Association for the Advancement of Science (Fellow, 1922; elected a "50-year Member," 1967)
American Mathematical Society
Mathematical Association of America (Charter Member)
Seismological Society of America
American Astronomical Society
Washington Academy of Sciences (Vice President, 1930)
Philosophical Society of Washington (President, 1930; Life Member, 1952)

Lambert was elected to the Cosmos Club of Washington in 1937.

Lambert's interest in the affairs of many of these scientific organizations continued until his death. His vitality and vigor astounded those who had known him through the years. In October 1966 he sold his home in Canaan and returned to Washington, living at the Cosmos Club. He told his friends, "I plan to stay here until I am carried out, either to the hospital or to the cemetery."

All of those who were fortunate enough to have been associated with Dr. Lambert as a scientific colleague, as an inquisitive student, or as friend or neighbor know of the sincere concern he had for the people who worked with him. His memory is endeared by them, not only for his unselfish cooperation in scientific research, but, more personally, for his quiet unselfish regard for his fellow men.

BIBLIOGRAPHY

KEY TO ABBREVIATIONS

Am. J. Sci. = American Journal of Science
Am. Math. Monthly = American Mathematical Monthly
Astron. J. = Astronomical Journal
Bull. Géod. = Bulletin Géodésique
Bull. Nat. Res. Council = Bulletin of the National Research Council
Gerlands Beitr. Geophys. = Gerlands Beiträge zur Geophysik
J. Wash. Acad. Sci. = Journal of the Washington Academy of Sciences
Trans. Am. Geophys. Union = Transactions of the American Geophysical
    Union

1906

A generalized trigonometric solution of the cubic equation.   Am.
    Math. Monthly, 13:73-76.
On the chord of contact of tangents to a conic.   Am. Math.
    Monthly, 13(8-9):159-60.

1920

The internal constitution of the earth.   J. Wash. Acad. Sci.,
    10:122-43.
An odd problem in mechanics.   Science, 51:271-72.
Physical laws underlying the scale of a sounding tube.   U.S. Coast
    and Geodetic Survey Special Publication No. 61. Washington,
    U.S. Govt. Print. Off. 45 pp.

1921

Some mechanical curiosities connected with the earth's field of
    force.   Am. J. Sci., 2:129-56.
The tendency of elongated bodies to set in the east and west direc-
    tion.   Nature, 108:528. (L)
With O. S. Adams.   Mathematical problems in the work of the
    United States Coast and Geodetic Survey.   Am. Math. Monthly,
    28:363-68.

1922

The latitude of Ukiah and the motion of the pole.   J. Wash. Acad.
    Sci., 12:26-43.

An investigation of the latitude of Ukiah, California, and of the motion of the pole. U.S. Coast and Geodetic Survey Special Publication No. 80. Washington, U.S. Govt. Print. Off. 111 pp.

The directive tendency of elongated bodies. Nature, 109:271-72.

The Eötvös balance. Bull. Nat. Res. Council, No. 17, p. 17.

The interpretation of apparent changes in mean latitude. Astron. J., 34:103-10.

1923

Elastic yielding of the earth's crust under a load of sedimentary deposits. Bulletin of the Geological Society of America, 34: 305-8.

The mechanics of the Taylor-Wegener hypothesis of continental migration. J. Wash. Acad. Sci., 13:448-50. (A)

1924

Mathematics and geophysics. Science, 59:30-32.

Earth tides and ocean tides. Nature, 113:889.

Effect of variations in the assumed figure of the earth on the mapping of a large area. U.S. Coast and Geodetic Survey Special Publication No. 100. Washington, U.S. Govt. Print. Off. 39 pp.

Forces tending to cause movements in the earth's crust. Bull. Nat. Res. Council, No. 41, p. 93. (A)

1925

Les marées de l'écorce terrestre et leurs rélations avec les autres branches de la géophysique. Bull. Géod., No. 5, pp. 41-47.

The variation of latitude. Bull. Géod., No. 6, pp. 105-13.

Can we explain gravitation? Scientific Monthly, 20:479-82.

1926

The figure of the earth and the new international ellipsoid of reference. Science, 63:242-46.

Miscellaneous geodetic data. International Critical Tables, 1:393-94.

La figure de la terre et le nouvel ellipsoide de référence international. Bull. Géod., No. 10, pp. 81-99.

1927

The variation of latitude and the fluctuations in the motion of the moon. J. Wash. Acad. Sci., 17:133-39.

1928

The importance from a geophysical point of view of a knowledge of the tides in the open sea. Bulletin N. 11 de la Section d'Océanographie du Conseil international de Recherches. 11 pp.

The figure of the earth and the parallax of the moon. Astron. J., 38:181-85.

Geodetic constants. J. Wash. Acad. Sci., 18:571-76.

1929

Bruns' term and the mathematical expression for the gravity anomaly. Gerlands Beitr. Geophys., 24:371-77.

A method of estimating tidal friction. Am. Math. Monthly, 36:243.

Astronomical methods of determining the figure of the earth. Am. J. Sci., 18:155-63.

With Oscar S. Adams. A form for the computation of geodetic positions. Bull. Géod., No. 22, pp. 55-63.

Geodesy. In: *Encyclopaedia Britannica,* 14th ed. (and subsequent eds.), Vol. 10, 7 pp. New York, Encyclopaedia Britannica, Inc.

The variation of latitude, tides and earthquakes. Proceedings of the Third Pan-Pacific Science Congress, Tokyo, 1926, pp. 1517-22.

1930

Methods of reducing gravity observations. Gerlands Beitr. Geophys., 26:185-88.

An approximate rule for the distance between the geoid and the spheroid on the assumption of complete isostatic compensation of the topography. Bull. Géod., No. 26, pp. 91-97.

The form of the geoid on the hypothesis of complete isostatic compensation. Bull. Géod., No. 26, pp. 98-106.

The reduction of observed values of gravity to sea level. Bull. Géod., No. 26, pp. 107-81.

Note on a recent article by Dr. Hopfner. Gerlands Beitr. Geophys., 26:182-84.

1931

Earth tides. Bull. Nat. Res. Council, No. 78, pp. 68-80.

Tidal friction. Bull. Nat. Res. Council, No. 78, pp. 81-99.

The shape and size of the earth. Bull. Nat. Res. Council, No. 78, pp. 123-50.

Note on the theoretical basis of isostasy. Am. J. Sci., 21:345-49.

With F. W. Darling. Tables for theoretical gravity, according to the new international formula. Bull. Géod., No. 32, pp. 327-40.

With Frank Schlesinger and E. W. Brown. The variation of latitude. Bull. Nat. Res. Council, No. 78, pp. 245-77.

Gravity. Trans. Am. Geophys. Union, 12:40-43. (Stockholm Meeting of the International Geodetic and Geophysical Union.)

1932

Stokes' formula in geodesy. Nature, 129:831-32.

1933

The earth as an engineering structure. Military Engineer, 25:461-65.

1934

Note on the reduction of gravity observations to sea level for the purpose of determining the geoid. Bull. Géod., No. 41, pp. 26-33.

1935

Geodetic astronomy in the United States. Bull. Géod., No. 47, pp. 371-81.

The Hayford-Bowie Tables and the definition of perfect isostasy. Zeitschrift für Geophysik, 11:35-39.

With C. H. Swick. Formulas and tables for the computation of geodetic positions on the international ellipsoid. U.S. Coast and Geodetic Survey Special Publication No. 200. Washington, U.S. Govt. Print. Off. 120 pp.

1936

The figure of the earth from gravity observations. J. Wash. Acad. Sci., 26:491-506.

Who shot those peas? Geodetic Letter, 3(3):1-10.

With F. W. Darling. Tables for determining the form of the geoid and its indirect effect on gravity. U.S. Coast and Geodetic Survey Special Publication No. 199. Washington, U.S. Govt. Print. Off. 130 pp.

Breitenschwankungen. In: *Handbuch der Geophysik,* ed. by Beno Gutenberg, Band 1, pp. 501-35. Berlin, Gebrüder Borntraeger.

1937

The analogue of Stokes' formula for the Prey and Bouguer gravity anomalies. Gerlands Beitr. Geophys., 49:199-209.

The external gravity-field and the interior of the earth. Trans. Am. Geophys. Union, 18(1):33-40.

An old answer to a present-day problem. Science, 86:79-80.

1938

With F. W. Darling. Formulas and tables for the deflection of the vertical. Bull. Géod., No. 57, pp. 29-71.

1940

The beginnings of mathematical geophysics in Great Britain. Trans. Am. Geophys. Union, 21(4):1068-72.

Report on earth tides. U.S. Coast and Geodetic Survey Special Publication No. 223. Washington, U.S. Govt. Print. Off. 29 pp.

1942

The distance between two widely separated points on the surface of the earth. J. Wash. Acad. Sci., 32:125-30.

1943

Notes on earth tides. Geophysics, 8:51-56.

1945

A possible case of fictitious continental drift. Science, 101:558-59.

Eclipses and earth surveys. Sky and Telescope, 4:8-10.

The international gravity formula. Am. J. Sci., 243-A, Daly Volume, pp. 360-92.

1947

Deflections of the vertical from gravity anomalies. Trans. Am. Geophys. Union, 28:153-56.

The use of values of gravity in the adjustment of the triangulation in Europe. Bull. Géod., 3:19-22.

1949

Comments on Arnold Court's article, "Refractive Temperature." Journal of the Franklin Institute, June, pp. 583-94.

Geodetic applications of eclipses and occultations. Extrait, Bull. Géod., 13:274-92.

1950

The International Geodetic Association (Die Internationale Erd-messung) and its predecessors. Extrait, Bull. Géod., 17:299-324.

1951

With F. W. Darling. Density, gravity, pressure and ellipticity in the interior of the earth. Chapter XIII in: *Internal Constitution of the Earth*, ed. by B. Gutenberg, pp. 340-63. New York, Dover Publications. 2d ed.

1953

Celestial flare triangulation. Engineering Experiment Station News, 25(3):20.

1960

Note on the paper of A. H. Cook, "The external gravity field of a rotating spheroid to the order of e^3." Geophysical Journal, 3(3):360-66.

1961

The gravity field of an ellipsoid of revolution as a level surface. Annales Academiae Scientiarum Fennicae, Series A, III, Geologica-Geographica, No. 57. 42 pp.

1966

The isostatic reduction of gravity data and its indirect effect. In: *Gravity Anomalies: Unsurveyed Areas*. Geophysical Monograph No. 9, pp. 81-84.

A list of unpublished papers by Dr. Lambert is deposited in the archives of the National Academy of Sciences, and the papers themselves are available for study in the Coast and Geodetic Survey Library, Washington, D.C.

(Editor's Note: In October 1970 the Coast and Geodetic Survey was combined with several other agencies in the formation of NOAA—National Oceanic and Atmospheric Administration. The Coast and Geodetic Survey is now the National Ocean Survey.)

Howard J. Lucas.

HOWARD JOHNSON LUCAS

March 7, 1885–June 22, 1963

BY WILLIAM G. YOUNG
AND SAUL WINSTEIN

HOWARD J. LUCAS was born to William W. Lucas and Marian Curtis Lucas in Marietta, Ohio, on March 7, 1885. He attended Ohio State University for both undergraduate and graduate work, receiving the B.S. degree in 1907 and the M.A. degree in 1908. Many years later, in 1953, he was awarded an Honorary D.Sc. degree by that institution. He became a Fellow in chemistry at the University of Chicago in 1909-1910, working toward a Ph.D. degree. At this point he was forced to leave school, owing to the death of his father, and he became Assistant Chemist in the U.S. Department of Agriculture (1910-1913). From 1913 to 1915 he served as Instructor at Throop College of Technology (which later became the California Institute of Technology). He was promoted to Associate Professor of Organic Chemistry in 1915 and to Professor in 1940. He served as Visiting Professor of the University of Hawaii in 1953 and Visiting Professor at Ohio State University in 1954-1955. Although he became Emeritus Professor of Organic Chemistry at the California Institute of Technology in 1955, he continued actively in research until shortly before his death.

Lucas was interested in the profession of chemistry from the time he joined the American Chemical Society in 1909.

He became active in the Southern California section of the society about 1916, serving on many committees until he became chairman of the section in 1931-1932. He helped promote an unusual high school chemistry contest, which is still an important activity of the section today.

Professor Lucas was honored by election to the National Academy of Sciences in 1957, after having been the second recipient of the American Chemical Society's award in Chemical Education, sponsored by the Scientific Apparatus Makers Association in 1953. The purpose of this award is to recognize outstanding contributions to chemical education. These recognitions came late in his career, primarily because his education was interrupted by the death of his father and because he joined the California Institute of Technology while it was in its infancy. He spent the better part of ten years working with several other talented people developing a curriculum which was based on extremely high standards and close working relationships between professor and student. As Cal Tech progressed, so did Lucas's opportunities to secure graduate students of high calibre. Although he was the only organic chemist on the staff in the early days, his influence and inspiration in his particular field caused many talented students to choose organic chemistry, despite the great attractiveness of the field of physical chemistry, at that time under Arthur A. Noyes.

Lucas's outstanding skills as an educator were devoted to bringing out the best efforts inherent in the individual as a student and a researcher in the field. His example of doing research himself, particularly in cooperation with his students in those fields of organic chemistry which could take advantage of the skills usually associated with physical chemistry, produced talented men who continued laying the foundation of what is now known as physical organic chemistry. All of the men who were associated with him as students considered him to be an excellent teacher. He gave one the feeling that he was sincerely interested in imparting knowledge and developing the student's laboratory skill. However, to quote one of Lucas's most successful students, "One needed to serve as a teaching assistant to obtain a real insight into Lucas, the teacher." All were amazed at the care that went into setting up and testing lecture demonstrations. The underlying principle of Professor Lucas's teaching method was to "get the student to think" and to "conduct experiments with the utmost accuracy and with carefully purified chemicals."

In trying to get the student to think, Professor Lucas emphasized the physical chemical side of organic chemistry. In so doing he did much to simplify organic chemistry for the student, tying it in with the chemistry the student already knew, especially at Cal Tech. Since there was no text available for this approach, Lucas wrote his own text, *Organic Chemistry,* which became a classic in the field. This book was one of the first to recognize the value of electronic interpretations in the field of organic chemistry, clearly relating organic chemistry to modern chemical theory.

The research program carried forward by Professor Lucas provided a substantial fraction of the theoretical basis of present-day organic chemistry. He did some of the very first research in physical organic chemistry.

When H. J. Lucas began his research, the electron-pair description of the covalent bond had just been recognized; he made the first clear application of the idea of electron displacement in molecules to the interpretation of the behavior of organic substances. He correlated the direction of addition of unsymmetrical reagents to olefins and other properties of molecules, such as acid strength, with relative electronegativities of substituent groups. He made a start on the more complex problem of electron displacement in aromatic substances and contributed to the understanding of aromatic substitution. His contributions and ideas were incorporated in the comprehensive electronic theory of organic reactions later developed mainly by the English.

Much of Professor Lucas's work involved unsaturated compounds. He and his students prepared pure cis- and trans-2-butenes and 2-pentenes. They carried out a comprehensive series of investigations which elucidated the kinetics and mechanisms of hydration of olefinic and acetylenic materials. Lucas's interest in the interpretation of the behavior of π-electron-containing materials led him to a study of the ability of olefins to complex with acceptor species such as silver ion and mercuric ion. This work and its interpretation anticipated by some ten years the more recent general concept of "π-complexes."

A good deal of Lucas's work dealt with the stereochemistry of materials with two asymmetric centers, such as glycols, epoxides, aminoalcohols, and dihalides, and the stereochemistry of their reactions. The work on substitution reactions of such materials led to the now generally recognized participation of neighboring functional groups in substitution reactions by way of cyclic intermediates such as ethylene bromonium and chloronium ions.

An interesting sideline carried along by Professor Lucas was qualitative organic analysis. Besides teaching this subject in an extremely fundamental manner, he made occasional original contributions to the field. For example, his hydrochloric acid-zinc chloride reagent for differentiation of primary, secondary, and tertiary alcohols is commonly known among organic chemists as the "Lucas reagent."

Professor Lucas died June 22, 1963, in Pasadena, California. He had been in poor health for some time because of a heart ailment.

BIBLIOGRAPHY

KEY TO ABBREVIATIONS

Ind. Eng. Chem., Anal. Ed. = Industrial and Engineering Chemistry, Analytical Edition
Ind. Eng. Chem. = Industrial and Engineering Chemistry (formerly Journal of Industrial and Engineering Chemistry)
J. Am. Chem. Soc. = Journal of the American Chemical Society
Org. Syn. = Organic Syntheses

1909

With W. McPherson. The action of unsymmetrical benzoyl-phenylhydrazine on orthobenzoquinone. J. Am. Chem. Soc., 31:281-84.

1913

The determination of nitrobenzene in peanut oil. J. Ind. Eng. Chem., 5:576-77.

1914

With R. del Valle Sárraga and J. Roman Benitez. A study of the milk of Puerto Rican cows. J. Ind. Eng. Chem., 6:22-24.

1917

With A. R. Kemp. The determination of silver in organic compounds. J. Am. Chem. Soc., 39:2074-78.

1921

With A. R. Kemp. Chromo-isomeric silver salts of pentabromophenol and a theory of chromo-isomerism of solid compounds. J. Am. Chem. Soc., 43:1654-65.

1924

With A. Y. Jameson. Electron displacement in aliphatic compounds. I. Electron displacement versus alternate polarity in carbon compounds. J. Am. Chem. Soc., 46:2475-82.

1925

With Hollis W. Moyse. Electron displacement in carbon compounds. II. Hydrogen bromide and 2-pentene. J. Am. Chem. Soc., 47:1459-61.

With Thomas P. Simpson and James M. Carter. Electron displacement in carbon compounds. III. Polarity differences in carbon-hydrogen unions. J. Am. Chem. Soc., 47:1462-69.

1926

Electron displacement in carbon compounds. IV. Derivatives of benzene. J. Am. Chem. Soc., 48:1827-38.

1927

With Murray N. Schultz. The sulfonation of *ortho*-toluidine and the preparation of sodium 6-chloro-5-nitro-*meta*-toluenesulfonate. J. Am. Chem. Soc., 49:298-302.

With Fred J. Ewing. A new method of preparing phosphorus pentafluoride. J. Am. Chem. Soc., 49:1270.

An all glass distilling tube without constriction. Ind. Eng. Chem., 19:680.

1928

With Nathan F. Scudder. The preparation of 2-bromo-*p*-cresol from *p*-nitrotoluene. J. Am. Chem. Soc., 50:244-49.

With John Buxton. The analysis of brominated cresols. J. Am. Chem. Soc., 50:249-52.

With Robert T. Dillon. The synthesis of 1-butene. J. Am. Chem. Soc., 50:1460-69.

With Robert T. Dillon. Some derivatives of *n*-heptane. J. Am. Chem. Soc., 50:1711-14.

1929

Electron displacement in carbon compounds. V. The addition of hydrogen chloride to 3-ethyl-2-pentene. J. Am. Chem. Soc., 51:248-53.

With Carlisle H. Bibb. Air oxidation of hydrocarbons catalyzed by nitrogen oxides. I. Natural gas. Ind. Eng. Chem., 21:633-35.

With Carlisle H. Bibb. Air oxidation of hydrocarbons catalyzed by nitrogen oxides. II. Benzene. Ind. Eng. Chem., 21:635-39.

With William G. Young and Robert Dillon. The synthesis of the isomeric 2-butenes. J. Am. Chem. Soc., 51:2528-34.

With William G. Young. Condensation of acetaldehyde with methylmalonic ester. Methylations with methyl bromide. J. Am. Chem. Soc., 51:2535-38.

With Edgar P. Valby. The ionization constant of *para*-cyano-benzoic acid. J. Am. Chem. Soc., 51:2718-20.

1930

With H. Darwin Kirschman and Baker Wingfield. A comparison method for determining ionization constants with a quinhy-drone reference electrode. J. Am. Chem. Soc., 52:23-28.

A new test for distinguishing the primary, secondary, and tertiary saturated alcohols. J. Am. Chem. Soc., 52:802-4.

With Robert T. Dillon and William G. Young. Qualitative estimation of the composition of butene mixtures by distillation methods. J. Am. Chem. Soc., 52:1949-53.

With Robert T. Dillon and William G. Young. The reaction rates of potassium iodide with 1,2- and 2,3-dibromobutane; the analysis of mixtures of the normal butenes. J. Am. Chem. Soc., 52:1953-64.

With William G. Young. The composition of butene mixtures resulting from the catalytic decomposition of the normal butyl alcohols. J. Am. Chem. Soc., 52:1964-70.

1933

With Yun-pu Liu. The nitration of *p*-cresol and of *p*-cresyl carbonate in the presence of sulfuric acid. J. Am. Chem. Soc., 55:1271-80.

1934

With W. F. Eberz. The hydration of unsaturated compounds. I. The hydration rate of isobutene in dilute nitric acid. J. Am. Chem. Soc., 56:460-64.

With W. F. Eberz. The hydration of unsaturated compounds. II. Equilibrium between isobutene and *tert*-butanol and the free energy of hydration of isobutene. J. Am. Chem. Soc., 56:1230-34.

With Yun-pu Liu. The hydration of unsaturated compounds. III. The hydration rate of trimethylethylene in aqueous solutions of acids. J. Am. Chem. Soc., 56:2138-40.

1935

With A. N. Prater and R. E. Morris. The reaction between oxygen and 2-butene. J. Am. Chem. Soc., 57:723-27.

Organic Chemistry. New York, American Book Company. vi + 686 pp.

1936

With E. R. Kennedy and C. A. Wilmot. The decomposition of di-*ortho*-tolyliodonium iodide. J. Am. Chem. Soc., 58:157-60.

With C. E. Wilson. Stereochemical relationships of the isomeric 2,3- butanediols and related compounds; evidence of Walden inversion. J. Am. Chem. Soc., 58:2396-2402.

1937

With W. F. Eberz, H. Welge, and D. M. Yost. The hydration of unsaturated compounds. IV. The rate of hydration of isobutene in the presence of silver ion. The nature of the isobutene-silver complex. J. Am. Chem. Soc., 59:45-49.

With R. H. Frieman and E. R. Kennedy. The hydration of unsaturated compounds. V. The rate of hydration of acetylene in aqueous solution of sulfuric acid and mercuric sulfate. J. Am. Chem. Soc., 59:722-26.

With S. Winstein. The hydration of unsaturated compounds. VI. The rate of hydration of trans-crotonaldehyde. The equilibrium between trans-crotonaldehyde and aldol in dilute aqueous solution. J. Am. Chem. Soc., 59:146-65.

With A. N. Prater. The isomeric 2-pentenes. J. Am. Chem. Soc., 59:1682-86.

With C. E. Redemann. The rapid saponification of esters by potassium hydroxide in diethylene glycol. An aid in identification and analysis. Ind. Eng. Chem., Anal. Ed., 9:521-22.

1938

With David Pressman. The determination of unsaturation in organic compounds by means of the mercury-catalyzed reaction with standard bromate-bromide solution. Ind. Eng. Chem., Anal. Ed., 10:140-42.

With S. Winstein. The coordination of silver ion with unsaturated compounds. J. Am. Chem. Soc., 60:836-48.

1939

With S. Winstein. Retention of configuration in the reaction of 3-bromo-2-butanols with hydrogen bromide. J. Am. Chem. Soc., 61:1576-80.

With S. Winstein. The reaction steps in the conversion of 2,3-diacetoxybutane to 2,3-dibromobutane. J. Am. Chem. Soc., 61:1581-84.

With D. Pressman. The hydration of unsaturated compounds. VII. The rate of hydration of crotonic acid; the rate of dehydration of beta-hydroxybutyric acid; the equilibrium between crotonic acid and beta-hydroxybutyric acid in dilute aqueous solution. J. Am. Chem. Soc., 61:2271.

With S. Winstein. The loss of optical activity in the reaction of the optically active *erythro-* and *threo-*3-bromo-2-butanols with hydrobromic acid. J. Am. Chem. Soc., 61:2845-48.

With F. R. Hepner and S. Winstein. The coördination complexes of mercuric ion with cyclohexene. J. Am. Chem. Soc., 61.3102-6.

With C. E. Redemann. Ionization constants and hydrolytic degradations of cyameluric and hydromelonic acids. J. Am. Chem. Soc., 61:3420-24.

1940

With C. E. Redemann. Some derivatives of cyameluric acid and probable structures of melam, melem, and melon. J. Am. Chem. Soc., 62:842-46.

With W. T. Stewart.   Esters of alginic acid.   J. Am. Chem. Soc.,
    62:1070-74.
With W. T. Stewart.   Oxidation of alginic acid by periodic acid.
    J. Am. Chem. Soc., 62:1792-96.
With David Pressman.   The hydration of unsaturated compounds.
    VIII. The rate of hydration of beta, beta-dimethylacrylic acid;
    the rate of dehydration and decarboxylation of beta-hydroxy-
    isovaleric acid.   J. Am. Chem. Soc., 62:2069-80.

1941

With M. J. Schlatter and R. C. Jones.   The isomeric 2,3-epoxy-
    pentanes and 2-pentenes. The extent to which mixtures of
    diastereomers are formed in reactions of some pentane com-
    pounds.   J. Am. Chem. Soc., 63:22-28.
With W. Baumgarten.   The reduction of tartaric acid.   J. Am.
    Chem. Soc., 63:1653-57.
With C. W. Gould, Jr.   The conversion of the 3-chloro-2-buta-
    nols to the 2,3-dichlorobutanes; evidence for a cyclic chloronium
    intermediate.   J. Am. Chem. Soc., 63:2541-50.

1942

With C. W. Gould, Jr.   Brucine as a reagent for partially re-
    solving bromoalkanes; the configuration of some diastereomeric
    dibromalkanes.   J. Am. Chem. Soc., 64:601-3.
With D. Pressman and L. Brewer.   The hydration of unsaturated
    compounds. IX. The oxonium complex constant of mesityl
    oxide.   J. Am. Chem. Soc., 64:1117-22.
With D. Pressman and L. Brewer.   The hydration of unsaturated
    compounds. X. The role of the oxonium complexes in the
    hydration of mesityl oxide and the dehydration of diacetone
    alcohol.   J. Am. Chem. Soc., 64:1122-28.
With D. Pressman. Hydration of unsaturated compounds. XI.
    Acrolein and acrylic acids.   J. Am. Chem. Soc., 64:1953-57.
With E. R. Kennedy.   Diphenyliodonium iodide.   Org. Syn., 22:52.
With E. R. Kennedy.   Iodobenzene dichloride.   Org. Syn., 22:69.

With E. R. Kennedy and M. W. Formo. Iodosobenzene. Org. Syn., 22:70.

With E. R. Kennedy. Iodoxybenzene. I. Disproportionation of iodosobenzene. Org. Syn., 22:72.

1943

With R. S. Moore and D. Pressman. The coördination of silver ion with unsaturated compounds. II. cis- and trans-2-pentene. J. Am. Chem. Soc., 65:227-29.

With F. W. Billmeyer, Jr. and D. Pressman. The coördination of silver ion with unsaturated compounds. III. Mixtures of trimethylethylene and cyclohexene. J. Am. Chem. Soc., 65:230-31.

1944

With W. T. Stewart and D. Pressman. The hydration of unsaturated compounds. XII. The rate of hydration of beta, beta-dimethylacrolein and its equilibrium with beta-hydroxy-isovaleraldehyde. J. Am. Chem. Soc., 66:1818-21.

1948

With H. K. Garner. The configuration of active 2,3-epoxybutane and erythro-3-chloro-2-butanol. J. Am. Chem. Soc., 70:990-92.

1949

With David Pressman. *Principles and Practice in Organic Chemistry.* New York, John Wiley & Sons, Inc.; London, Chapman & Hall, Ltd. xi + 557 pp.

1950

With F. W. Mitchell, Jr. and H. K. Garner. Acetolysis of the p-toluenesulfonates of the 2,3-butanediols. J. Am. Chem. Soc., 72:2138-44.

With H. K. Garner. 1,2-dimethylethyleneiodonium ions as intermediates in reactions of the 3-iodo-2-butanols. J. Am. Chem.
Soc., 72:2145-50.

With John Michael O'Gorman. Hydrolysis of the acetal of D-
(+)-2-octanol. J. Am. Chem. Soc., 72:5489-90.

With M. S. Guthrie. Geometrical isomerism of propylene acetals.
J. Am. Chem. Soc., 72:5490-91.

With F. W. Mitchell, Jr. and C. N. Scully. Cyclic phosphites of
some aliphatic glycols. J. Am. Chem. Soc., 72:5491-97.

With H. K. Garner. Preparation and hydrolysis of some acetals
and esters of D(−)2,3-butanediol. J. Am. Chem. Soc., 72:5497-
5501.

With F.W. Mitchell, Jr. Phosphonation with a phosphite ester
of propanediol. J. Am. Chem. Soc., 72:5779.

1951

With P. J. Leroux. L(−)-2-butanol from D(−)2,3-butanediol.
J. Am. Chem. Soc., 73:41-42.

With W. Fickett and H. K. Garner. The configuration of optically
active 1,2-dichloropropane. J. Am. Chem. Soc., 73:5063-67.

With H. Lemaire. Measurement of the basic strength of weak
bases in glacial acetic acid. J. Am. Chem. Soc., 73:5198-5201.

1952

With F. H. Dickey and W. Fickett. Stereoisomeric 2,3-butanedia-
mines, 3-amino-2-butanols and 2,3-dimethyl-ethyleneimines;
stereochemistry of the opening and closing of the imino ring.
J. Am. Chem. Soc., 74:944-51.

With G. K. Helmcamp. Stereochemistry of the reaction of 2,3-
epoxybutane with alcohols. J. Am. Chem. Soc., 74:951-54.

With F. R. Hepner and K. N. Trueblood. Coördination of silver
ion with unsaturated compounds. IV. The butenes. J. Am.
Chem. Soc., 74:1333-37.

With K. N. Trueblood. Coördination of silver ion with unsaturated compounds. V. Ethylene and propene. J. Am. Chem. Soc., 74:1338-39.

1954

With Alan E. Comyns. The system: silver perchlorate-dioxane. J. Am. Chem. Soc., 76:1019-20.

With Robert E. Kofahl. Coördination of polycyclic aromatic hydrocarbons with silver ion; correlation of equilibrium constants with relative carcinogenic potencies. J. Am. Chem. Soc., 76:3931-35.

1955

With R. Ghirardelli. Stereochemistry of the ring opening of 2,3-iminobutane by acetic acid. J. Am. Chem. Soc., 77:106.

With Henry Lemaire. The mercury-catalyzed addition of acetic acid to 3-hexyne. J. Am. Chem. Soc., 77:939-46.

With Paul Schlichta and John K. Inman. The preparation and configuration of D(−)-4,5-dimethyl-1,3-dioxolane. J. Am. Chem. Soc., 77:3784-85.

1956

With W. Smith Dorsey. Coördination of silver ion with unsaturated compounds. VII. 3-hexyne. J. Am. Chem. Soc., 78:1665-69.

1957

With R. Ghirardelli. Stereochemistry of the opening of the imine ring with ethylamine. J. Am. Chem. Soc., 79:734-41.

With George K. Helmkamp and Forrest L. Carter. Coördination of silver ion with unsaturated compounds. VIII. Alkynes. J. Am. Chem. Soc., 79:1306-10.

With Alan E. Comyns. Coördination of silver ion with unsaturated compounds. IX. Solid complexes of silver salts with cyclohexene, α-pinene and β-pinene.   J. Am. Chem. Soc., 79:4339-41.

With Alan E. Comyns.   Coördination of silver ion and unsaturated compounds. X. Complexes of silver perchlorate and silver nitrate and alkynes.   J. Am. Chem. Soc., 79:4341-44.

With Gabriel J. Buist.   Basicity constants and rates of hydration of some imines.   J. Am. Chem. Soc., 79:6157-60.

ALDEN HOLMES MILLER

February 4, 1906–October 9, 1965

BY ERNST MAYR

ALDEN HOLMES MILLER was born at Los Angeles, California, February 4, 1906, and died of a heart attack at Clear Lake, California, on October 9, 1965. The most impressive aspect of his all-too-short life was the range of his activities. His premature death left a painful gap in the institutions which he had served with so much distinction and in the branch of biological science to which he had contributed so significantly.

It is no accident that Alden Miller became a naturalist. Loye Miller, his beloved father, "Padre" to his friends, was one of the enthusiastic group of California naturalists, and, even before he could walk, young Miller was forever out in the field with his parents. He did not escape the "pack rat affliction" of the young naturalist and made his mother's life miserable by trying to raise pollywogs in the bathroom sink and by converting a corner of his bedroom into a museum. How much Alden admired his father is obvious not only from the close contact he had with him all his life and the choice of his career, but also in the selection of specific lines of research (avian paleontology, anatomy, and vocalization). Both father and mother gave him a love for music which was heightened by the fact that he had "absolute pitch" and a fine voice. He was blessed being raised in a happy family, although he tended to shyness and may well have occasionally felt overshadowed by the radiant personality of his universally popular father. He entered the University of California at Los Angeles, where his father was also teaching, in 1923 and earned his A. B. degree in 1927.

During this time he became engaged to Virginia Dove, a fellow student at UCLA, whom he married in August 1928. Their marriage was a very harmonious one, owing to a similarity of interests and their love and respect for each other. Alden was a kind and thoughtful father, guiding his three children in their education and leisure-time activities. The happy family life of the Millers was a joy and example to their many friends.

In college Alden Miller majored in zoology and chemistry, but he simultaneously studied music under John Smallman and developed a beautiful and well-trained voice. As a result, he became the baritone soloist in one of Los Angeles' largest churches, the First Congregational. Toward the end of his undergraduate days, he had to make a vital decision. Should he choose music as his profession, as he was strongly urged by his musician friends, or should he become a biologist? He finally decided that he would have a richer life if he became a scientist, and he enrolled as a graduate student with Joseph Grinnell in Berkeley. After this decision was made, his professional life was as straightforward and uncomplicated as any professional life can be in these complex and rapidly changing times. He remained associated with the Berkeley campus of the University of California until his death, and found it possible to develop his diverse interests and abilities within the framework of this one institution.

Miller soon became an enthusiastic, almost passionate Grinnellian. Grinnell's methods of field work, of data collecting, and of presenting the results in subsequent scientific publications were unconsciously adopted by Miller, and much of this procedure was retained by him after his interests had outgrown Grinnell's traditional objectives. In the 1920s, Grinnell was a leader and pioneer. He was the first to develop some of the best-known concepts of ecology, such as the niche and competitive exclusion, and pioneered in various other areas of evolutionary biology, particularly the study of geographic variation in relation to climate and physical environment. Grinnell's ideal was to get away from the anecdotal approach of the traditional naturalist. His aim was to make natural history scientific by accuracy of recording, precision of description, and quantitative analysis of the data. Alas, this purely inductive method often overwhelms the investigator. Some of Grinnell's many students were rightly ridiculed for the publication of awesome mountains of undigested raw data. Alden Miller was far too good a scientist to go to such extremes, and yet, throughout his life, he had a tendency to give a greater amount of his strength and time to the gathering and presentation of data than they were worth. The systematist, using this word in the broadest possible sense, faces a genuine methodological dilemma. He cannot make any generalizations without the gathering of abundant comparative data, and yet, unless he is extremely careful, he may lose sight of the forest for the trees.

One of the major objectives of Grinnell's school was to determine the precise distribution of each species of terrestrial vertebrates in California and adjacent states and to specify its dependence on certain landscape types and climatic zones. A second objective was to analyze the impact of the distribution on the geographic variation of each species. The needed information was gathered on a multitude of field trips to all parts of California and adjacent states. The findings were presented in two types of publication. One was a series of monographs on the vertebrates of specific areas, and Miller was co-author of two volumes in this series, *The Vertebrate Animals of the Providence Mountains* (1948) and *The Lives of Desert Animals in Joshua Tree National Monument* (1964). Two major summaries were the other outcome of this research. The massive data gathered during a lifetime of faunistic researches were published by Grinnell and Miller, in 1944, as *The Distribution of the Birds of California* (608 pages and 57 figures, mostly maps). This formed the basis of *An Analysis of the Distribution of the Birds of California,* published by Miller in 1951, carried out entirely in the classical terms of life zones and biotic provinces, and vegetational associations as distinguished by the plant ecologists. As in much of the early ecological work, there was rarely a rising above the purely descriptive level. Yet, it must not be overlooked that this type of work has established an excellent basis for the conservationist, for the geographer, for wildlife management departments, and for all those who conduct more ambitious work in the field of ecology.

Miller's bibliography contains a total of 258 papers. They range from a new locality record of the black-bellied plover, published when he was just eighteen years old, to work on mammals, fossils, anatomy, physiology, systematics, behavior, and various areas of environmental and evolutionary biology.

Miller's Ph.D. thesis (1931), a broad-gauge study of the American shrikes (*Lanius*), foreshadows many of the lines of his future research. The first part of this monograph is devoted to a painstaking description of geographic and individual variation of the two species, one of the first ornithological papers giving detailed statistics of differences in measurable characters of sexes, age groups, and geographic races.

The degree of precision pioneered in this monograph set new standards and had a lasting impact on American ornithology.

The second half of this monograph is devoted to a detailed study of the natural history of American shrikes, much of it based on Miller's own field work. The breadth of his interests is best indicated by some of the section headings, such as migration, habitats, territory, courtship, nest-building, eggs, incubation, growth of young (16 pages), second and third broods, food, foraging, impaling instinct, digestion, preening and bathing, modes of progression, vocal notes, causes of death, and age. Fifteen other papers in his bibliography are devoted to various aspects of avian biology dealing with personal observations of courtship display, territorial habits, parental care (including distraction displays), and stages of the life cycle.

A special part of his thesis dealt with an analysis of plumages and molts. Physiologists and particularly endocrinologists have long known that a close study of molts and the sequence of plumages reveals a great deal about the annual cycle of hormonal levels. The "geography" of feather tracts is important also as taxonomic character in birds, and, realizing this, Miller devoted much study to this subject, so much indeed that he became the outstanding American authority in this field. A foreign author recently wrote me plaintively, "No one in America is qualified to review my book on molts, now that Alden Miller has died."

In spite of the wealth of descriptive detail presented by Miller, what he was really interested in was questions of causation. He said of his studies of the molts of the Loggerhead Shrike that they "have demonstrated that a pronounced geographic variation in the completeness of the first fall molt exists within this species. The variation appears to be associated not only with migration and with length of summer season but also with the structural features that differentiate subspecies." In a later paper (1933), he writes, "Experimental methods have been open to criticism from the standpoint of the naturalist because of the artificiality of the conditions attending the experiments. It appears, however, that in the analysis of Phainopepla [desert bird] plumage there is an opportunity to observe a natural experiment which under perfectly normal conditions seems to corroborate certain of the principles discovered by the experimentalists in the laboratory. By studying a group of immature Phainopeplas which have been preserved at varying stages of the body molt and with varying appearance of black pigmentation, we have, in a sense, a continuous picture of the period when the testes is apparently attaining full hormone secreting function." These comments foreshadow Miller's later intensive population studies of the hormonal and environmental factors controlling reproduction in birds.

Some thirty of Miller's publications, including his *Lanius* and *Junco* monographs, are in the field of taxonomy. Miller was the first and soon the leading proponent of population systematics among American ornithologists. He argued convincingly at a time when he was almost alone in these views that species and subspecies should not be conceived in the classical typological manner but as variable populations. He concluded a lecture at the International Ornithological Congress at Oxford in 1934 with these words: "The illustrations which the genus *Junco* offers should serve to point an inquiring finger at the simplicity of concepts of species and subspecies still retained by many persons, and should induce the student of taxonomy to search more thoroughly for the true nature of species." In seven revisions, he studied the geographic variation of certain North American birds with whole population samples. In each case a careful statistical analysis was under-

taken and an attempt made to correlate the observed variation in size, proportions, and coloration with the variation
of the environment. His *Speciation in the Avian Genus Junco*
(1941) was considered, at the time of its publication, "the
finest study of this sort in the ornithological literature" and
still deserves this evaluation. Unfortunately, Miller presented
his findings in the Grinnellian tradition as a straightforward
taxonomic revision, and some of his most interesting and
novel evolutionary findings were recorded, in a fragmented
way, under the heading of various junco subspecies. Consequently, this superb piece of research did not become nearly
as widely known outside the small circle of specialists as it
deserved. Its publication (1941) was timely, indeed, because
it was at this period that Goldschmidt vigorously promoted
the viewpoint that geographic variation and isolation were
of no evolutionary consequence and had nothing to do with
species formation. Miller proved conclusively that geographic
races in juncos are incipient species, and show, indeed, such a
perfect transition from local race to full species that to this
date (1972) there is not yet unanimity among ornithologists
as to which group of populations should be considered species
and which others subspecies. Miller was quite justified in
concluding that "the genus *Junco* contributes a rather complete exemplification of the stages and processes that lead to
the first milepost in the evolutionary path, the full species."

His junco work foreshadows much that Miller continued
to pursue during the ensuing ten or fifteen years. For instance,
when geographic isolates among the juncos secondarily come
into contact again, they show a lesser or greater amount of
hybridization in this zone of contact regardless of the degree
of morphological difference between the two populations.
Miller was greatly interested in three aspects of this hydridi-
zation. First, to what extent the analysis of the hybrid flocks

sheds light on the amount of genetic divergence that had taken place in the parental population; particularly, which characters would seem to have an oligogenic basis and would show well-defined segregation and what other characters would seem to be polygenic and intergrade gradually. The second question he pursued was to what extent behavioral barriers had arisen during the preceding isolation that would prevent complete interbreeding of the populations. And finally, he was concerned in the role which differences in habitat selection (ecological preference) played in reenforcing the behavioral barriers between incipient species. He successfully reared hybrid juncos in the laboratory and came back to the problem of hybridization again and again in subsequent publications. His student C. G. Sibley, and in turn Sibley's students, have continued to study various aspects of hybridization between natural populations.

In the course of time, Miller became the outstanding authority on the taxonomy of the birds of western North America. Naturally, he was chosen by A. Wetmore to serve on the committee charged with the preparation of the fifth edition of the *Check-List of North American Birds* and to be responsible for the information relating to the birds of western North America. In this capacity, he had to do a great deal of *ad hoc* research, subsequently incorporated in about a dozen supplements to the previous Check-List. He had an even greater share in the *Distributional Check-List of the Birds of Mexico* and he also helped Peters in the *Check-List of Birds of the World,* co-authoring with John Davis the account of the family Mimidae (mockingbirds). All of this entailed painstaking critical work with museum specimens and in the library, and Miller's contribution was always thoroughly sound and completely reliable.

Loye Miller, Alden's father, was one of the pioneers in the study of the paleontology of American birds. It is only natural that his son should have developed an interest in this formerly so-neglected area of ornithology. Even though birds have more species (8,600 recent species) than any other group of terrestrial vertebrates, they have been much neglected by paleontologists, bird fossils being generally of small size, lacking teeth, and possessing fragile bones. It requires real expertise to identify fossil bird bones, which is the reason that most work on avian paleontology is done by ornithologists. The first of Miller's twenty-seven publications on fossil birds was published when he was twenty-three years old; the last one posthumously. These publications fall rather clearly into two periods. In the earlier, covering the 1930s and early 1940s, he worked on the Tertiary and Pleistocene fauna of western North America. A second period began when he accompanied R. A. Stirton to Australia in 1961. His exciting discoveries of fossil flamingos and ratites in Australia are a major contribution, shared with Stirton. As a good naturalist, Miller was very much interested in the composition of fossil faunas and in the information they gave on the ecological conditions which prevailed at the time of the deposit. His paper on "An Avifauna from the Lower Miocene of South Dakota" (1944) well represents his approach.

From his father, Miller acquired also a considerable interest in anatomy, particularly functional anatomy, reflected in eight papers on the subject. Most of these are of little importance, dealing with such matters as his discovery of a buccal pouch in the Rosy Finch and the vocal apparatus of various species of owls. His most important contribution is a monograph on the structural modifications in the Hawaiian Goose (*Nesochen*), quite rightly called, in the subtitle, "A Study in Adaptive Evolution." This species, quite closely related to the North American Canada Goose, has become sedentary and largely terrestrial. In a superb functional anatomical analysis, Miller shows in how many different ways this shift in the adaptive zone had affected the skeleton and muscles of the Hawaiian Goose, particularly its locomotory apparatus.

Miller was an enthusiastic field man. Although he did a lot of his research in the laboratory, his heart was in the outdoors. He had thoroughly accepted the Grinnellian view that the animal was part of nature and had to be studied as part of nature. We have no records of how many field trips he undertook with his father and as a student, but the field notebook which he kept after joining the Museum of Vertebrate Zoology contains records on 53 trips between 1930 and 1965. Most of these were undertaken to poorly known areas of California and adjacent states (Oregon, Nevada, Arizona, etc.), but from the 1940s on he visited also Mexico, Panama, Colombia, the Galapagos Islands, Australia, and New Guinea. He did not undertake these trips as a leisurely tourist but devoted every minute to making observations, recording these painstakingly, and adding to his collections. The last specimen collected by Alden Miller, catalogued in the Museum of Vertebrate Zoology, was a song sparrow collected on September 26, 1955, in Mendocino County. This brought the field number for specimens personally collected by him to 12,564. Only he who knows how much work it is to make up a bird skin and how far into the night one has to work to prepare the yield of a successful day will appreciate the significance of this figure. In the 1920s and up to World War II, a graduate student at the Museum of Vertebrate Zoology working for a Ph.D. degree had to take a summer field trip unless he was already an experienced hand. In those days, the end of the semester was a time of great excitement around the Museum, with field parties getting ready to leave for here, there, and everywhere, and envy on the part of the "unchosen" for those lucky enough to be participants. Of late, after the general direction of the field had changed, the organization of official field parties was largely given up.

Miller himself was a superb field man. All of his students are unanimous in praising the acuity of his senses, his unerring ability to identify birds from even a fraction of song or call note (his outstanding musical ability was no doubt helpful), his determined planning, and his tireless dedication. One anecdote illustrates Miller's mastery in the field. On an overnight field trip to a waterfowl refuge in the Sacramento Valley, while supper was being prepared at dusk an anomalous bird call was heard and Miller said without the slightest hesitation, "Rock Wren." Since this camp, surrounded by tule marshes and ponds, was a totally unsuited locality for a rock inhabitant, the students were quite sure that their professor for once had goofed. Yet, next morning, they found the Rock Wren on a nearby lumber pile. The anecdote illustrates not only Miller's uncanny ability in identifying bird sounds but also his confidence in his ear. When he was sure of what he had heard, he would not say, "Sounds like a Rock Wren," but simply, "Rock Wren," no matter how unlikely the locality.

Seasonal phenomena are one of the most impressive aspects of animal life. Miller shared with other naturalists the excitement produced by William Rowan's discovery of photoperiodicity. This is evident from his review of Rowan's book in 1930 even though his own experimental researches on this problem did not begin until 1945. As an undergraduate at UCLA, he took courses with a well-known endocrinologist, Bennet Allen, who had made significant contributions to the understanding of the relationship between the pituitary body and amphibian pigmentation. Miller served as research assistant to Allen and learned to hypophysectomize amphibian embryos and larvae. He did more such work at Berkeley in Richard M. Eakin's laboratory in 1937, but never published his results. It was not until Albert Wolfson did a Ph.D. thesis under Miller's guidance, dealing with aspects of photoperiodicity, that Miller himself entered this field. He was particularly concerned with the causation of the so-called "refractory period," a period after the breeding season during which birds fail to respond (with an increase of gonad size) to an increase in day length. The literature was quite confused, and different authors championed essentially three different causations (or various combinations). According to one, the refractory period was due to a specific environmental condition ("decreasing day length"). Miller demonstrated that this could not be correct. Added illumination, even when starting soon after the end of the previous breeding season and continued for almost an entire year, not only failed to induce a gonadal response but even prevented an increase of gonad size at the time when this took place in control birds. Nor could an internal rhythm be the entire answer. By keeping birds under midwinter light conditions for an entire year, he proved that there was a very slight increase (from one to four grams) in testis size owing to the internal rhythm, but nothing like the several hundredfold increase that occurred after added illumination. Obviously then a rather specific inhibition had to be involved.

This still left quite uncertain what cause and target of the inhibition were, a puzzle that Miller also solved. A dramatic response of the testes during the refractory period to treatment with the pituitary hormone gonadotropin demonstrated that refractoriness is an inherent property not of the gonads but rather of the entire hormonal system governed by the pituitary. Miller, furthermore, provided new evidence that different species respond differently with respect to the length and intensity of their refractoriness and that caution is necessary in extrapolating from one species to another. What impressed Miller particularly in this research was the close correlation between physiological phenomena and the climatic conditions under which each species and, in fact, each local population of each species lived and reproduced. Latitude and degree of migratoriness were accurately reflected in the photo-period response.

Miller's research so far had been done with North Temperate species and populations of the sparrow genus *Zonotrichia*. At this point, Miller had the brilliant idea of investigating the physiological control of breeding seasons at a locality where seasonal variation of day length is at a minimum, that is, directly on the equator. In 1949 and 1950 he began an extended project of studying periodicity in wild birds in Colombia at localities that are no more than $3\frac{1}{2}°$ latitude from the equator. Of ten species that were regularly sampled during three equally spaced periods of a year, eight showed no indication of a breeding season. Some breeding individuals were found in any period that was sampled. This finding corresponded closely to those in other tropical areas. But Miller was not satisfied with this. He asked himself, what happens to a given individual? Up to now his results had reflected the conditions as shown by the average of the species population. In his ensuing research he founded what constituted a new branch of biology, population endocrinology: he followed the endocrine cycle of an entire population of free-living bird individuals.

The planning and execution of the analysis of the breeding cycle in the Andean Sparrow (*Zonotrichia capensis*) is a model of its kind. In the course of a year 160 individuals of this species were captured in a restricted area and individually color-marked. The age of younger birds was determined by plumage condition and examination of the ossification of the skull. The breeding condition of males was determined by examination of testis size through laparotomy. These operations had to be conducted so skillfully that the birds could be released at once and continue their normal activities. The operations caused no apparent debilitation of the birds, even though some birds were laparotomized three or four times. The results showed that each individual normally goes through two complete cycles each year averaging six months in duration. The breeding condition of males lasts about four months, while the intervening period of regression, rest, and recrudescence of the testes occupies two months. This research was rounded out and brought to completion by bringing a sample of living birds to Berkeley and exposing them to various light regimes, but was finally terminated by Miller's death.

An appreciation of Alden Miller would be incomplete that did not mention his substantial contribution as an academic administrator. The late J. B. S. Haldane always emphasized the benefits of human polymorphism without which our institutions could hardly function. Our universities are excellent testimony for this observation. We have a generous sprinkling of brilliant but often quite irresponsible individuals who do not possess the foggiest notion of how to translate their ideas into action and how to reconcile them with existing institutions. They could not keep a university functioning smoothly, considering that they are far too undisciplined to attend meetings regularly, to know how to draft an agenda, or to chair an orderly meeting. Fortunately, there is also a handful of efficient and selfless individuals at each of our universities who are more interested in the well-being of the university than in the promotion of their own egos. Alden H. Miller was such an individual, and yet, by his actions, he refuted everything that we usually say when slandering university administrators. Miller never sought an administrative career of any kind. In principle, he disliked administrative posts that were not directly connected with his scientific interests, and when accepting such positions, he insisted on being relieved at the earliest opportunity. Nevertheless, he was unanimously praised as an excellent administrator. He saw his own involvement in the governance of the university, and that of his colleagues, as the logical and necessary extension of that faculty self-government of which Berkeley had always been proud. The epitome of this attitude is that if you are asked to perform a service, to fill an office, or to chair a committee, you have the responsibility to do so unless the task is physically impossible or is so extraneous to your experience that you honestly believe you could not discharge it properly.

Miller's full involvement with academic duties started in 1950, and in the last fifteen years of his life he served on no less than thirty committees of the University of California, of seven of which he was chairman. This service included committees on the college, campus, and state level. In the College of Letters and Science, he was Vice Chairman of the College Faculty and Chairman of its Executive Committee in 1961-1962. He was Chairman of the Budget Committee from 1957 to 1961. When Chancellor Glenn Seaborg went to Washington to head the AEC and Vice Chancellor for Academic Affairs Strong moved up, Miller became Vice Chancellor of Academic Affairs, 1961-1962 and 1963-1964. He served on promotion, curriculum, research, and publication committees. Yet, he steadfastly refused administrative appointments that would have made the continuation of his research career impossible.

By inclination Miller was conservative rather than a great innovator. His contribution to administrative matters, in addition to his efficiency and integrity, was that he could analyze situations objectively, determine what was feasible and what was not, and provide a necessary balance to "weigh out" new ideas. His spirit of dedication was never more evident than at the time of crisis in the Department of Paleontology (such as occurs so often in university departments), and the only solution seemed to be the dissolution of the department and reassignment of its faculty. Miller volunteered at this stage to assume acting chairmanship of the department for a year because he felt that the department was serving a useful purpose and should be continued. He soon worked out the source of the difficulties, proposed the needed actions, and turned a viable department back to the university at the end of his term. This was all done in a pure spirit of public service, since Miller himself derived no benefits from the assignment. Indeed, some of his associates have questioned whether he did not go too far in fulfilling this and other services to the community, since there was no doubt that he was constantly overburdened with administrative chores. There is, indeed, some evidence that his leadership as Director of the Museum of Vertebrate Zoology suffered from the harassment of his many-sided academic duties. There is much to indicate that his fatal heart condition might well have been brought about by these stresses.

It must not be forgotten that his work for the university was only one of his many administrative loads. Miller was very active in several of the national ornithological organizations, such as the Cooper Ornithological Society and the American Ornithologists' Union, and he served these organizations on their councils, as an officer, and in numerous other ways. He was President of the American Ornithologists' Union from 1953 to 1955 and Chairman of its Check-List Committee at the time of his death. From 1939 on, he served as the editor of *The Condor* and raised its standards to such a level of excellence that it was considered by many to be America's leading ornithological journal. Here again he displayed the virtues of unselfishness, conscientiousness, and integrity that distinguished all of his activities. One of his associates remembers that when they arrived late in the evening in Los Angeles after a tiring drive from Berkeley, Miller did not go to bed as his companion did but started editing proof of the current issue of *The Condor* and kept at it until nearly midnight. If he had not driven himself like this, the issue might have been late! Except for the German *Journal für Ornithologie,* all ornithological journals of that period were essentially devoted to faunistics and taxonomy. Miller sponsored a policy, by no means approved by the old-timers, to include manuscripts on experimental researches and to shift the balance from faunistics and systematics to ecology, physiology, and behavior. At one stage the new policies resulted in an actual rebellion of some of the older bird watching–avicultural members which required prompt and decisive action by Miller to prevent a dissolution of the Cooper Ornithological Society. It was a great source of satisfaction to him that in a subsequent vote his action was endorsed by about 98 percent of the membership.

His reputation as a person of efficiency and integrity and his ability as a troubleshooter resulted in his election as President of the International Commission for Zoological Nomenclature, a well-known hotbed of dissension. He had just started to exercise his talents in this new office when he was suddenly taken away.

Various ornithological societies honored him by election to offices and honorary memberships. In 1943 he was awarded the Brewster Medal of the American Ornithologists' Union, and his election to the National Academy of Sciences came in 1957.

In his personality and character, he displayed the usual contradictions. For instance, self-confidence and shyness would seem to be incompatible traits. Yet, what Miller wrote of his own teacher, Joseph Grinnell, was quite literally true of himself also: "His self-confidence was not much revealed in public. An innate reserve and shyness and a distain for ostentation [concealed it]." Miller kept his feelings to himself, to such an extent that he appeared cold to those who did not really know him well. Yet, the example he set through his complete integrity and fairness, through the high standards he demanded, through his own hard work and his many-sided achievements, evoked a good deal of hero worship among his students. Even where they disagreed with him in certain scientific interpretations, they admired him as a human being and emulated him in many ways. He was dedicated to his family, but there were only a few of his students and colleagues who considered Miller a close personal friend. He had a quiet, almost shy humor, largely unknown except to his closest associates.

Whether it was hero worship for his father and for his teacher, Joseph Grinnell, or an innate tendency, there is no doubt that Miller was strongly inclined to be conservative. This tendency affected his judgment with respect to the strategy of scientific publishing, policy formation in the Museum of Vertebate Zoology, planning of research, or other issues. He was never rude to anyone; indeed, an unfailing courtesy was one of his characteristic traits. He avoided arguments and unpleasantness as much as he possibly could, but when a conflict became inevitable, as happened two or three times in his life, he fought the issue with determination to a conclusive end. As he grew older, his personality became increasingly warmer. Quite evidently his former insecurity abated when he had proved himself so eminently successful in his chosen fields of endeavor.

Perhaps Miller's outstanding character trait was his tremendous drive to do research and fulfill his professional obligations. He would let nothing else interfere with these aims. His capacity to organize work and make every minute count was quite extraordinary and was carried out without any fanfare. He always kept some minor tasks on his desk (such as proof to be read) to be done in the few minutes between appointments. His ability to compartmentalize was almost proverbial. A few minutes after a very emotional and controversial meeting had broken up, one might find Miller calmly working on a manuscript.

He was quite Spartan in his ability to endure privations and physical pain without a word of complaint. Some fifteen years before his death he had an extremely painful bone condition in his foot, later corrected by surgery, but this did not prevent him from continuing in his daily routine. And although he limped badly and sometimes had to use a cane, he even went on a field trip to Mexico with some associates. As one of them wrote me, "His foot hurt like hell, but he hobbled around, putting up his 15 bird skins a day without complaint. On one occasion, he got out of the Museum truck and put the sore foot right into a squirrel hole, twisting it badly. He righted himself, said 'Damn!' and stomped off."

On his field trips, he was able to do with a minimum of comfort and it was lucky that his wife was equally able to cope with such an austere life. Indeed, much of the credit for the achievements of his collecting trips should go to her, for she was at his side in the field as often as possible, and always after the children were grown. Whether it was in the rain forests of Colombia or in the fly-infested desert of Central Australia, she served as a field assistant, doing her share in preparing specimens and taking care of the camp chores, always cheerful even under the most adverse conditions. The Millers were often teased because they went camping as if they were gypsies, with virtually no equipment except for sleeping bags, a food box, and a couple of old car-spring leaves to be used as fire irons over a camp fire. As his wife wrote, "Alden never complained about heat, cold, flies, or any physical discomfort, and by his example, taught me and all the children not to complain but to accept things as they are."

Miller had a considerable impact on American science. He exercised his influence in three capacities, as a scientist (through his published work), as an academic administrator, and as an educator, in the broadest sense of this word. He, more than anyone else, was responsible for the transformation of American ornithology from what might be called "glorified bird watching" to a legitimate branch of biology. He and his students were interested not only in birds as such but also in birds as suitable material for the study of challenging biological problems. By the breadth and quality of his work, he set new standards of excellence which have had a lasting impact. Berkeley became the training center of students to be raised in this new image of ornithology, "The MVZ School of Ornithology" as it was often called. No less than thirty-one graduate students took their Ph.D. degree with him, and in view of the fact that so many of them now occupy prominent positions in American universities, it would seem worthwhile to list them in the chronological order of their degree: T. H. Eaton, Jr. (1933), W. L. Engels (1937), E. T. Hooper (1939), F. Richardson (1939), F. H. Test (1940), H. I. Fisher (1942), A. Wolfson (1942), C. A. Reed (1943), A. S. Leopold (1944), F. A. Pitelka (1946), J. T. Marshall, Jr. (1948), C. G. Sibley (1948), R. W. Storer (1949), C. B. Koford (1950), J. Davis (1950), T. R. Howell (1951), G. W. Salt (1951), K. L. Dixon (1953), T. L. Rodgers (1953), D. E. Bowers (1954), D. W. Johnston (1954), R. A. Norris (1954), R. F. Johnston (1955), R. K. Selander (1956), R. I. Bowman (1957), J. Mary Taylor (1959), R. C. Banks (1961),

G. F. Fisler (1961), N. K. Johnson (1961), R. B. Payne (1965), and E. O. Willis (1965). Miller was always available for consultation if the student wanted to discuss his thesis with him, but he left it up to the student to take the initiative. He felt that the student would learn more if he had to find his own way than if the professor supervised him at every step. The great variety of thesis projects indicates how much freedom he gave to his students. The lack of domination is also indicated by how rarely Miller appears as a co-author in any of the papers done by students. Virtually the only exceptions are where he employed students as research assistants in his own research. He had a way of encouraging his students when they were doing well. His great innate courtesy expressed itself in the fact that he seemed to lean over backwards to avoid being critical. He thought the student could learn most by watching others at work, and this is one of the reasons why he set such an outstanding example of dedicated work and efficiency.

Miller was only thirty-four years old when, in 1940, he took over the directorship of the Museum of Vertebrate Zoology after the premature death of Joseph Grinnell. He served as the director of this important university museum for a period of twenty-six years. In spite of certain innovations, it is evident that Miller considered it his task to maintain the Grinnellian tradition. Field work remained the key activity. The delimitation of biotic districts and the determination of intraspecific geographic variation were considered major tasks. He deviated from tradition in one respect, by enlarging the geographic framework beyond the western states to include Mexico and South America and eventually even the Australian region. Also his interests were broader than those of Grinnell, as indicated not only by his work in paleontology and anatomy but particularly by his research in reproductive physiology. Indeed, he felt that an ornithologist should be interested in all biological aspects of birds, rather than becoming a narrow specialist. Consequently he frowned on the idea of establishing a separate physiological and behavior group in the Museum. With the Grinnellian tradition so well established, he considered it his role as director to serve as chief administrator rather than as team leader. Combined with his conservatism, all this tended to favor the status quo. This tendency was reenforced by the Museum's appointment policy. As long as the emphasis of the research in the Museum was on California, it seemed natural that positions should be filled by young vertebrate biologists trained in California, preferably in the Museum itself. The result was extreme inbreeding of the staff of the Museum (and of the attached Hastings Reservation). Seth Benson, Frank Pitelka, Starker Leopold, Ned Johnson, Jean Linsdale, and John Davis were all home products. This did not encourage pioneering in new directions.

Whether it was because Miller was conservative by nature or whether it was his great sense of loyalty to Joseph Grinnell, the fact is that Miller continued many of the old traditions of the Grinnell School long after the law of diminishing returns had taken its toll. His determination to continue collecting trips and the publication of faunistic reports were symptoms of his attitude. The fact of the matter is that developments in evolutionary biology were faster than the changes in Miller himself. Science thrives on breakthroughs and controversies. When the battle over the cause of evolution was won, when the polytypic species had been adopted by vertebrate taxonomists, when the role of the environment as chief factor of selection had been universally acknowledged, a change in the interests of students occurred. They lost interest in field trips, and recruitment into vertebrate zoology became more difficult. The excitement of the 1930s and 1940s in the new systematics, culminating in a crop of nine Ph.D.'s in the Museum of Vertebrate Zoology in the early 1950s, declined quite noticeably. By this time, Miller's own energy and attention were largely occupied with his crushing burden of academic administration, and the criticism that the Museum no longer had the aura of excitement of former decades was heard increasingly often. Perhaps it is asking too much that one center should display continuous leadership, particularly after some of its outstanding students had established flourishing new centers at other universities. This is a familiar phenomenon in academic life.

By inclination and as a follower of Grinnell, Miller was committed to the inductive method. Yet, it is not altogether true, as has sometimes been stated, that he was uninterested in generalizations. Not only is an appreciable section of his junco monograph devoted to generalizations but Miller published six smaller essays which deal with generalizations and theoretical issues. Each of them is still worth reading and some of them had a considerable impact when first published, such as that on habitat selection (1942), on population size in birds (1947), on the role of key adjustments in the origin of higher taxa (1950), and on the role of ecological factors in the rate of speciation (1956). Nevertheless, Miller was more of a particularist than a synthesizer. He never published a major book dealing with any of the topics with which he was most familiar. This is why he was best known to those who worked in the same field and with the same material. It is unquestionably in ornithology that he had his greatest impact and where his loss is felt most acutely.

BIBLIOGRAPHY

KEY TO ABBREVIATIONS

Audubon Mag. = Audubon Magazine
J. Mammal. = Journal of Mammalogy
Proc. Biol. Soc. Wash. = Proceedings of the Biological Society of Washington
Proc. Nat. Acad. Sci. = Proceedings of the National Academy of Sciences
Record S. Australian Mus. = Record of the South Australian Museum
Univ. Calif. Publ. Geol. Sci. = University of California Publications in Geological Sciences
Univ. Calif. Publ. Zool. = University of California Publications in Zoology
Wilson Bull. = Wilson Bulletin

1924

The black-bellied plover at Buena Vista Lake. Condor, 26:106.

1925

The boom-flight of the Pacific nighthawk. Condor, 27:141-43.

1928

The status of the cardinal in California. Condor, 30:243-45.
The molts of the loggerhead shrike *Lanius ludovicianus* Linnaeus. Univ. Calif. Publ. Zool., 30(13):393-417.

1929

A new race of black-chinned sparrow from the San Francisco Bay district. Condor, 31:205-7.
Additions to the Rancho La Brea avifauna. Condor, 31:223-24.
The passerine remains from Rancho La Brea in the paleontological collections of the University of California. Univ. Calif. Publ. Geol. Sci., 19(1):1-22.

1930

With S. B. Benson. The summer resident birds of the boreal and transition life-zones of Mount Pinos, California. Condor, 32:101-4.
The new races of the loggerhead shrike from western North America. Condor, 32:155-56.

The status of *Lanius borealis* as a species. Condor, 32:163-64.

With L. Miller. A record of the scarlet tanager for California. Condor, 32:217.

1931

Observations on the incubation and the care of the young in the jacana. Condor, 33:32-33.

An auklet from the Eocene of Oregon. Univ. Calif. Publ. Geol. Sci., 20(3):23-26.

Notes on the song and territorial habits of Bullock's oriole. Wilson Bull., 43:102-8.

The breeding of the mockingbird in the San Francisco Bay district. Condor, 33:219.

Systematic revision and natural history of the American shrikes (Lanius). Univ. Calif. Publ. Zool., 38:11-242.

1932

An extinct icterid from Shelter Cave, New Mexico. Auk, 49:38-41.

Observations on some breeding birds of El Salvador, Central America. Condor, 34:8-17.

The fossil passerine birds from the Pleistocene of Carpinteria, California. Univ. Calif. Publ. Geol. Sci., 21(7):169-94.

The summer distribution of certain birds in Central and Northern Arizona. Condor, 34:96-99.

Bird remains from Indian dwellings in Arizona. Condor, 34:138-39.

1933

Postjuvenal molt and the appearance of sexual characters of plumage in *Phainopepla nitens*. Univ. Calif. Publ. Zool., 38:425-46.

With H. Howard. Bird remains from cave deposits in New Mexico. Condor, 35:15-18.

Distributional notes from the northwest coast district of California. Condor, 35:36-37.

The inner abdominal feather region in brooding woodpeckers. Condor, 35:78-79.

The red tree-mouse preyed upon by the spotted owl. J. Mammal., 14:162.

With S. F. Light. *General Zoology, Laboratory Manual, Zoology 1-A.* University of California Syllabus Series, No. 247. Berkeley, University of California Press. 110 pp.

With T. T. McCabe. Geographic variation in the northern water-thrushes. Condor, 35:192-97.

The Canada jays of northern Idaho. Transactions of the San Diego Society of Natural History, 7:287-98.

With E. R. Hall. Arrangement of the obturator muscles, with notes on the other muscles of the thigh, in the dwarf wapiti (*Cervus nannodes Merriam*). J. Mammal., 14:358-61.

1934

With J. F. Ashley, Jr. Goose footprints on a Pliocene mud-flat. Condor, 36:178-79.

The vocal apparatus of some North American owls. Condor, 36:204-13.

Field experiences with mountain-dwelling birds of southern Utah. Wilson Bull., 46:156-68.

Winter occurences of saw-whet owl and Nuttall woodpecker in desert areas. Condor, 36:252.

1935

With T. T. McCabe. Racial differentiation in *Passerella (Melospiza) lincolnii.* Condor, 37:144-60.

Further comments on the cowbirds of the San Francisco bay region. Condor, 37:217-18.

Some breeding birds of the pine forest mountains, Nevada. Auk, 52:467-68.

The vocal apparatus of the elf owl and spotted screech owl. Condor, 37:288.

1936

An isolated colony of the gray-headed pika in Nevada. J. Mammal., 17:174-75.

Tribulations of thorn-dwellers. Condor, 38:218-19.

With L. Miller. The northward occurrence of *Bufo californicus* in California. Copeia, 3:176.

The identification of juncos banded in the Rocky Mountain states. Birdlore, 38:429-33.

1937

The nuptial flight of the Texas nighthawk. Condor, 39:42-43.

Structural modifications in the Hawaiian goose (*Nesochen sandvicensis*), a study in adaptive evolution. Univ. Calif. Publ. Zool., 42(1):1-80.

A comparison of behavior of certain North American and European shrikes. Condor, 39:119-22.

Notes on the saw-whet owl. Condor, 39:130-31.

With S. F. Light. *General Zoology, Laboratory Manual, Zoology 1A.* University of California Syllabus Series, No. 263. Berkeley, University of California Press. v + 110 pp.

Biotic associations and life-zones in relation to the Pleistocene birds of California. Condor, 39:248-52.

A cassin kingbird in San Joaquin County, California. Condor, 39:258.

1938

Fork-tailed petrel in San Francisco Bay region. Condor, 40:45.

Hybridization of juncos in captivity. Condor, 40:92-93.

A summer record of the white-winged crossbill in Oregon. Condor, 40:226.

With H. I. Fisher. The pterylosis of the California condor. Condor, 40:248-56.

Problems of speciation in the genus Junco. In: *Proceedings of the Eighth International Ornithological Congress,* Oxford, 1934, pp. 277-84. Oxford, Oxford University Press.

1939

The breeding Leucostictes of the Wallowa Mountains, Oregon. Condor, 41:34-35.

With H. Howard. The avifauna associated with human remains at Rancho La Brea, California. Carnegie Institution of Washington Publication No. 514, pp. 39-48.

Status of the breeding Lincoln's sparrows of Oregon. Auk, 56:342-43.

With L. V. Compton. Two fossil birds from the lower Miocene of South Dakota. Condor, 41:153-56.

With S. F. Light. *General Zoology, Laboratory Manual, Zool-*

ogy 1A. University of California Syllabus Series, No. 270. Berkeley, University of California Press. v + 100 pp.

Avian fossils from the lower Miocene of South Dakota. Bulletin of the Geological Society of America, Vol. 50, No. 12, Part II, pp. 1971-74.

Analysis of some hybrid populations of Juncos. Condor, 41:211-14.

Birds of the alpine zone of Mount Shasta, California. Condor, 41:218-19.

Foraging dexterity of a lazuli bunting. Condor, 41:255-56.

1940

Hybrid between *Zonotrichia coronata* and *Zonotrichia leucophrys*. Condor, 42:45-48.

Field technique in collecting for a research museum. Museum News, 17:6-8.

An early record of the dickcissel in Arizona. Condor, 42:125.

A transition island in the Mohave Desert. Condor, 42:161-63.

The pine grosbeak of the Cascade Mountains, Washington. Auk, 57:420-21.

Climatic conditions of the Pleistocene reflected by the ecologic requirements of fossil birds. In: *Proceedings of the Sixth Congress of the Pacific Science Association*, University of California at Berkeley, Stanford University, and San Francisco, pp. 807-10. Berkeley, University of California Press.

1941

The buccal food-carrying pouches of the rosy finch. Condor, 43:72-73.

With F. E. Peabody. An additional Pleistocene occurrence of the murre, *Uria aalge*. Condor, 43:78.

Rufous-crowned sparrow of southeastern New Mexico. Auk, 58:102

The significance of molt centers among the secondary remiges in the falconiformes. Condor, 43:113-15.

Speciation in the avian genus Junco. Univ. Calif. Publ. Zool., 44:173-434.

Racial determination of Bewick wrens in the western Great Basin region. Condor, 43:250-51.

With C. G. Sibley. A Miocene gull from Nebraska. Auk, 58: 563-66.

A review of centers of differentiation for birds in the western Great Basin region. Condor, 43:257-67.

1942

With C. G. Sibley. An Oligocene hawk from Colorado. Condor, 44:39-40.

Habitat selection among higher vertebrates and its relation to interspecific variation. American Naturalist, 76:25-35.

American scoter at Alameda. Gull, 24:15.

With C. G. Sibley. A new species of crane from the Pliocene of California. Condor, 44:126-27.

Differentiation of the oven-birds of the Rocky Mountain region. Condor, 44:185-86.

Shower bathing of a spotted towhee. Condor, 44:232.

1943

Preface. *Philosophy of Nature: Selected Writings of a Western Naturalist,* by Joseph Grinnell, pp. vii-x. Berkeley, University of California Press.

A California condor bone from the coast of southern Oregon. Murrelet, 23:77.

With H. Twining. Winter visitant rosy finches in northeastern California. Condor, 45:78.

A new race of Canada jay from coastal British Columbia. Condor, 45:117-18.

With S. F. Light and F. A. Pitelka. *General Zoology, Laboratory Manual, Zoology 1A.* Berkeley and Los Angeles, University of California Press. v + 114 pp.

A record of the western tree sparrow in southern California. Condor, 45:160.

A new race of brown-headed chickadee from northern Washington. Occasional Papers, Museum of Zoology, Louisiana State University, 14:261-63.

Census of a colony of Caspian terns. Condor, 45:220-25.

1944

Specific differences in the call notes of chipmunks. J. Mammal., 25:87-89.

With F. A. Pitelka. List of birds of the Berkeley campus. Berkeley, Museum of Vertebrate Zoology. 4 pp.

With M. S. Ray. Discovery of new vireo of the genus Neochloe in southwestern Mexico. Condor, 46:41-45.

Specimens of the Pacific golden plover from California. Condor, 46:130.

An avifauna from the lower Miocene of South Dakota. Univ. Calif. Publ. Geol. Sci., 27(4):85-99.

With A. Wetmore, H. Friedmann, F. C. Lincoln, J. L. Peters, A. J. van Rossem, J. Van Tyne, and J. T. Zimmer. Nineteenth supplement to the American ornithologists' union check-list of North American birds. Auk, 61:441-64.

Second nestings in the wren-tit. Condor, 46:299.

With Joseph Grinnell. *The Distribution of the Birds of California*. Berkeley, Cooper Ornithological Club. 608 pp.

1945

Birds of the yellow pine association of Potosi Mountain, Southern Nevada. Condor, 47:130-31.

With A. Wetmore, H. Friedmann, F. C. Lincoln, J. L. Peters, A. J. Van Rossem, J. Van Tyne, and J. T. Zimmer. Twentieth supplement to the American ornithologists' union check-list of North American birds. Auk, 62:436-49.

Further records of birds from central California. Condor, 47:217-18.

1946

Vertebrate inhabitants of the piñon association in the Death Valley region. Ecology, 27:54-60.

A method of determining the age of live passerine birds. Bird-Banding, 17:33-35.

Social parasites among birds. Scientific Monthly, 62:238-46.

Endemic birds of the Little San Bernardino Mountains, California. Condor, 48:75-79.

With A. Wetmore, H. Friedmann, F. C. Lincoln, J. L. Peters, A. J. van Rossem, J. Van Tyne, and J. T. Zimmer. Twenty-first supplement to the American ornithologists' union check-list of North American birds. Auk, 63:428-32.

The identity of the orange-crowned warblers of the Santa Monica Mountains, California. Condor, 48:181.

The western tanager summer resident in Marin County. Gull, 28:33.

1947

The structural basis of the voice of the flammulated owl. Auk, 64:133-35.

A new genus of icterid from Rancho La Brea. Condor, 49:22-24.

The range of the ruffed grouse in California. California Fish and Game, 33:53-54.

The tropical avifauna of the upper Magdalena Valley, Columbia. Auk, 64:351-81.

With A. Whitmore, H. Friedmann, F. C. Lincoln, J. L. Peters, A. J. van Rossem, J. Van Tyne, and J. T. Zimmer. Twenty-second supplement to the American ornithologists' union check-list of North American birds. Auk, 64:445-52.

Arizona race of acorn woodpecker vagrant in California. Condor, 49:171.

Panmixia and population size with reference to birds. Evolution, 1:186-90.

The refractory period in light-induced reproductive development of the golden-crowned sparrow. Anatomical Record, 99:40.

1948

Further observations on variation in canyon wrens. Condor, 50:83-85.

White-winged Junco parasitized by cowbird. Condor, 50:92.

The whistling swan in the upper Pliocene of Idaho. Condor, 50:132.

With A. Wetmore, H. Friedmann, F. C. Lincoln, J. L. Peters, A. J. van Rossem, J. Van Tyne, and J. T. Zimmer. Twenty-third supplement to the American ornithologists' union check-list of North American birds. Auk, 65:438-43.

With D. H. Johnson and M. D. Bryant. The vertebrate animals of the Providence Mountains area of California. Univ. Calif. Publ. Zool., 48:221-376.

A new subspecies of eared poor-will from Guerrero, Mexico. Condor, 50:224-25.

The refractory period in light-induced reproductive development of golden-crowned sparrows. Journal of Experimental Biology, 109:1-11.

With R. M. Eakin and H. S. Reed. Sumner Cushing Brooks, 1888-1948. In: *In Memoriam,* pp. 1-5. Berkeley, University of California Press.

1949

Potentiality for testicular recrudescence during the annual refractory period of the golden-crowned sparrow. Science, 109:546.

With A. Wetmore, H. Friedmann, F. C. Lincoln, J. L. Peters, A. J. van Rossem, J. Van Tyne, and J. T. Zimmer. Twenty-fourth supplement to the American ornithologists' union check-list of North American birds. Auk, 66:281-85.

With F. A. Pitelka. *List of the Birds of the Berkeley Hills.* Berkeley, Museum of Vertebrate Zoology. 4 pp.

Some concepts of hybridization and integradation in wild populations of birds. Auk, 66:338-42.

1950

Temperatures of poor-wills in the summer season. Condor, 52:41-42.

A new name for the Canada jay of the Rainbow Mountains of British Columbia. Condor, 52:46.

Some ecologic and morphologic considerations in the evolution of higher taxonomic categories. In: *Ornithologie als biologische Wissenschaft. Festschrift zum 60. Geburtstag von Erwin Stresemann (22. November 1949),* pp. 84-88. Heidelberg, Carl Winter Universitätsverlag GmbH.

Harold Michner, 1882-1949. Condor, 52:95.

Lanius ludovicianus gambeli Ridgway. California shrike. Habits. In: *Life Histories of North American Wagtails, Shrikes, Vireos, and Their Allies.* U.S. National Museum Bulletin, 197:157-79.

With A. Wetmore, H. Friedmann, F. C. Lincoln, J. L. Peters, J. Van

Tyne, and J. T. Zimmer. Twenty-fifth supplement to the American ornithologists' union check-list of North American birds. Auk, 67:368-70.

With R. W. Storer. A new race of *Parus sclateri* from the Sierra Madre del Sur of Mexico. Journal of the Washington Academy of Sciences, 40:301-2.

1951

With S. B. Benson and R. C. Stebbins. *Natural History of the Vertebrates.* Zoology 113—spring semester. Laboratory and field work, University of California Syllabus Series, Syllabus WH. Berkeley, University of California Press. 39 pp.

The "rodent-run" of the green-tailed towhee. Ibis, 93:307-8.

A comparison of the avifaunas of Santa Cruz and Santa Rosa Islands, California. Condor, 53:117-23.

With L. Miller. Geographic variation of screech owls of the deserts of western North America. Condor, 53:161-67.

With A. Wetmore, H. Friedmann, F. C. Lincoln, J. L. Peters, J. Van Tyne, and J. T. Zimmer. Twenty-sixth supplement to the American ornithologists' union check-list of North American birds. Auk, 68:367-69.

Further evidence on the refractory period in the reproductive cycle of the golden-crowned sparrow, *Zonotrichia coronata.* Auk, 68:380-83.

An analysis of the distribution of the birds of California. Univ. Calif. Publ. Zool., 50:531-644.

1952

Two new races of birds from the upper Magdalena Valley of Colombia. Proc. Biol. Soc. Wash., 65:13-17.

With A. Wetmore, H. Friedmann, F. C. Lincoln, J. L. Peters, J. Van Tyne, and J. T. Zimmer. Twenty-seventh supplement to the American ornithologists' union check-list of North American birds. Auk, 69:308-12.

The generic name of the white-bellied wren of Mexico. Condor, 54:322.

Supplementary data on the tropical avifauna of the arid upper Magdalena Valley of Colombia. Auk, 69:450-57.

1953

More trouble for the California condor.   Condor, 55:47-48.

Preface.   *The California Condor,* by C. Koford, pp. vii-viii.   Research Report No. 4.   New York, National Audubon Society.

The incubation period of the Hutton vireo.   Condor, 55:221.

With A. Wetmore, H. Friedmann, F. C. Lincoln, J. Van Tyne, and J. T. Zimmer.   Twenty-eighth supplement to the American ornithologists' union check-list of North American birds.   Auk, 70:359-61.

The case against trapping California condors.   Audubon Mag., 55:261-62.

A fossil hoatzin from the Miocene of Colombia.   Auk, 70:484-89.

1954

The occurrence and maintenance of the refractory period in crowned sparrows.   Condor, 56:13-20.

With A. Wetmore, H. Friedmann, D. Amadon, F. C. Lincoln, G. H. Lowery, Jr., F. A Pitelka, J. Van Tyne, and J. T. Zimmer.   Twenty-ninth supplement to the American ornithologists' union check-list of North American birds.   Auk, 71:310-12.

With R. T. Moore.   A further record of the slaty finch in Mexico.   Condor, 56:310-11.

Nomenclature of the black-throated sparrows of Chihuahua and western Texas.   Condor, 56:364-65.

1955

Record of the least flycatcher in central British Columbia.   Condor, 57:62-63.

The avifauna of the Sierra del Carmen of Coahuila, Mexico.   Condor, 57:154-78.

The expression of innate reproductive rhythm under conditions of winter lightning.   Auk, 72:260-64.

With A. Wetmore, H. Friedmann, D. Amadon, F. C. Lincoln, G. H. Lowery, Jr., F. A. Pitelka, J. Van Tyne, and J. T. Zimmer.   Thirtieth supplement to the American ornithologists' union check-list of North American birds.   Auk, 72:292-95.

The breeding range of the black rosy finch.   Condor, 57:306-7.

A hybrid woodpecker and its significance in speciation in the genus Dendrocopos. Evolution, 9:317-21.

Acorn woodpecker on Santa Catalina Island. Condor, 57:373.

Breeding cycles in a constant equatorial environment in Colombia, South America. In: *Acta XI Congressus Internationalis Ornithologici,* pp. 495-503. Basel, 1954. Birkhauser Verlag, Basel and Stuttgart.

Concepts and problems of avian systematics in relation to evolutionary processes. Chapter 1 in: *Recent Studies in Avian Biology,* ed. by A. Wolfson, pp. 1-22. Urbana, University of Illinois Press.

1956

With W. C. Russell. Distributional data on the birds of the White Mountains of California and Nevada. Condor, 58:75-77.

With R. I. Bowman. Fossil birds of the late Pliocene of Cita Canyon, Texas. Wilson Bull., 68:38-46.

With R. I. Bowman. A fossil magpie from the Pleistocene of Texas. Condor, 58:164-65.

With A. Wetmore, H. Friedmann, D. Amadon, F. C. Lincoln, G. H. Lowery, Jr., F. A. Pitelka, J. Van Tyne, and J. T. Zimmer. Thirty-first supplement to the American ornithologists' union check-list of North American birds. Auk, 73:447-49.

Ecologic factors that accelerate formation of races and species of terrestrial vertebrates. Evolution, 10:262-77.

Northward vagrancy of the Scott oriole. Condor, 58:452.

1957

With S. B. Benson and R. C. Stebbins. *Natural History of the Vertebrates.* Zoology 113. Laboratory and field work, University of California Syllabus Series, No. 358. Berkeley, University of California Press. 42 pp.

In memoriam: Adriaan Joseph van Rossem. Auk, 74:20-27.

With R. M. Eakin and G. H. Ball. Harold Kirby, 1900-1952, Professor of Zoology. In: *In Memoriam,* pp. 73-75. Berkeley, University of California Press.

Migratory flight of a Zonotrichia at 10,000 feet above ground level. Condor, 59:209-10.

With A. Wetmore, H. Friedmann, D. Amadon, F. C. Lincoln, G. H. Lowery, Jr., J. L. Peters, F. A. Pitelka, A. J. van Rossem, J. Van Tyne, and J. T. Zimmer. *Check-List of North American Birds,* 5th ed. New York, American Ornithologists' Union. xiii + 691 pp.

With H. Friedmann, L. Griscom, and R. T. Moore. *Distributional Check-List of the Birds of Mexico.* Pacific Coast Avifauna Series No. 33, Part II, pp. 203-470. Los Angeles, Cooper Ornithological Society.

1958

Reproductive periods in birds near the equator. Caldasia, 8: 295-300.

1959

Reproductive cycles in an equatorial sparrow. Proc. Nat. Acad. Sci., 45:1095-1100.

With F. A. Pitelka. *List of the Birds of the Berkeley Hills.* Berkeley, Museum of Vertebrate Zoology, 4 pp.

Response to experimental light increments by Andean sparrows from an equatorial area. Condor, 61:344-47.

A new race of nighthawk from the upper Magdalena Valley of Colombia. Proc. Biol. Soc. Wash., 72:155-57.

1960

With John Davis. Family Mimidae. In: *Check-List of Birds of the World,* ed. by Ernst Mayr and James C. Greenway, Jr., Vol. IX, pp. 440-58. Cambridge, Museum of Comparative Zoology.

A blackish race of the Gray Seedeater of northern South America. Condor, 62:121-23.

Adaptation of breeding schedule to latitude. In: *Proceedings of the XIIth International Ornithological Congress,* Helsinki, 1958, Vol. II, pp. 513-22. Helsinki, International Ornithological Society.

Additional data on some Colombian birds. Novidades Colombianas, I:235-37.

The slaty spinetail. Condor, 62:413.

1961

Molt cycles in equatorial Andean sparrows. Condor, 63:143-61.

With R. A. Stirton and R. H. Tedford. Cenozoic stratigraphy

and vertebrate paleontology of the Tirari Desert, South Australia. Record S. Australian Mus., 14:19-61.

1962

Bimodal occurrence of breeding in an equatorial sparrow. Proc. Nat. Acad. Sci., 48:396-400.

With J. Davis. Further information on the Caribbean Martin in Mexico. Condor, 64:237-39.

The history and significance of the fossil *Casuarius lydekkeri*. Records of the Australian Museum, 25:235-37.

1963

Seasonal activity and ecology of the avifauna of an American equatorial cloud forest. Univ. Calif. Publ. Zool., 66:1-74.

The fossil flamingos of Australia. Condor, 65:289-99.

The vocal apparatus of two South American owls. Condor, 65: 440-41.

With E. Mayr, R. W. Storer, and E. Stresemann. *Tanagra* Linnaeus 1764 and *Tanagra* Linnaeus 1766 (aves): proposed use of plenary powers to end confusion. Bulletin of Zoological Nomenclature, 20:301-2.

Photoregulative and innate factors in the reproductive cycles of an equatorial sparrow. In: *Proceedings of the XVIth International Congress of Zoology,* ed. by John A. Moore, p. 166. Washington, National Research Council.

Fossil ratite birds of the late tertiary of South Australia. Record S. Australian Mus., 14:413-20.

The curator as a research worker. Curator, 6:282-86.

1964

A new species of warbler from New Guinea. Auk, 81:1-4.

Desert adaptations in birds. In: *Proceedings of the XIIIth International Ornithological Congress,* Vol. II, pp. 666-74. Baton Rouge, The American Ornithologists' Union, Museum of Zoology, Louisiana State University.

With E. McMillan. Hepatic tanager vagrant to coastal section of California. Condor, 66:308.

Mockingbirds and thrashers. Chapter in: *Song and Garden Birds of North America,* pp. 196-207. Washington, D.C., National Geographic Society.

With R. C. Stebbins. *The Lives of Desert Animals in Joshua Tree National Monument.* Berkeley, University of California Press. 452 pp.

Mockingbird. In: *A New Dictionary of Birds,* ed. by A. L. Thomson, pp. 479-81. Centenary publication of the British Ornithologists' Union. New York, McGraw-Hill Book Co., Inc.

J. Grinnell. Systematic Zoology, 13:235-42.

1965

With Ian I. McMillan and Eben McMillan. Hope for the California Condor. Audubon Mag., 67:38-41.

Capacity for photoperiodic response and endogenous factors in the reproductive cycles of an equatorial sparrow. Proc. Nat. Acad. Sci., 54:97-101.

The syringial structure of the Asiatic owl, *Phodilus.* Condor, 67:536-38.

1966

The fossil pelicans of Australia. Memoirs of the Queensland Museum, 14:181-90.

Animal evolution on islands. In: *The Galapagos,* ed. by Robert I. Bowman, pp. 10-17. Proceedings of the symposia of the Galapagos International Scientific Project. Berkeley and Los Angeles, University of California Press.

An evaluation of the fossil Anhingas of Australia. Condor, 68:315-20.

With V. D. Miller. The behavioral ecology and breeding biology of the Andean sparrow, *Zonotrichia capensis.* Caldasia, 10:83-154.

Amphispiza belli nevadensis (northern sage sparrow). Bulletin of the U. S. National Museum, No. 237, Part 2, pp. 1004-13. *Amphispiza belli canescens* (California sage sparrow), *ibid.,* pp. 1013-15; *Amphispiza belli belli, ibid.,* pp. 1015-19; *Amphispiza belli clementeae, ibid.,* pp. 1019-20; *Amphispiza belli cinerea* (gray sage sparrow), *ibid.,* pp. 1020-21. (Short articles in life histories of North American cardinals, grosbeaks, buntings, towhees, finches, sparrows, and allies.)

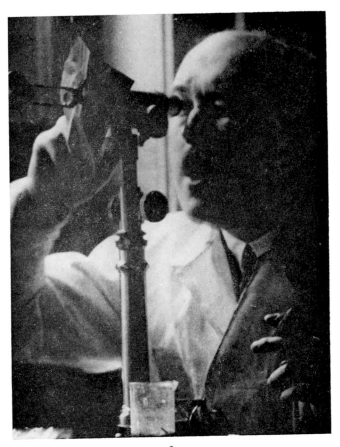

O. Stern

OTTO STERN

February 17, 1888–August 17, 1969

BY EMILIO SEGRÈ

OTTO STERN was born to a family of prosperous German Jewish millers and grain merchants on February 17, 1888, at Sohrau, upper Silesia, now Zory in Poland. Otto was one of five children, two brothers and three sisters. The father, Oscar, had married Eugenie Rosenthal, of Rawitsch. The family moved to Breslau in 1892 and thus Otto went to school there; his home, however, strongly supplemented the school instruction, and offered to Otto ample occasion for reading scientific books for children, hearing instructive conversation, and even for making chemical experiments. He attended the Johannes Gymnasium in Breslau from 1897 to 1906, at which date he obtained the *Abitur* certificate. As usual with German students, he wandered from one university to another; he went to Freiburg im Breisgau, to Munich, and finally returned to Breslau, where he spent most of his university years studying chemistry, and especially physico-chemistry. During his university years he attended lectures by Sommerfeld on mathematical physics, and by Rosanes on mathematics. The latter was the man from whom Max Born, also a student at Breslau, but a few years older than Stern, learned matrix algebra. Stern, however, did not learn much mathematics at school. Among his physics teachers were

Pringsheim and Lummer, famous for their experimental work on blackbody radiation, and also Schaefer, the author of a most popular book on classical theoretical physics, but here too the formal classwork did not prove very profitable for him. He liked physics and studied it in books; in particular he mastered Boltzmann's work on statistical mechanics, and Clausius on thermodynamics. Physico-chemistry at the time flourished in Germany: Nernst and Haber were among its luminaries, and, in Breslau, Abegg and especially Sackur had a great influence on Stern. It was under the guidance of Sackur that in 1912 Stern did his doctoral dissertation on the kinetic theory of osmotic pressure in concentrated solutions. The subject was Stern's own choice. This work consists of a theoretical part and a longer experimental part in which the theory is applied to CO_2 solutions in different solvents.

After receiving his Ph.D. degree, Stern took advantage of his economic independence to join Albert Einstein at Prague. He said many years later that what prompted him to take this fateful step was a "spirit of adventure." He had not met Einstein before but he knew he was a great man, at the center of modern developments in physics. Sackur, his professor, talked to Haber who knew Einstein, and Einstein was willing to accept him.

Stern was with Einstein from the spring of 1912 until 1914, first in Prague and then in Zurich, where in 1913 he became *Privatdozent* for physico-chemistry at an unusually early age. This period had a deep influence on him. Although Stern was primarily trained as a physico-chemist, he found plenty to talk about with Einstein. It was from Einstein that he learned what were the really important problems of contemporary physics: the nature of the quantum of light with its double aspect of particle and wave, the nature of atoms, and relativity, although the last was not much discussed by them because Stern was not deeply interested in it. Einstein at that time was studying radioactivity and the decay law. This research brought later fruits in his famous analysis of radiation where he extended the law to the probability of emission of quanta. Einstein had a great respect for thermodynamics and statistical mechanics and used these disciplines in an uncanny way to establish properties of quantized systems. Stern became also most proficient in the same direction. They wrote a paper together on the then actual problem of the zero-point energy of a harmonic oscillator, trying to calculate its influence on the specific heat of H_2. They tried to obtain experimental evidence from the existing data in favor of the (1/2) hν value of the energy of the ground state of the harmonic oscillator.

Shortly thereafter Stern wrote the first of his papers of great permanent value, "The Calculation of the Entropy Constant of the Perfect Monatomic Gas." Classical thermodynamics leaves an arbitrary constant in the expression of the entropy of a perfect gas. Such a constant, unlike the arbitrary constant in energy, has observable consequences. For instance, it influences the vapor pressure of a gas in thermodynamical equilibrium with a solid. Much effort had been devoted to the theoretical calculation of this entropy constant, which appeared to be connected to quantum phenomena, and in fact Sackur and Tetrode had found a formula for the entropy constant. Their arguments, however, were not very substantial. We know now that this was so because a perfect monatomic gas at low temperature shows degeneracy phenomena which must be treated with one of the quantum statistics, Bose-Einstein or Fermi-Dirac. Their discovery lay far in the future and thus it was not possible to calculate directly the entropy constant. Stern bypassed the difficulty by considering the gas only at high temperature where classical

Boltzmann statistics is adequate and the degeneracy phenomena have disappeared, leaving their trace only in the entropy constant. He then put the gas in equilibrium with an idealized solid modeled on the one frequency crystal used by Einstein in his theory of the specific heat. The solid obeys the Nernst Theorem, which says that its entropy at absolute zero vanishes, and this takes care of the quantum aspects. Calculating the equilibrium thermodynamically and by kinetic theory applied to the model, Stern found the entropy constant confirming the Sackur-Tetrode result in an unobjectionable fashion.

This masterful paper had considerable influence on later developments; for instance, Fermi studied it thoroughly before he discovered the Fermi statistics. Stern himself extended the results obtained to diatomic molecules and applied again the method of comparing results obtained by classical thermodynamics and molecular models.

The informal teaching from Einstein was supplemented in Zurich by long discussions with Debye, Herzfeld, and especially Ehrenfest, who visited there for a prolonged period. Thus Stern became well acquainted with the problems of quantum theory before the revolutionary application of the quantum ideas to the hydrogen atom by Bohr. Nevertheless, when the Bohr paper appeared and was studied by Stern and von Laue, both in Zurich, it shocked them by the novelty of the ideas propounded. After having discussed the paper on a long walk, they decided to take an oath, "If this nonsense of Bohr should in the end prove to be right we will quit physics." They did not suspect what was in store for them.

When World War I broke out in August 1914, Stern was drafted in the German army, first as a private and later as a noncommissioned officer, and was assigned to meteorological work on the Russian front at Lomsha in Poland. The meteorological observations had sometimes to be done at temperatures of —30° C., and it was necessary to follow the balloons for as long as thirty minutes. Between observations, however, there was time for theoretical physics, and Stern pursued his studies on the Nernst Theorem, investigating its validity in solid solutions. In one paper Stern showed a deep understanding of the nature of the third law of thermodynamics and concluded that it was universally valid provided the system has *one* lowest energy state. The energy states of a mixed crystal were further investigated in another Lomsha paper in which Stern became an expert on determinants. He received from home the books he needed for this work. This is perhaps the only paper in which there is a trace of mathematical virtuosity; otherwise Stern uses everywhere only the simplest mathematics.

The Nernst Theorem was a subject of deep interest to Stern all his life. In America many years later he had long friendly arguments with the physical chemists in Berkeley when he tried to explain his point of view to people such as G. N. Lewis. Although Stern was right, he did not always succeed in convincing his opponents. In his last years he came to attribute to the Nernst Theorem a fundamental character which gave him hope to find there a foundation for quantum mechanics. The last paper he wrote, in 1962, is on this subject.

During the war Unteroffizier Otto Stern met Leutnant James Franck, in France, it seems, and the informality between a lieutenant and a noncommissioned officer surprised the German military, to say the least. Late in the war Nernst obtained Stern's transfer to an office in the War Department in Berlin. Stern continued there to use as much time as he could to pursue scientific questions. Max Born, A. Landé, and others were at work in the same office. The supervisor was R. Ladenburg, later of Princeton University. Nernst visited very frequently. It seems that pure physics interested the group much more than their official tasks. In this period Stern also met M. Volmer, who became a lifelong friend. Stern, Volmer, and James Franck used to take long walks together discussing science and politics.

They must also have found time for experimental work, because in January 1919, barely two months after the armistice that ended World War I, Stern and Volmer submitted for publication a paper on the decay time of fluorescence. The experimental work had been accomplished in Nernst's institute. Another interesting paper of that period was an attempt with Volmer to separate by diffusion a hydrogen of mass 2 from ordinary hydrogen. The motivation of this work was the hypothesis that ordinary hydrogen of atomic weight 1.008 might contain about 4 parts per thousand of the heavier isotope. The attempt failed but was prophetic.

In 1915 Stern had been admitted as *Privatdozent* for theoretical physics at Frankfurt am Main but could not take the position because of the war. Von Laue was then the professor of theoretical physics at Frankfurt. At the end of the war von Laue wished to go to Berlin, and Born, who was then at Berlin as professor of theoretical physics, exchanged his chair with him and went to Frankfurt. Stern became Born's assistant.

During the war, or even earlier, Stern had learned of the invention of molecular beams by the French physicist Dunoyer. He immediately saw the vast possibilities of this discovery. A molecular beam is obtained by letting molecules of a gas stream freely in a vacuum from the orifice of an "oven"; a partition with a slit separates the space in which the molecules enter from another evacuated chamber. Molecules which thread the orifice of the oven and the slit fly undisturbed in the second chamber and form the "molecular beam." It is essential for the working of the system that the vacuum be such that the mean free path of the molecules is large compared with the dimensions of the apparatus. The molecules in the molecular beam are free, not subject to collisions, and for this reason the method is especially suited to the study of questions relating to schematic simple situations such as are often considered in theoretical physics. In fact, many *Gedankenexperimenten* dear to the hearts of theoreticians involve molecular beams. It is thus no wonder that the method appealed to a professor of theoretical physics and a person whose previous successes lay more in the field of theory than in that of experiment. In Stern's own words, "The most distinctive characteristic property of the molecular ray method is its simplicity and directness. It enables us to make measurements on isolated neutral atoms or molecules with macroscopic tools. For this reason it is especially valuable for testing and demonstrating directly fundamental assumptions of the theory."

As soon as Stern arrived at Frankfurt he started experiments using the new technique. In this he not only had the enthusiastic support of Born, his superior, but the latter even gave some public lectures to collect funds needed by Stern for building the apparatus. Stern had performed experiments before in Breslau, but never anything so ambitious. Stern's abilities were more in the direction of planning and evaluating experiments than in executing them; he liked to associate with skilled experimenters who could complement his talents. Thus we find him associated, in succession, with Gerlach, Estermann, Knauer, and Frisch.

It must be realized that vacuum techniques in 1919 were still primitive, compared with present ones, and that the simple generation of a molecular beam was a major achievement. The vacuum was often obtained by a diffusion pump, but coconut charcoal cooled by liquid air was still the most efficient pump.

Ramsey grease was extensively used on ground joints and else-where. The final vacuum was tested by observing the aspect of a discharge in a Geissler tube. The estimated pressure achieved was 10^{-4} mm of Hg.

As time went on the techniques were steadily improved, but they remained on an artisanlike basis. Stern himself was a good glass blower and had much interest in technical details, fully aware of their importance for the final results of the experiment. Alternately a professor of physical chemistry and of theoretical physics, interested in the most fundamental ques-tions of science, he knew that the way to their solution passed through minute technical details. Thus he had great, if dif-ferent, rapport both with his colleague Pauli and with the mechanics who built his apparatus in Frankfurt and Hamburg. He had uncommon ingenuity and delighted in any ingenious "trick" he could invent. His respect for the shop and the machinists and his contempt for sloppy work are interestingly demonstrated by a footnote to a paper on the monochro-matization of de Broglie waves of helium atoms. The toothed wheels used in his monochromator were supposed to have 400 teeth. They were built using a precision lathe and according to the instructions given with the machine. They turned out to be mislabeled and to have 408 teeth! Stern was unaware of this fact and had found a discrepancy between his result on λ and the de Broglie formula $\lambda = h/mv$ greater than the estimated experimental errors until on disassembling the ap-paratus he was able to clear the mystery. However, he told the facts in the paper, advertising by name the firm that had built the lathe.

Stern's laboratory remained in the forefront of the art of making molecular beams and in a situation of virtual monopoly for about fifteen years. Until about 1934, all important experi-ments using molecular beams originated in his laboratory;

furthermore, all successive molecular beam laboratories were founded by people who had learned from Stern, or by pupils of his pupils.

The first experiment he tackled at Frankfurt was the direct verification of the Maxwellian distribution of velocities. It is noteworthy that Stern thought that in the beam the velocity distribution should follow the law

$$dn = Cv^2 \, dv \, e^{-mv^2/2kT}$$

where dn is the number of molecules with velocity between v and v + dv, C is a normalization constant, and the other symbols have the usual meaning. Einstein pointed out to him that the true law to be expected was

$$dn = C'v^3 \, dv \, e^{-mv^2/2kT}$$

Experiment confirmed the predictions of kinetic theory: although, as Stern wrote, there could be little doubt that kinetic theory was correct, a direct measurement of the molecular speed was new.

This work, finished in 1920, was immediately followed by an experiment of revolutionary import: the famous Stern-Gerlach experiment on space quantization. In Bohr's theory of the atom, as then understood, the angular momentum of the atom was expected to have a component in the direction of an external magnetic field having the values $nh/2\pi$ with n integral $\neq 0$. For the case $n = \pm 1$ the atom had two possible orientations. This apparently strange prediction, if correct, should have given, classically, a birefringence of the gas, because the index of refraction for rays polarized in a direction perpendicular or parallel to the magnetic field should have been different. No such birefringence had been observed. This fact, plus the difficulty of reconciling the Bohr prediction with Larmor's theorem, which seemed to preclude a mechanism for the fixed orientation of the component of the angular momentum, worried Stern. One morning he woke up early and was lying in bed cogitating on these problems when the thought came to him that the difficulty could be tackled directly by the molecular beam method. Associated with the atomic angular momentum should be a magnetic moment $\mu = eh/4\pi mc$, and in an inhomogeneous magnetic field having a certain value of $\partial H_z/\partial z$ the atom is subject to a force

$$\mu \frac{\partial H_z}{\partial z}$$

This force produces a deflection of the molecular beam, easily calculable from elementary mechanics and the geometry of the apparatus. In the classical hypothesis there should be a continuum distribution of deflections corresponding to all possible orientations of the magnetic moment. According to the hypothesis of space quantization, on the other hand, the beam should split into a discrete number of components. Stern decided to try this experiment and, in collaboration with W. Gerlach, using a beam of silver atoms, carried it through in the years 1920-1923. The ultimate conclusion was the experimental proof of the space quantization and the measurement of the magneton, $eh/4\pi mc$. Stern and Gerlach devoted five papers to the description of this memorable experiment, which was a turning point in the study of the mechanics of the atom. In the last, most comprehensive paper they described all the technical refinements developed. Of course, reading it with hindsight one wonders why the interpretation of the experiment did not point to the electron spin. Stern said in his old age that the surprise and the excitement of the result were overwhelming. He had started the experiment without knowing what to expect. The classical arguments and the quantum arguments were both strong and he wavered from day to day in his expectations. The experiment was really a question put to Nature, to use Stern's own words, and the final result was a surprise. It could not, however, be completely understood without spin and quantum mechanics, both still in the future.

In the meantime Stern had been called as professor of theoretical physics at Rostock and thus left Frankfurt even before the termination of the Stern-Gerlach experiment, returning to Frankfurt during vacations in order to finish the experiment. He held the Rostock position for a short time only; from September 1921 to December 1922. The University of Hamburg then offered him the position of ordinarius for physico-chemistry and promised him a special laboratory for molecular beams, which in due course was built in the Jungiusstrasse. His colleagues, Koch, Lenz, R. Minkowski, Unsöld, and the younger theoreticians mentioned later, contributed to create a pleasant and stimulating atmosphere. Stern enjoyed their company even outside the institute, and they helped him solve the severe space problems which arose while the new institute for Stern was being built. Stern remained at Hamburg until the advent of Hitler forced him to emigrate, and while there he accomplished the greater part of his work.

Although work with molecular beams was to remain his main activity, it was not his only interest, and in the year 1924 we find an important paper of pure physico-chemistry on the theory of the electrolytic double layer which contains ideas important even for practical applications in mineral flotation, plus another paper on the equilibrium between matter and radiation which has had considerable following among the cosmologists.

In 1926 Stern inaugurated a series of papers which he called Untersuchungen zur Molekularstrahlmethode (U.z.M.) This series reached No. 30 before it ended with the words "Nevertheless the experiments had to be prematurely interrupted owing to external causes," meaning that the institute had been in effect dismantled by the Nazis. In the first of the U.z.M. dated September 1926, Stern explains the advantages and disadvantages of the method, discusses technical details, and then gives the program for future work. In this section he mentions (1) the measurement of magnetic moments of molecules, including those due to the electrons, to the nucleus, and those induced by diamagnetic action; (2) electric dipole moments, including the so-called permanent dipole moment as well as moments of higher order (quadrupoles); (3) the measurement of the field of force of molecules (molecular forces); (4) fundamental problems such as the recoil on emission of a quantum, the de Broglie waves of matter, and others. The execution of this colossal program kept him busy and gave work to many assistants, students, postdoctoral fellows, and guests of his institute. Among his assistants were, chronologically, I. Estermann, F. Knauer, R. Schnurmann, and O. R. Frisch; students were E. Landt, A. Leu, E. Wrede, B. Lammert, and M. Wohlwill; among the guests or postdoctoral fellows were T. E. Phipps, I. Rabi, E. Segrè, J. B. Taylor, L. C. Lewis, and J. Josephy.

The formidable program in U.z.M. No. 1 was almost entirely executed during Stern's tenure at Hamburg. The most notable result, most notable because totally unexpected, was the determination of the magnetic moment of the proton to an accuracy of about 10 percent as 2.5 nuclear magnetons. Before the experiment started, several theoreticians had deemed it a waste of time and effort, so sure were they that the magnetic moment of the proton was one nuclear magneton. This experiment was supplemented, in the last days of the Hamburg laboratory, by the measurement of the magnetic moment of the deuteron. The experiments on the de Broglie waves of the He atoms confirmed in a striking fashion the results predicted by quantum mechanics, but gave also some unexpected results on the interaction of atoms with surface lattices. However, when these elegant and conclusive experiments on the wave aspects of helium atoms were published they did not cause surprise because quantum mechanics was by then so solidly established that one could not doubt the outcome. Stern himself felt that the experiments were perhaps not sufficiently appreciated. He always loved them and thought that the diffraction of a helium atom, a true chunk of matter, was more significant than the diffraction of an electron.

With the Stern-Gerlach experiment, Stern had acquired worldwide fame and became a frequent visitor to foreign countries, including the United States. He had a special preference for Berkeley, in part because he liked his colleagues in chemistry and physics there, in part because he was very sensitive to its pleasant climate. The University of California invited him as a visiting professor and gave him an honorary degree of LL.D. in 1930. In 1933 Professor G. N. Lewis gave him a precious few drops of D_2O with which Stern measured the magnetic moment of the deuteron. Stern recognized immediately the potentialities of the cyclotron and as early as 1931 reported in Europe on the work of Lawrence and his associates with great enthusiasm. However, when Stern was forced to emigrate he did not receive an offer from Berkeley.

Stern also attended regularly the Copenhagen conferences in Bohr's institute and participated very actively in European meetings.

When the Fermi group, somewhat isolated in Rome, decided to send some of its younger members to learn modern experimental techniques abroad, it befell me to go to Hamburg for about a year on a Rockefeller Fellowship starting in 1931. Stern was then at the peak of his powers and I intended to learn all I could from him. The first thing I noticed was his habit of calculating everything amenable to calculation, of measuring everything he could, and of not proceeding unless theory and experiment agreed or he had found the reason for the disagreement. He was most systematic and meticulous; for example, he never relented until the shape and intensity of a molecular beam were those he had calculated before starting the experiment. He was interested in minute technical details and showed me how to hunt for leaks in an apparatus, but otherwise left me pretty much to my own resources. Being in a room near his laboratory, I could go and see him and Frisch work on their experiments. Frisch gave me numerous technical suggestions. There was considerable discussion on the theoretical aspects of the work of the laboratory and I wrote to my friends in Rome and told them during vacations about the problems in Hamburg: Hamburg had had a distinguished succession of professors of theoretical physics— Lenz, Jordan, Pauli, Gordon, Jensen—but in 1932 there was a sort of interregnum and outside help was particularly welcome. This is why in the U.z.M. publications of that period one finds mention of Majorana, Einaudi, Wick, Fermi, Fano, and others. They were all in Rome, admired Stern's work, and liked to help, even at a distance, by solving the problems I reported to them from Hamburg.

The experiment on which I worked purported to demonstrate the dynamics of the establishment of space quantization, by flipping over oriented potassium atoms. It had been started by Stern and Phipps, but left unfinished when Phipps's fellowship ended. I inherited his apparatus, but could not make much headway until on reading Maxwell's *Electricity* I found a trick by which one could achieve a certain magnetic field configuration essential to the success of the experiment. The experiment is of some historical interest because its results elicited a remarkable explanation from Rabi, who connected them with nuclear spin.

Stern's extremely successful work at Hamburg came to an end in August 1933 with his resignation, which was caused by the Nazis. The pretext was the dismissal of his colleague and old pupil Estermann and an order to remove Einstein's portrait from his office. He emigrated, and whatever was left of the institute, deprived of its soul, soon petered out. The Carnegie Institute of Technology at Pittsburgh, Pennsylvania, created a research professorship for Stern and he reestablished there a molecular beam laboratory with the help of Estermann. They did valuable work in molecular beams and obtained some pioneering results, without the use of molecular beams, when, together with O. C. Simpson and J. Halpern, they showed that parahydrogen has a much greater transparency than orthohydrogen for slow neutrons. This fact determines the sign of the singlet n-p scattering length as opposite to that of the triplet. Another paper by Estermann, Lewis, and Stern is devoted to the measurement of the change in density of potassium chloride upon X-ray irradiation. This paper was connected with some war work.

Stern and his associates further perfected the Hamburg techniques but did not use the new powerful resonance methods that Rabi and his associates were then developing, and through which they were reaching precision in the measurement of magnetic moments unattainable by Stern's methods.

Stern was naturalized as an American citizen on March 8, 1939, and during World War II served as a consultant to the War Department. At the end of the war, Stern resigned his Pittsburgh position and retired, making his home in Berkeley where he had two sisters. He visited Europe almost every year, especially Switzerland, attracted by the mountains of the Engadine, his favorite places being Chantarella in the Engadine and Zurich, where he could have the company of his old friend Pauli. He never revisited Germany nor collected the German pension due him, expressing in this way his abomination for Nazism. On the other hand, he maintained cordial relations with several of his old German friends, and as soon as it was possible, at the end of the war, supplied them with packages of some of the amenities or necessities of life they were missing. He managed also to see them, outside of Germany.

Stern never married. As a young bachelor he liked to dance, and was a good tennis player. By the time he lived in Hamburg he had become somewhat of a *bon vivant*. He went only to the best hotels, liked good cuisine, excellent cigars, and in general all the refinements of life. He had many friends among physicists: Lise Meitner, his colleagues at Hamburg, Franck, von Laue, Bohr, Volmer, and others were close to him and he saw them relatively frequently. He was always invited to conferences because he always had something important to say.

He was easily accessible, at least by German standards of the time, to his students and postdoctoral fellows, with whom he had lunch regularly. He went frequently to the movies, but had to be told by his companion Pauli whether he had already seen the film or not.

When Stern came to the United States he tended to isolate himself. After retiring from Pittsburgh, in Berkeley, he attended the Physics colloquium regularly. During his last years he remained interested in the great discoveries in particle physics and astrophysics. A few days before his death he argued vehemently in favor of explaining the enormous energy output of quasars by a reaction between matter and antimatter and was dissatisfied that astrophysicists rejected that interpretation! On his seventieth birthday, the practitioners of the art of molecular beams honored him with a special book devoted to him, but by then he was seldom seen at any meetings. A few old friends visited him occasionally and he received them with unvariable courtesy, although it seemed clear that the thing he cherished most was his privacy.

Stern was stricken by a heart attack while at the movies and died in Berkeley on August 17, 1969, at the age of eighty-one. He had been elected to the National Academy of Sciences in 1945; he was also a member of the Royal Danish Academy since 1936, and of the American Philosophical Society of Philadelphia. He received the Nobel Prize in Physics for 1943.

Stern was one of the greatest physicists of this century. He wrote relatively few papers, but of what power were those he did write! The reader does not know whether to admire most the simplicity and profundity of the theoretical ideas, the ingenuity of the techniques employed, or the inescapable force of the conclusions.

The material for this biographical sketch comes from papers kindly made available by the heirs of Otto Stern and from materials in the Archives of the American Physical Society. An autobiographical tape dictated by Stern exists at the Eidgenossische Technische Hochschule in Zurich, but was not made available to me. I am indebted also to Professors R. Minkowski and I. Estermann for pertinent information.

BIBLIOGRAPHY

KEY TO ABBREVIATIONS

Ann. Physik = Annalen der Physik
Phys. Rev. = Physical Review
Physik. Z. = Physikalische Zeitschrift
Z. Electrochem. = Zeitschrift für Electrochemie
Z. Physik = Zeitschrift für Physik
Z. physik. Chem. = Zeitschrift für physikalische Chemie

1912

Zur kinetischen Theorie des osmotischen Druckes konzentrierter
    Loesungen und ueber die Gueltigkeit des Henryschen Gesetzes
    fuer konzentrierte Loesungen von Kohlendioxyd in organi-
    schen Loesungsmitteln bei tiefen Temperaturen. Dissertation
    Universitaet Breslau 1912. Z. Physik. Chem., 81:441.

1913

Zur kinetischen Theorie des Dampfdrucks einatomiger fester Stoffe
    und ueber die Entropiekonstante einatomiger Gase. Physik.
    Z., 14:629.
With A. Einstein. Einige Argumente fuer die Annahme einer
    Molekularen Agitation beim absoluten Nullpunkt. Ann.
    Physik, 40:551.

1914

Zur Theorie der Gasdissoziation.   Ann. Physik, 44:497.

1916

Die Entropie fester Loesungen.   Ann. Physik, 49:823.
Ueber eine Methode zur Berechnung der Entropie von Systemen
    elastische gekoppelter Massenpunkte.   Ann. Physik, 51:237.

1919

With M. Born. Ueber die Oberflaechenergie der Kristalle und
    ihren Einfluss auf die Kristallgestalt. Sitzungsberichte, Preuss-
    ische Akademie der Wissenschaften, 48:901.
With M. Volmer. Ueber die Abklingungszeit der Fluoreszenz.
    Physik. Z., 20:183.

With M. Volmer. Sind die Abweichungen der Atomgewichte von der Ganzzahligkeit durch Isotopie erklaerbar. Ann. Physik, 59:225.

Molekulartheorie des Dampfdrucks fester Stoffe und Berechnung chemischer Konstanten. Z. Electrochem., 25:66.

1920

With M. Volmer. Bemerkungen zum photochemischen Aequivalentgesetz vom Standpunkt der Bohr-Eisteinschen Auffassung der Lichtabsorption. Zeitschrift für wissenschaftliche Photographie, Photophysik und Photochemie, 19:275.

Eine direkte Messung der thermischen Molekulargeschwindigkeit. Physik. Z., 21:582.

Zur Molekulartheorie des Paramagnetismus fester Salze. Z. Physik, 1:147.

Eine direkte Messung der thermischen Molekulargeschwindigkeit. Z. Physik, 2:49. Nachtrag dazu, 3:417.

1921

Ein Weg zur experimentellen Pruefung der Richtungsquantelung im Magnetfeld. Z. Physik, 7:249.

With W. Gerlach. Der experimentelle Nachweis des magnetischen Moments des Silberatoms. Z. Physik, 8:110.

1922

With W. Gerlach. Der experimentelle Nachweis der Richtungsquatelung im Magnetfeld. Z. Physik, 9:349.

With W. Gerlach. Das magnetische Moment des Silberatoms. Z. Physik, 9:353.

Ueber den experimentellen Nachweis der raeumlichen Quantelung im elektrischen Feld. Physik. Z., 23:476.

1923

With I. Estermann. Ueber die Sichtbarmachung duenner Silberschichten auf Glas. Z. physik. Chem., 106:399.

Ueber das Gleichgewicht zwischen Materie und Strahlung. Z. Electrochem., 31:448.

1924

Zur Theorie der elektrolytischen Doppelschicht. Z. Electrochem., 30:508.

With W. Gerlach. Ueber die Richtungsquantelung im Magnetfeld. Ann. Physik, 74:673.

1926

Transformation of atoms into radiation. Transactions of the
Faraday Society, 21:477-78.
Zur Methode der Molekularstrahlen I. Z. Physik, 39:751.
With F. Knauer. Zur Methode der Molekularstrahlen II. Z.
Physik, 39:764.
With F. Knauer. Der Nachweis kleiner magnetischer Momente
von Molekuelen. Z. Physik, 39:780.
Bemerkungen ueber die Auswertung der Aufspaltungsbilder bei
der magnetischen Ablenkung von Molekularstrahlen. Z. Phy-
sik, 41:563.
Ueber die Umwandlung von Atomen in Strahlung. Z. physik.
Chem., 120:60.

1928

With F. Knauer. Ueber die Reflexion von Molekularstrahlen.
Z. Physik, 53:779.
With G. Hevesy. Fritz Haber's Arbeiten auf dem Gebiet der phy-
sikalischen Chemie und Elektrochemie. Naturwissenschaften,
16:1062.

1929

With F. Knauer. Intensitaetsmessungen an Molekularstrahlen
von Gasen. Z. Physik, 53:766.
Beugung von Molekularstrahlen. Naturwissenschaften, 17:391.

1930

With F. Knauer. Bemerkung zu der Arbeit von H. Mayer "Ueber
die Gueltigkeit des Kosinusgesetzes der Molekularstrahlen."
Z. Physik, 60:414.
Beugungserscheinungen an Molekularstrahlen. Physik. Z., 31:953.
With I. Estermann. Beugung von Molekularstrahlen. Z. Physik,
61:95.

1931

With I. Estermann and R. Frisch. Monochromasierung der de
Broglie-Wellen von Molekularstrahlen. Z. Physik, 73:348.

With I. Estermann and R. Frisch. Versuche mit monochromati-
schen de Broglie-Wellen von Molekularstrahlen. Physik. Z.,
32:670.

1932

With R. Frisch, T. E. Phipps, and E. Segrè. Process of space
quantisation. Nature, 130:892.

With R. Frisch. Die spiegelnde Reflexion von Molekularstrahlen.
Naturwissenschaften, 20:721.

1933

With R. Frisch. Anomalien bei der spiegelnden Reflektion und
Beugung von Molekularstrahlen an Kristallspaltflaechen I. Z.
Physik, 84:430.

With R. Frisch. Ueber die magnetische Ablenkung von Wasserstoffmolekuelen und das magnetische Moment des Protons I.
Z. Physik, 85:4.

With R. Frisch. Ueber die magnetische Ablenkung von Wasserstoffmolekuelen und das magnetische Moment des Protons.
Leipziger Vortraege, p. 36.

With R. Frisch. Beugung von Materiestrahlen. *Handbuch der
Physik* XXII. II. Teil. Berlin, Verlag Juilus Springer.

With I. Estermann and R. Frisch. Magnetic moment of the
proton. Nature, 132:169.

With I. Estermann. Ueber die magnetische Ablenkung von Wasserstoffmolekuelen und das magnetische Moment des Protons
II. Z. Physik, 85:17.

With I. Estermann. Eine neue Methode zur Intensitaetsmessung
von Molekularstrahlen. Z. Physik, 85:135.

With I. Estermann. Ueber die magnetische Ablenkung von iso-
topen Wasserstoffmolekuelen und das magnetische Moment des
"Deutons." Z. Physik, 86:132.

1934

With I. Estermann. Magnetic moment of the deuton. Nature,
133:911.

Bemerkung zur Arbeit von Herrn Schueler: Ueber die Darstellung
der Kernmomente der Atome durch Vektoren. Z. Physik, 89:
665.

1935

Remarks on the measurement of the magnetic moment of the proton. Science, 81:465.

1937

A new method for the measurement of the Bohr magneton. Phys. Rev., 51:852.

With J. Halpern, I. Estermann, and O. C. Simpson. The scattering of slow neutrons by liquid ortho- and parahydrogen. Phys. Rev., 52:142.

With I. Estermann and O. C. Simpson. The magnetic moment of the proton. Phys. Rev., 52:535.

1947

With I. Estermann and O. C. Simpson. The free fall of atoms and the measurement of the velocity distribution in a molecular beam of cesium atoms. Phys. Rev., 71:238.

With I. Estermann and S. N. Foner. The mean free paths of cesium atoms in helium, nitrogen, and cesium vapor. Phys. Rev., 71:250.

1948

The method of molecular rays. In: *Les Prix Nobel en 1946*, ed. by M. P. A. L. Hallstrom *et al.*, pp. 123-30. Stockholm, Imprimerie Royale. P. A. Norstedt & Söner.

1949

With I. Estermann and W. J. Leivo. Change in density of potassium chloride crystals upon irradiation with X-rays. Phys. Rev., 75:627.

On the term $k \ln n$ in the entropy. Reviews of Modern Physics, 21:534.

1962

On a proposal to base wave mechanics on Nernst's theorem. Helvetica Physica Acta, 35:367.

THOMAS GORDON THOMPSON

November 28, 1888–August 10, 1961

BY ALFRED C. REDFIELD, CLIFFORD A. BARNES, AND FRANCIS A. RICHARDS

T HOMAS GORDON THOMPSON was the first American chemist to devote his major efforts to investigating the chemistry of sea water. As such, he played a pioneering role in initiating in this country interest in an aspect of oceanography which had previously been examined primarily by European investigators. His influence in the establishment of the Oceanographic Laboratories at the University of Washington placed him and that university among the leaders in the recognition of the teaching of oceanography as a proper function of institutions of higher learning.

Thompson was born in Rose Bank, Staten Island, New York, on November 28, 1888, the son of John Haslam Thompson and Mary Elizabeth Langdon. His father born in Jersey City, New Jersey, died when Thompson was nine. His mother, born in Elizabeth, New Jersey, died in 1934. There was one brother, John Headen Thompson.

On June 22, 1922, Thompson married Harriet Galbraith, born in Winnipeg, Canada, on February 3, 1893. She preceded him in death on July 31, 1951. They had three children: Thomas Gordon, Jr., born October 3, 1923; John Souter, born September 8, 1925; and Harriet, born April

30, 1931. On July 14, 1954, Thompson married Mrs. Isabel Harris Costigan, and he legally adopted Mrs. Costigan's two younger children, Gary and Charles.

His last public act in science was the reading of two papers at the International Oceanographic Congress in New York in August and September, 1959, the year of his retirement. A slow physical deterioration began soon after which ended in his death on August 10, 1961.

Thompson's youth was spent in Brooklyn where he attended the Brooklyn Commercial High School. Although his adult career was in the State of Washington, he retained to the end of his life an accent that testified to his youthful environment. His "Brooklynese" was a distinction that he carefully cultivated, even correcting his children's pronunciation from time to time. They, however, resisted and they speak as do their western neighbors.

On graduating from high school in 1906 he secured a job as assistant chemist in the control laboratories of the American Brass Company. This experience evidently turned his attention to analytical chemistry—a discipline which dominated all his later work. He subsequently entered Clark University, graduating with a Bachelor of Arts degree in 1914. With the support of a Carnegie scholarship from the British Iron and Steel Institute, he then went to the University of Washington for graduate study. He received the degree of Master of Science in 1915 and of Doctor of Philosophy in Chemistry in 1918. His doctoral dissertation, "Preservation of Iron and Steel by Means of Passivifying Factors," was prepared under the direction of Professor Horace G. Byers.

Thompson was appointed Acting Instructor of Chemistry at the University of Washington in 1918 and Assistant Professor of Chemistry in 1919; he was promoted to Associate Professor in 1923, to Professor in 1929, and retired as Professor Emeritus in 1959.

As head of the division of analytical chemistry, Thompson established courses in qualitative and quantitative analysis which set a standard of care and precision that has indelibly marked the character of the hundreds who came under his watchful eye. His inexorable demand for integrity during the student's first contact with chemical experiments was an object lesson that all remember. Let the budding analyst caught in poor technique or sloppy procedure beware. "Never in my wildest dreams did I ever expect to see such a thing" was his cry when an innocent student was caught violating good analytical procedure. Unforgettable though the chastisement may have been, it was always kindly; its purpose was to correct, not to scold or punish. Though he was a strict taskmaster, the humanity of his personality was always present to encourage the disheartened young man. As a tribute to his work in chemical education, the Thomas Gordon Thompson Fund for graduate fellowships in chemistry was established at the University of Washington by Samuel G. Baker, one of his students.

In later years, as Thompson became more exclusively concerned with the sea, he expressed regret that many of his students had not continued their work on the chemistry of sea water. The fact was that until after World War II very little support was available to chemical oceanographers. Up to that time, the number of sea water chemists in this country could be counted on the fingers of one hand. Thompson's students were trained primarily to be chemists, and as such many found attractive positions in the academic world and in industry. They retain a nostalgia for their earlier association with oceanography and for their personal relationship with "Tommy," as they all think of their Professor. Others, however, have attained influential positions in oceanography as he desired.

Fifteen students obtained their doctoral degrees under his direction: Devadattish Devaputra, 1931; Lacey H. Evans, 1932; Bertram D. Thomas, 1933; Henry E. Wirth, 1935; Iver Igelsrud, 1936; Clifford A. Barnes, 1937; Raymond W. Bremner, 1937; Joseph R. Goodman, 1941; Randall E. Hamm, 1941; John P. Tully, 1948; Francis A. Richards, 1950; Seth D. Reeder, 1951; Tsiahwa J. Chow, 1953; Kurt H. Nelson, 1953; and James A. Gast, 1959.

An outstanding characteristic of Thompson was his interest in the scientific and personal careers of his students. He realized that his colleagues and underlings were human and he felt that their lives were a part of his life. The pride he took in his graduate students and the contact he retained with them was characteristic of his warm personality. An album of photographs of his students was his cherished possession, and his records as to their wives, children, and well-being were complete, so far as he could keep them. His concern was for them as people as well as for them as students and colleagues.

The Oceanographic Laboratories at the University of Washington were established as a result of a recommendation by a committee of the National Academy of Sciences in 1931 and Thompson was selected as director. To increase his effectiveness in this position, he was given a grant by the Rockefeller Foundation for six months' travel to study oceanographic and marine laboratories throughout northern Europe. This trip, and a similar one made possible by a travel grant from the Academy in 1933, to visit laboratories in southern Europe and northern Africa, helped shape many of the policies and procedures of the new institution in Seattle.

The Oceanographic Laboratories were an interdepartmental institution, the staff of which was drawn from the departments of physics, chemistry, bacteriology, botany, and zoology in the University. Graduate degrees were granted by these departments to those who worked in the Laboratories. Thompson served as director for twenty years, until 1951 when Oceanography was established as a department in the University.

Under Thompson's thoughtful guidance a small research vessel, the *Catalyst,* was built for the Laboratories and was put into operation in 1932. Into her 75-foot length were packed accommodations for a crew of three and bunks for thirteen "scientists," together with a laboratory for chemical work and the special gear required for collecting samples at sea. The head was convertible at need to serve as a bacteriological laboratory. One of his students has written:

"The final result was a trifle top-heavy, which accounted for the great amplitude of roll and prevalence of *mal de mer* among the devoted passengers and crew. Tommy—sometimes called "The Admiral" under these circumstances—was a man of courage, the first to master his discomfort and to carry on in the face of adverse winds and waves. Seeing him in oilskins on the somewhat perilous platform hanging over the ship's side, superintending the collection of a water sample from the depths was to sense his persistent interest in the mystery of the sea."[1]

In spite of her limitations, the *Catalyst* served admirably for her intended purpose, to take students to sea and give them firsthand experience with the problems of scientific work in that unstable medium. In this, Thompson was somewhat before the times—female students were encouraged and sometimes even recruited to share the experience of cruises in the inshore waters of the coast.

[1] B. D. Thomas, *Journal of Marine Research,* 17 (1958):11.

During Thompson's directorship, the laboratory at Friday Harbor, off the mouth of Puget Sound, became the summer field station of the Oceanographic Laboratories. Courses were given in oceanography, as well as in the usual divisions of marine biology, with frequent day trips to observe and study the rich life and the active movement of the local waters. The Director made his residence among the students and they came to know him more intimately than was possible at the University in Seattle. One of the courses instituted at Friday Harbor was a general oceanography course to which the instructors in the various disciplines contributed. Typical of Thompson's delight in naming things and people was his reference to the course as "Omnology."

In the days before large-scale federal sponsorship of research in universities, research budgets were often minuscule or nonexistent. To ensure that he could carry out viable research, he and Mrs. Thompson budgeted one-tenth of his salary for his research—an investment that brought both of them much satisfaction.

The bibliography indicates that Thompson's first papers were on somewhat unrelated problems in inorganic and biological chemistry—subjects evidently dictated by the varied interests of his masters. In selecting a specialty in which to pursue chemical research that would benefit his newly chosen home in the Pacific Northwest, he and Dr. H. K. Benson looked over the promising opportunities for research in the area. Benson chose the chemical problems of the forest and forest products and Thompson those of the sea. His interest in the sea and its chemistry was aroused in part as the result of the construction of the Lake Washington Ship Canal, which allowed sea water to flow into the Lake. His first publication on the consequences of this development appeared in 1925. Three years later he was writing on the sea water of the San Juan Archipelago and in 1930 on the hydrography of the Gulf of Alaska and on ionic ratios in the waters of the North Pacific Ocean. Thus, in half a dozen years the analytical chemist became an oceanographer. This expansion of his interest was by no means an abandonment of his primary discipline, but rather a recognition of a field ripe for its application.

Thompson's most important contribution to the data of science is his work on the minor elements in sea water. These substances occur in such small concentrations in the ocean that their determination presents difficult analytical problems. Thompson developed and applied improved methods for the study of the concentrations of these elements and their variation in the waters of the sea. His work included studies on aluminum, boron, copper, iron, manganese, nickel, strontium, silicon, bromine, iodine, phosphates, and nitrates. As a superb analytical chemist, he achieved results that have not been subject to successful challenge.

He was also interested in the relation of the chemical properties of sea water to its physical properties; namely, its specific gravity, refractivity, and electrical conductivity. His work with B. D. Thomas and C. L. Utterback on the last-named provided the basic data for the development of modern methods for determining the salinity of sea water. He contributed to physical chemistry by examining the equilibria in saturated solutions of the major salts of sea water. His study of the isotopic composition of sea water, made in 1935, before the mass spectrometer had superseded densiometric methods of determination, evidenced his readiness to explore new fields as they were opened up by scientific advances. On the practical side, he made inquiry into the possibilities of desalting sea water by freezing.

In addition to these varied chemical studies, Thompson

published in collaboration with others many papers on the descriptive oceanography of the North Pacific Ocean and of the local coast. It is noteworthy that most of his publications appeared under joint authorship, a circumstance which testifies to his pleasure in collaborating with others and which perhaps explains the diversity of the subjects on which he published.

Thompson served in the Chemical Warfare Service of the U.S. Army during both world wars. In 1917 he served as a private for a month at Camp Lewis, Washington, and for two months with the Gas Defense Service in the laboratories of the National Carbon Company of Cleveland, Ohio. Commissioned as First Lieutenant, he worked on the chemistry of war gases in the Geophysical Laboratory at Washington, D.C., in the laboratories of Ohio State University and Johns Hopkins University, and at the Edgewood Arsenal. In July 1918 he was transferred to the Chemical Warfare Service with the rank of Captain.

Following the outbreak of World War II, he was commissioned Colonel in the Chemical Warfare Service in 1942 and was a member of the Chemical Warfare Board during 1943-1944. He was Technical Director of the San Jose Project, a secret investigation on jungle warfare conducted in Panama, in 1944-1946. He was also a member of a committee of the Office of Scientific Research and Development, U.S.N.

In many ways a most unmilitary man, Thompson took his military role seriously. His final promotion to Colonel was recognition of the chemist's contribution to the defense of his country. His career was an example of the willing sacrifices of scientists to that end.

Among his services to the scientific community, Thompson was a representative of the National Academy of Sciences–National Research Council at the meetings of the International Geodetic and Geophysics Union in Stockholm (1930), Lisbon (1933), Edinburgh (1936), and Washington (1939), and was Chairman of the International Committee on Oceanography for the Pacific Science Congress from 1935 to 1953.

Thompson served also as Chairman of the Puget Sound Section, American Chemical Society (1915); as President of the Pacific Division, American Association for the Advancement of Science (1946-1947); as Chairman of the Standing Committee on Oceanography of the Pacific Science Congress (1929); as Chairman of the Committee on Methods and Units for Chemical Oceanography of the International Association of Physical Oceanography (1936); as a Representative to the Pacific Science Congresses in Vancouver (1933), San Francisco (1936), and New Zealand (1949); as President of the Oceanography Section of the American Geophysical Union (1934-1937); on the Foreign Relations Committee of the National Research Council (1935); as President of the Oceanographic Society of the Pacific (1935-1942); on the Editorial Board of the *Journal of Marine Research* (1937 until his death); as Chairman of the U.S. Committee on Oceanography of the Pacific of the National Research Council (1948).

Five outstanding honors were tendered to Thompson: the award of the Alexander Agassiz Gold Medal of the National Academy of Sciences "for his original contributions to the science of the ocean" in 1948; election to the National Academy of Sciences in 1951; the publication in 1958 of a volume of scientific papers "dedicated to Thomas Gordon Thompson on the occasion of his seventieth birthday by some of his friends and associates in appreciation of his profound influence on the development of oceanography";[2] the presenta-

[2] Published as Vol. 17, 1958, of the *Journal of Marine Research* by the Sears Foundation for Marine Research.

tion to him on May 25, 1960, of a Certificate for "distinguished service to the people of Washington" by Governor Albert Rossilini; and the christening of the Auxiliary General Oceanographic Research Ship No. 9 as the *Thomas G. Thompson.* The ship is a 209-foot vessel especially designed and built under U.S. Navy auspices for oceanographic research at the University of Washington.

Thompson carried the warmth, earthy humor, and good fellowship which marked his dealings with students and colleagues into his off-campus life. Children and enormous ice cream confections were both passions of his, and, to the kids' great delight, he chose to enjoy them simultaneously. There were no happier occasions at the Friday Harbor laboratory than when, in the midafternoon, the call would go out, "Come on, kids, let's go," and all in sight were loaded into Tommy's car for a trip to the drugstore for sodas, sundaes, and banana splits—all as guests of the director.

A gifted storyteller, he had an anecdote for every occasion, sometimes irreverent, sometimes macabre, sometimes highly topical, but always funny, never unkind, and frequently repeated. In World War II, he lost his hearing in one ear, but he claimed always to have been tone-deaf. He would remark that his ear for music was so bad he couldn't tell the difference between "Nearer My God to Thee" and "The Star-Spangled Banner," so he always stood up for both.

Card games—particularly bridge and cribbage—were a great joy to him, and he played with extreme skill as well as a highly amusing running commentary on the poor quality of his hand. "How would God play a hand like this?" Although not highly active politically he was a staunch Democrat and was one of those few who predicted, within a few electoral votes, the unexpected election of Truman over Dewey in 1948.

Philately was a serious hobby of his and he accumulated a large and valuable collection. A special interest was Central American air mail stamps, but he probably most enjoyed his exchanges with foreign scientists and the receipt of foreign covers mailed to him by friends. When on trips out of the country, he delighted in writing his friends back home and decorating the envelopes with collections of stamps.

During World War II, McConnell Island, a 33-acre island in the San Juan Archipelago, became available for purchase, and by the judicious sale of some of his more valuable stamps, Thompson raised money to buy it. After his return from army duty, he and his family began to develop the island, finally building a home of native stone and driftwood. The island was a place of beauty and delight to Tommy, and to his many visitors. In one of the last summers he spent there, over 700 visitors were recorded in the guest book—a fair indication of the friendship and esteem in which he was held.

BIBLIOGRAPHY

KEY TO ABBREVIATIONS

Am. Coll. Soc. Mag. = American College Society Magazine
Am. J. Sci. = American Journal of Science
Anal. Chem. = Analytical Chemistry
Bot. Gaz. = Botanical Gazette
Bull. Nat. Res. Council = Bulletin of the National Research Council
Deep-Sea Res. = Deep-Sea Research
Ind. Eng. Chem., Anal. Ed. = Industrial and Engineering Chemistry, Analytical Edition
J. Am. Chem. Soc. = Journal of the American Chemical Society
J. Chem. Educ. = Journal of Chemical Education
J. Conseil, Conseil Perm. Internat. Exploration Mer = Journal du Conseil, Conseil Permanent International pour l'Exploration de la Mer
J. Ind. Eng. Chem. = Journal of Industrial and Engineering Chemistry
J. Marine Res. = Journal of Marine Research
Proc. ——— Pacific Sci. Congr. = Proceedings of the ——— Pacific Science Congress
Publ. Puget Sound Biol. Sta. = Publications of the Puget Sound Biological Station
Trans. Am. Geophys. Union = Transactions of the American Geophysical Union
Univ. Wash. Publ. Oceanogr. = University of Washington Publications in Oceanography

1915

Total amino nitrogen in the seedlings of the Alaska pea. J. Am. Chem. Soc., 37:230-35.
With H. K. Benson. The tannin content of Pacific Coast conifers. J. Ind. Eng. Chem., 7:915-18.

1916

Preservation of iron and steel by means of passivifying factors. Carnegie Scholarship Memoirs, Iron Steel Institute, London, 7:232-98.

1919

With G. B. Rigg. Colloidal properties of bog water. Bot. Gaz., 68:367-79.

1920

Preservation of Iron and Steel by Means of Passivifying Factors.
Seattle, H. C. Pigott Printing Concern. 39 pp. (Ph.D. Thesis,
University of Washington, 1918.)

With F. J. Kopp. Pressures produced by the action of sulfur
monochloride upon β, β-dichloroethyl sulfide. J. Ind. Eng.
Chem., 12:1056-59.

With Henry Odeen. The solubility of β, β'-dichloroethyl sulfide
in petroleum hydrocarbons and its purification by extraction
with these solvents. J. Ind. Eng. Chem., 12:1057-62.

With John H. Black. The intersolubility of chloropicrin and
water. J. Ind. Eng. Chem., 12:1066-67.

1921

With J. H. Black and G. T. Sohl. The intersolubility of beta-beta-
dichloroethyl sulfide and ethyl alcohol. J. Am. Chem. Soc.,
43:877-79.

1923

With G. B. Rigg and W. L. Gilliland. The influence of plants
on the air in houses. American Journal of Botany, 10:383-86.

With H. K. Benson and G. S. Wilson. The chemical utilization
of wood in Washington. Engineering Experiment Station,
University of Washington, Bulletin 19. Seattle, University of
Washington Press. 160 pp.

1924

Chemistry: its accomplishments and possibilities. Am. Coll. Soc.
Mag., pp. 41-63.

Important questions and answers on chemistry. Am. Coll. Soc.
Mag., pp. 64-120.

1925

With E. V. Smith. The control of sea water flowing into the Lake
Washington Ship Canal. Ind. Eng. Chem., 17:1084-93.

1927

With E. V. Smith. Salinity of the Lake Washington Ship Canal. A study of conditions affecting the flow of sea water into the canal system. Engineering Experiment Station, University of Washington, Bulletin 41. Seattle, University of Washington Press. 104 pp.

With Committee. Correlations of high school and college chemistry. J. Chem. Educ., 4:640-56.

With E. V. Smith. Occurrences of hydrogen sulfide in the Lake Washington Ship Canal. Ind. Eng. Chem., 19:822-23.

With G. B. Rigg, J. R. Lorah, and K. T. Williams. Dissolved gases in waters of some Puget Sound bogs. Bot. Gaz., 84:264-78.

With J. R. Lorah and G. B. Rigg. The acidity of the waters of some Puget Sound bogs. J. Am. Chem. Soc., 49:2981-88.

With J. R. Lorah and K. T. Williams. Improved apparatus for the removal of dissolved gases from water. J. Am. Chem. Soc., 49:2991-94.

With J. W. Lang and Lucile Anderson. The sulfate-chloride ratio of the waters of the North Pacific. Publ. Puget Sound Biol. Sta., 5:277-92.

1928

With F. A. Rantz. The status of chemical education in the high schools of the State of Washington. School Science and Mathematics, 28:68-73.

The standardization of silver nitrate solutions used in chemical studies of sea waters. J. Am. Chem. Soc., 50:681-85.

With G. H. Hitchings and S. P. Todd. The chemistry of the waters of Argyle Lagoon, II. Publ. Puget Sound Biol. Sta., 5:325-32.

With Phoebe Blalock. A chemical study of the waters of Argyle Lagoon. Publ. Puget Sound Biol. Sta., 5:341-53.

With R. C. Miller. Apparatus for the micro-determination of dissolved oxygen. Ind. Eng. Chem., 20:774.

With R. C. Miller. Differences observed in the condition of the sea water at the margins of two opposing tidal currents. Science, 68:517-18.

With M. W. Johnson and S. P. Todd. The sea water at the Puget Sound Biological Station from September 1926 to September 1927. Publ. Puget Sound Biol. Sta., 6:371-91.

1929

An experiment demonstrating the slow miscibility of two liquids of different densities. J. Chem. Educ., 6:523.

With R. C. Miller, G. H. Hitchings, and S. P. Todd. Studies of the sea water near the Puget Sound Biological Station during the summer of 1927. Publ. Puget Sound Biol. Sta., 7:65-99.

With M. W. Johnson. The sea water at the Puget Sound Biological Station from September 1927 to September 1928. Publ. Puget Sound Biol. Sta., 7:119-28.

1930

With C. C. Wright. Ionic ratios in the waters of the North Pacific Ocean. J. Am. Chem. Soc., 52:915-21.

With H. H. Gran. The diatoms and the physical and chemical conditions of the sea water of the San Juan Archipelago. Publ. Puget Sound Biol. Sta., 7:169-204.

A progress report on ionic ratios and specific gravity of sea water. In: *Contributions to Marine Biology*, pp. 79-81. Stanford, Stanford University Press.

With M. W. Johnson. The sea water at the Puget Sound Biological Station from September 1928 to September 1929. Publ. Puget Sound Biol. Sta., 7:345-68.

With Richard Van Cleve. Determination of the chlorinity of ocean waters. Report of the International Fisheries Commission, No. 3. Victoria, Canada, International Fisheries Commission. 14 pp.

With G. F. McEwen and Richard Van Cleve. Hydrographic sections and calculated currents in the Gulf of Alaska, 1927-28. Report of the International Fisheries Commission, No. 4. Victoria, Canada, International Fisheries Commission. 36 pp.

1931

Oceanographic program at the University of Washington. Trans. Am. Geophys. Union, Twelfth annual meeting, pp. 173-74.

With Henry E. Wirth. The specific gravity of sea water at zero depths in relation to the chlorinity. J. Conseil, Conseil Perm. Internat. Exploration Mer, 6:232-40.

With W. R. Johnson and Henry E. Wirth. The sulfate-chlorinity ratio in ocean waters. J. Conseil, Conseil Perm. Internat. Exploration Mer, 6:246-51.

With R. U. Bonnar. The buffer capacity of sea water. Ind. Eng. Chem., Anal. Ed., 3:393-400.

1932

With E. G. Moberg. Some problems of oceanographic chemistry. Scientific Monthly, 34:442-45.

With R. W. Bremner and I. M. Jamieson. Occurrence and determination of iron in sea water. Ind. Eng. Chem., Anal. Ed., 4:288-90.

The physical properties of sea water. Bull. Nat. Res. Council, 85:63-94.

With R. J. Robinson. Chemistry of the sea. Bull. Nat. Res. Council, 85:95-203.

With D. Devaputra and C. L. Utterback. The radioactivity of sea water. J. Conseil, Conseil Perm. Internat. Exploration Mer, 7:358-66.

1933

With H. J. Taylor. Determination and occurrence of fluorides in sea water. Ind. Eng. Chem., Anal. Ed., 5:87-89.

With B. D. Thomas. Lithium in sea water. Science, 77:547-48.

1934

With B. D. Thomas and C. L. Utterback. The electrical conductivity of sea water. J. Conseil, Conseil Perm. Internat. Exploration Mer, 9:28-35.

With C. L. Utterback and B. D. Thomas. Refractivity-chlorinity-temperature relationships of ocean waters. J. Conseil, Conseil Perm. Internat. Exploration Mer, 9:35-38.

With H. G. Houlton. Determination of silicon in sea water. Ind. Eng. Chem., Anal. Ed., 5:417-18.

With B. D. Thomas and C. A. Barnes. Distribution of dissolved oxygen in the North Pacific Ocean. In: *James Johnston Memorial Volume,* pp. 203-34. Liverpool, University Press of Liverpool.

With R. J. Robinson. The sea water of the Puget Sound region. Proc. 5th Pacific Sci. Congr., Vol. 3, pp. 2101-7. Victoria and Vancouver, Canada. Toronto, University of Toronto Press.

With N. M. Carter, E. G. Moberg, and Tage Skogsberg. The reporting of data in oceanographical chemistry. Proc. 5th Pacific Sci. Congr., Vol. 3, pp. 2123-27. Victoria and Vancouver, Canada. Toronto, University of Toronto Press.

1935

With T. L. Wilson. The occurrence and determination of manganese in sea water. J. Am. Chem. Soc., 57:233-36.

With H. E. Wirth and C. L. Utterback. Distribution of isotopic water in the sea. J. Am. Chem. Soc., 57:400-4.

With R. W. Bremner. The determination of iron in sea water. J. Conseil, Conseil Perm. Internat. Exploration Mer, 10:33-38.

With R. W. Bremner. The occurrence of iron in the waters of the north-east Pacific Ocean. J. Conseil, Conseil Perm. Internat. Exploration Mer, 10:39-47.

With C. A. Barnes and F. A. Zeusler. Summary of the oceanographic investigations of Bering Sea and Bering Strait. Trans. Am. Geophys. Union, 16th annual meeting, pp. 258-64.

The oceanographic laboratories of the University of Washington. Collecting Net, 10:281-84.

1936

With Iver Igelsrud. Equilibria in the saturated solutions of salt occurring in sea water. I. The ternary systems $MgCl_2$-KCl-H_2O, $MgCl_2$-$CaCl_2$-H_2O, $CaCl_2$-KCl-H_2O, and $CaCl_2$-$NaCl$-H_2O at O°. J. Am. Chem. Soc., 58:318-22.

With L. D. Phifer. The plankton and the properties of the surface waters of the Puget Sound region. Univ. Wash. Publ. Oceanogr., 1:111-34.

With Iver Igelsrud and R. J. Robinson. The distribution of phosphates in the sea water of the northeast Pacific. Univ. Wash. Publ. Oceanogr., 3:1-34.

The motorship *Catalyst*: a seagoing laboratory. J. Chem. Educ., 13:203-9.

With G. F. McEwen and Richard Van Cleve. Hydrographic sections and calculated currents in the Gulf of Alaska, 1929. Report of the International Fisheries Commission, No. 10. Victoria, Canada, International Fisheries Commission. 32 pp.

With K. T. Williams. Experiments on the effect of sphagnum on the pH of salt solutions. International Revue of Hydrobiology, 33:271-75.

With Iver Igelsrud. Equilibria in the saturated solutions of salts occurring in sea water. II. The quaternary system of $MgCl_2$-$CaCl_2$-KCl-H_2O at 0°. J. Am. Chem. Soc., 58:2003-9.

1937

Oceanographical work in Bering Sea. Geographical Review, 27:701-2.

The oceanographic laboratories of the University of Washington. Biologist, 18:160-70.

With H. E. Wirth and C. L. Utterback. Note on determination of heavy water in ocean waters. Transactions and Proceedings of the Royal Society of New Zealand, 67:113.

With R. J. Robinson. The reporting of chemical oceanographic data. Procès Verbaux, Association Internationale des sciences physiques de l'océan, Vol. 2, pp. 68-69, Edinburgh, September 1936. Liverpool, University Press of Liverpool.

With C. A. Barnes. Investigations in Bering Sea and North Pacific. Procès Verbaux, Association Internationale des sciences physiques de l'océan, Vol. 2, pp. 109-10. Edinburgh, September 1936. Liverpool, University Press of Liverpool.

With C. A. Barnes and F. A. Zeusler. Investigations in Bering Sea and Bering Strait. Procès Verbaux, Association Internationale des sciences physiques de l'océan, Vol. 2, p. 111, Edinburgh, September 1936. Liverpool, University Press of Liverpool.

With Iver Igelsrud. The solubility of boron in the waters of the North Pacific. Procès Verbaux, Association Internationale des sciences physiques de l'océan, Vol. 2, p. 155, Edinburgh, September 1936. Liverpool, University Press of Liverpool.

With R. W. Bremner. The electrical conductances of standard

potassium chloride solutions throughout the temperature range 0 to 25°.   J. Am. Chem. Soc., 59:2372-74.

With L. D. Phifer.   Seasonal variations in the surface waters of San Juan Channel during the five year period, January 1931 to December 30, 1935.   J. Marine Res., 1:34-59.

1938

With Iver Igelsrud and B. M. G. Zwicker.   The boron content of sea water and of marine organisms.   Am. J. Sci., 35:47-63.

With Kenneth T. Barkey.   Observations on fjord-waters.   Trans. Am. Geophys. Union, 19th annual meeting, pp. 254-60.

With R. W. Bremner and C. L. Utterback.   Specific gravities of pure and mixed salt solutions in the temperature range 0 to 25°.   J. Am. Chem. Soc., 60:2616-18.

With C. A. Barnes.   Physical and chemical investigations in Bering Sea and portions of the North Pacific Ocean.   Univ. Wash. Publ. Oceanogr., 3:35-79; appendix: 1-164.

1939

With R. W. Bremner and C. L. Utterback.   Electrical conductances of pure and mixed salt solutions in the temperature range 0 to 25°.   J. Am. Chem. Soc., 61:1219-23.

With R. J. Robinson.   Notes on the determination of dissolved oxygen in sea water.   J. Marine Res., 2:1-8.

With H. M. Haendler.   The determination and occurrence of aluminum in sea water.   J. Marine Res., 2:12-16.

1940

With J. R. Goodman and F. A. Zeusler.   Observations on the waters of the Arctic Ocean off the Alaskan coast.   Procès Verbaux, Association Internationale des sciences physiques de l'océan, Vol. 3, pp. 160-61. Washington, D.C., September 1939. Liverpool, University Press of Liverpool.

With F. A. Zeusler and J. R. Goodman.   Summary of observations in Bering Sea and Bering Strait in 1937 and 1938.   Procès Verbaux, Association Internationale des sciences physiques de l'océan, Vol. 3, pp. 162-63. Washington, D.C., September 1939. Liverpool, University Press of Liverpool.

With J. R. Goodman. Characteristics of the waters in sections from Dutch Harbour, Alaska, to the Strait of Juan de Fuca, and from the Strait of Juan de Fuca to Hawaii. Procès Verbaux, Association Internationale des sciences physiques de l'océan, Vol. 3, pp. 186-88. Washington, D.C., September 1939. Liverpool, University Press of Liverpool.

With R. J. Robinson. Tidal cycle variations in the composition of sea water. Procès Verbaux, Association Internationale des sciences physiques de l'océan, Vol. 3, p. 189. Washington, D.C., September 1939. Liverpool, University Press of Liverpool.

With D. H. Anderson. The determination of the alkalinity of sea water. J. Marine Res., 3:224-29.

With J. R. Goodman. Characteristics of the waters in sections from Dutch Harbor, Alaska, to the Strait of Juan de Fuca, and from the Strait of Juan de Fuca to Hawaii. Univ. Wash. Publ. Oceanogr., 3:81-103; appendix: 1-48.

Activities of the oceanographic laboratories of the University of Washington. Proc. 6th Pacific Sci. Congr., Vol. 3, pp. 127-37. University of California at Berkeley, Stanford University, and San Francisco. Berkeley and Los Angeles, University of California Press.

1941

With R. E. Hamm. Dissolved nitrogen in the sea water of the Northeast Pacific with notes on the total carbon dioxide and the dissolved oxygen. J. Marine Res., 4:11-27.

With R. E. Hamm. Specific gravities and electrical conductances of some calcium sulfate solutions and mixtures of sodium chloride and calcium sulfate. J. Am. Chem. Soc., 63:1418-22.

1942

With Edwin Karpi. The bromine-chlorinity ratio of sea water. J. Marine Res., 5:28-36.

With J. R. Goodman, J. H. Lincoln, and F. A. Zeusler. Physical and chemical investigations: Bering Sea, Bering Strait, Chukchi

Sea during the summers of 1937 and 1938. Univ. Wash. Publ. Oceanogr., 3:105-9; appendix: 1-117.

War gases: facts for air raid wardens and every civilian. In: *War Gases,* pp. 25-37. Seattle, Civilian Protection Division, Washington State Defense Council.

1943

Two lecture demonstrations (on the behavior of war gases). J. Chem. Educ., 20:377, 398.

1948

With Bjorn Helland-Hansen and J. P. Jacobsen. Chemical methods and units. Publications Scientifiques, Association Internationale des sciences physiques de l'océan, No. 9. 28 pp.

With R. J. Robinson. The determination of phosphates in sea water. J. Marine Res., 7:33-41.

With R. J. Robinson. The determination of nitrites in sea water. J. Marine Res., 7:42-48.

With R. J. Robinson. The determination of silicate in sea water. J. Marine Res., 7:49-55.

1950

With G. J. Lewis, Jr. The effect of freezing on the sulfate/chlorinity ratio of sea water. J. Marine Res., 9:211-17.

With J. P. Jacobsen and R. J. Robinson. A review of the determination of dissolved oxygen in sea water by the Winkler method. Publications Scientifiques, Association Internationale des sciences physiques de l'océan, No. 11. 22 pp.

1952

With T. J. Chow. The determination and distribution of copper in sea water. I. The spectrophotometric determination of copper in sea water. J. Marine Res., 11:124-38.

With F. A. Richards. The estimation and characterization of plankton populations by pigment analyses. II. A spectrophotometric method for the estimation of plankton pigments. J. Marine Res., 11:156-72.

Report by the chairman of the International Committee on the

Oceanography of the Pacific. Proc. 7th Pacific Sci. Congr., Vol. 3, pp. 136-42. Auckland and Christchurch, New Zealand, 1949. Wellington, R. E. Owen, Government Printer.

Report on the oceanographic laboratories of the University of Washington. Proc. 7th Pacific Sci. Congr., Vol. 3, pp. 164-68. Auckland and Christchurch, New Zealand, 1949. Wellington, R. E. Owen, Government Printer.

1954

With K. H. Nelson. Desalting sea water by freezing. Refrigerating Engineering, 62:44-48, 90.

With K. H. Nelson. Deposition of salts from sea water by frigid concentration. J. Marine Res., 13:166-82.

With T. J. Chow. Seasonal variation in the concentration of copper in the surface waters of San Juan Channel, Washington. J. Marine Res., 13:233-44.

1955

With T. J. Chow. Flame photometric determination of strontium in sea water. Anal. Chem., 27:18-21.

With T. J. Chow. Flame photometric determination of calcium in sea water and marine organisms. Anal. Chem., 27:910-13.

With T. J. Chow. A non-metallic water sampler. Deep-Sea Res., 2:200-3.

With T. J. Chow. The strontium-calcium atom ratio in carbonate-secreting marine organisms. Deep-Sea Res., Suppl. 3:20-39.

1956

With K. H. Nelson. Concentration of brines and deposition of salts from sea water under frigid conditions. Am. J. Sci., 254: 227-38.

With Taivo Laevastu. The determination and occurrence of nickel in sea water, marine organisms and sediments. J. Conseil, Conseil Perm. Internat. Exploration Mer, 21:125-43.

1957

With J. P. Tully. Report of the standing committee on oceanography of the Pacific. Proc. 8th Pacific Sci. Congr., Vol. 3, pp. 3-8. University of the Philippines, Diliman, Quezon City, 1953. Quezon City, National Research Council of the Philippines, University of the Philippines.

With J. P. Tully. A summary of Pacific oceanography, 1949-53. Proc. 8th Pacific Sci. Congr., Vol. 3, pp. 9-22. University of the Philippines, Diliman, Quezon City, 1953. Quezon City, National Research Council of the Philippines, University of the Philippines.

Pacific oceanography in the United States. Proc. 8th Pacific Sci. Congr., Vol. 3, pp. 93-114. University of the Philippines, Diliman, Quezon City, 1953. Quezon City, National Research Council of the Philippines, University of the Philippines.

Fresh water from the sea. In: *1957 Technicon Yearbook*, pp. 96-100, 158. New York, American Technicon Society.

1958

A short history of oceanography with emphasis on the role played by chemistry. J. Chem. Educ., 35:108-12.

With J. A. Gast. Determination of the alkalinity and borate concentration of sea water. Anal. Chem., 30:1549-51.

With Taivo Laevastu. Soluble iron in coastal waters. J. Marine Res., 16:192-98.

1959

With J. A. Gast. Evaporation of boric acid from sea water. Tellus, 11:344-47.

1960

With R. A. Barkley. Determination of chemically combined iodine in sea water by amperometric and catalytic methods. Anal. Chem., 32:154-58.

With Richard A. Barkley. The total iodine and iodate-iodine content of sea-water. Deep-Sea Res., 7:24-34.
With Taivo Laevastu. Determination and occurrence of cobalt in sea water. J. Marine Res., 18:189-93.

1964

With Tadashiro Koyama. Identification and determination of organic acids in sea water by participation chromatography. Journal of the Oceanographic Society, Japan, 20:209-20.

Dwight Wilson

DAVID WRIGHT WILSON

January 4, 1889–July 13, 1965

BY ERIC G. BALL AND
JOHN M. BUCHANAN

I N HIS LIFETIME David Wright Wilson spanned the period of
the birth and maturation of modern biochemistry in the
United States. His knowledge of the field was thus intimate
and personal and lent much to his perspective and enthusiasm for biochemistry. This knowledge also contributed greatly
to his effectiveness as a teacher. He was quick to grasp the
significance of important discoveries and often pioneered in
their further development.

Wright, as he was known to his friends, was born in Knox-
ville, Iowa, on January 4, 1889. Both of his parents were
descended from Yeates Conwell and were cousins many times
removed. Yeates Conwell and his wife, Rebecca Fisher, arrived from the British Isles in 1699 and settled in Delaware.
Another early ancestor was Alexander Ewing, who emigrated
to the colonies about 1700 from Londonderry, Ireland. Ewing's
son, John, an astronomer and mathematician, was pastor of
the First Presbyterian Church of Philadelphia and second
provost of the University of Pennsylvania (1799-1802). Shortly
after Wright became professor and head of the Department
of Physiological Chemistry at the University of Pennsylvania,
his first child was born and named John Ewing. The death

of this beloved son at the age of eleven was a lifelong grief to him and to his wife, Helene.

Wright himself described his early environment as typical of a happy home in a small town in the Middle West. His father, James Ewing Wilson, was a graduate of Washington College. A Civil War injury had made his father extremely deaf. As a result he was forced to choose a livelihood where hearing was not essential and was employed as a bookkeeper in a bank. Wright's mother was Katherine Wright Wilson. As a boy, Wright enjoyed playing baseball, and fishing with his uncle in a river some three or four miles from his home. His uncle owned a drugstore where Wright worked during school vacations. At an early age he became interested in printing presses and by the time he was in high school he was the proud owner of a foot press which printed a page 10×12 inches. On this he printed the high school paper.

In 1906, the year the American Society of Biological Chemists was founded, Wright entered Grinnell College and leaned toward a career as a journalist. Stimulated by Professor Walter Scott Hendrixson, he became interested in chemistry. Professor Hendrixson received his Ph.D. degree in chemistry at Harvard in 1893 and in 1894-1895 studied in Berlin and Göttingen. In his senior year Wright and one other student took a special course in physiological chemistry. In 1910 there could not have been very many opportunities for an undergraduate in the United States to enroll in such a course. The die was apparently now cast, but was it? Upon graduation Wright entered graduate school in the Department of Chemistry at the University of Illinois. There he assisted in teaching and carried out his first research on excessive water drinking with Professor P. B. Hawk. Hawk had come to the University of Illinois in 1907 as professor of physiological chemistry, after serving four years at the University of Pennsylvania as demonstrator in physiological chemistry. It is interesting to note that Hawk at Pennsylvania served under John Marshall, whom Wright was to succeed in 1922 as head of the Department of Physiological Chemistry. The summer of 1911 was spent by Wright at the University of Illinois completing his work for the master's degree, which he received in the spring of 1912.

The fall of 1911 found Wright earning a living working at the New York Hospital under the supervision of Stanley Benedict. His job there was to carry out food analyses on diets that were fed to cancer patients. This was obviously a year of decision for Wright as to his future career. Excerpts from a line-a-day diary which he kept best illustrate this.

"*October 4*—This morning Dr. Benedict took me over and introduced me to New York Hospital and my laboratory. It's a nice, roomy well equipped laboratory and I'm quite satisfied.

"*November 6*—My work is hard now on account of the food analysis which takes more time than it should.

"*November 10*—I am commencing to get control of my work. Have stopped analyzing the beef tea, oatmeal and potatoes, but am still bothered by the milk.

"*December 2*—A year ago I was almost decided for physiological, now I'm strongly favoring organic."

(During the Christmas vacation Wright went to Baltimore to attend meetings of the Physiological Society and the American Society of Biological Chemists where he met Professor Mendel of Yale. He went on to Washington to attend a meeting of the chemists where he met Otto Folin of Harvard. As a result his interest in physiological chemistry was apparently rekindled, as the following diary entries show.)

"*January 26*—This afternoon I went up and interviewed Professors Morgan and Bogert on physiological chemistry. Professor Morgan advised it quite strongly.

"February 13—Have decided to go to Yale next year.

"March 23—Dr. Benedict was over and offered me the work for next year at General Memorial Hospital at $1400 or $800 with assistant and chance to work at Cornell Medical for Ph.D. The last sounds good and I'll see about it.

"April 3—A letter from Yale announces I have been appointed to a $400 fellowship with free tuition. That is $400 more than I expected. I'll probably take it, but will see Mendel first.

"April 6—Professor Mendel came over to the laboratory this morning and talked about plans for next year and research in particular.

"April 14—Accepted the Yale fellowship."

Thus it was that Wright began work for his Ph.D. degree in the first laboratory of physiological chemistry in this country, established in 1874 under Russell H. Chittenden. In 1912 Chittenden was still head of the department at Yale, but his duties as Director of the Sheffield Scientific School consumed such a large proportion of his time that Mendel was responsible for instruction and guidance in research. At the time of Wright's arrival at Yale, Mendel, in collaboration with T. B. Osborne, was studying the nutritive properties of various purified proteins and observing the inadequacies of various synthetic diets for the growth of rats. Yet for some reason that is not clear Wright undertook for his thesis work a study of the nonprotein water-soluble nitrogen extractables from the muscles of a variety of marine forms. Perhaps Mendel was looking ahead to the role that he suspected unidentified low-molecular-weight compounds must play in nutrition. But why the use of marine forms? In any case, Wright's training under Benedict on various analytical procedures undoubtedly stood him in good stead in these studies. In the years that followed, Wright was to return from time to time to studies on muscle extractives from species of both marine and land forms.

In 1914 Wright completed his work for the Ph.D. degree and accepted a position with Walter Jones in the Physiological Chemistry Department at the Johns Hopkins Medical School. He immediately displayed there an interest in the application of biochemical methods to the solution of clinical problems, an interest which was to remain with him throughout his life. This interest took many forms, from active collaboration in investigations to the encouragement and support of research by his clinical colleagues. During his years at Johns Hopkins he was a member of a group which called themselves "The Riders and Drivers Club." Wright was apparently the only non-M.D. in a group of young physicians who, as one of them has stated, recognized "no barriers between the basic science departments and the clinical departments." At that time the group included such well-known names of today as A. R. Dochez, James L. Gamble, George A. Harrop, Robert F. Loeb, and Walter W. Palmer, among others.

While at Johns Hopkins, Wright worked one summer for the Federal Bureau of Fisheries at Muscatine, Iowa, some hundred miles east of his birthplace. There he studied the chemical composition of fish blood. Another summer he worked at the Mayo Clinic, Rochester, Minnesota, where he discovered the first spontaneously crystallizable Bence-Jones protein. It is interesting to note that during his period at Johns Hopkins, Wright apparently did not become actively engaged in the field of nucleic acid in which his chief, Walter Jones, was one of the leading investigators of the day. Many years later Wright did take up investigations in the field of purines and pyrimidines.

World War I interrupted Wright's sojourn at Johns Hopkins. On June 11, 1917, he started work at New Haven as Junior Physiologist in the Bureau of Mines at a salary of $1500. There he joined his former teachers, F. P. Underhill and Yandell Henderson, in an investigation on poisonous gases for the Army and Navy. On October 1 he was promoted to the rank of Assistant Physiologist at a salary of $2400. Late in the fall of 1917 a method had been worked out for the relief of edema following chlorine inhalation. In order that he might be sent abroad to try out the treatment, Wright applied for a commission in the U.S. Army. On January 11, 1918, he accepted a commission as First Lieutenant in the Sanitary Corps of the Army.

On February 8, 1918, Wright embarked for England; he landed in Liverpool eight days later and was immediately transferred to Blois, France. It was here that the clearing-house for all casual officers was located. On March 1 he reported to Paris, the center of gas warfare activities for the Allies. His diary records that here he met Walter B. Cannon of Harvard and Haldane, Douglas, and Barcroft of the British school of physiologists, among others. Two weeks later he was sent to Porton, the center of research activities on gas warfare in England. During this period he had volunteered along with others to try out suits designed to protect soldiers from mustard gas in a wood heavily contaminated with the gas. He incurred severe gas burns and because of his devotion to duty was recommended for special distinction. He returned briefly to Chaumont, France, after the Armistice and was discharged on January 9, 1919, with the rank of Captain.

In 1922 he was appointed head of the Department of Physiological Chemistry at the University of Pennsylvania. The chair he occupied there, originally called the Chair of Chemistry and Toxicology, and named after Benjamin Rush, was the oldest in the Medical School of the University of

Pennsylvania. It had been separated into two seats—one occupied by Dr. John Marshall and the other by Dr. Alonzo E. Taylor. With the appointment of Dr. Wilson the decision was made to return to a one-man administration. The quarters occupied by the department were located in the basement and were far from spacious or luxurious. Wright proceeded to build up a young and well-balanced staff. Among the appointments made during the early years were James C. Andrews, physical chemistry; W. D. Langley, organic chemistry; James H. Jones, Nutrition; and George E. Simpson, who had received his Ph.D degree in physiological chemistry at Yale in 1920.

It was in the fall of 1926 that one of the authors of this memoir (E.G.B.), intent upon obtaining a Ph.D. degree in physical chemistry but short of financial means to attain this goal, accepted a position as research assistant to Wright. The new assistant, though reasonably competent at quantitative techniques, was totally ignorant of physiological chemistry. Encouraged by Wright to attend seminars and the lectures in biochemistry to medical students, the research assistant found himself enthusiastically enrolled as a graduate student by the end of the first year.

These were exciting and stimulating years for a young person to be in the department. Plans were well along for a new building which would house physiological chemistry and anatomy. Though Wright was knee-deep in blueprints, he always found time to discuss, in his typically quiet and relaxed manner, whatever problems arose. He made you feel that your problems were all-important. Contact with the clinical areas was afforded through Wright's continuing interest in fostering relationships between these areas and biochemistry. David L. Drabkin, an M.D., was appointed to the staff in 1926, and during this period Charles Johnson, a young surgeon, was a postdoctoral fellow and Joseph Stokes, a pediatrician, was mastering the techniques of total base determinations.

The years 1930-1940 were a period of steady and consistent growth of the new department. During this time the nature of the research problems began to change considerably in emphasis. Whereas acid-base studies had received primary attention in Wright's laboratory prior to 1930, in this later period he revived an earlier interest in nitrogenous extractives of muscle. In 1931 he spent a sabbatical leave in the laboratory of Dr. Barger at the University of Edinburgh. Over the next decade a number of papers appeared on the occurrence, isolation, and structure of octopine, carnosine, and anserine and on the chemical synthesis and metabolism of 1-methyl histidine.

In 1936 Dr. Samuel Gurin joined the staff of the Department of Physiological Chemistry and was to have a considerable influence on the direction of the laboratory, first as a close friend and colleague of Wright Wilson, then as the Chairman of the Department at Wright's retirement, and finally as Dean of the Medical School. Soon after his arrival on the campus a fruitful collaboration was established with Wright and Carl Bachman of the Department of Obstetrics-Gynecology for the isolation of a gonadotrophic hormone from pregnancy urine. This research investigation was profitable at both the scientific and clinical levels. To quote from a letter from Dr. Bachman: "Over the ensuing six years the above enterpsise eventually involved about twelve members of the two departmental staffs. More than twenty-five reports were published in the periodical literature of our respective scientific and clinical fields. The program was terminated only when, in 1942, the exigencies of World War II necessitated curtailment. Whatever benefits Wright and his group may have obtained from these joint activities, there can be little doubt that the rewards for our own group were both substantial and enduring. . . . Of paramount importance was the beneficial influence that the enterprise had—and continues to have—on the conduct of the clinical, teaching and investigative activities of our group in obstetrics-gynecology. Our staff continues to approach all assignments in the spirit of academic medicine."

This program illustrates in best form the type of collaboration between clinicians and biologists that Wright hoped for upon coming to the University of Pennsylvania, and finally achieved.

A similar cordial relationship also existed with the Department of Research Surgery headed at different times by Dr. I. S. Ravdin and Dr. Jonathan Rhoads. Many projects were jointly undertaken by staff members in this department and the Biochemistry Department, possibly because Dr. Harry Vars occupied quarters in the latter department and enjoyed appointments in both. One of the most unexpected fruits of this cordial relationship was a collaborative effort between Dr. Gurin, Dana Crandall, and Robert Ravdin, the son of Dr. I. S. Ravdin. In 1945 Bob Ravdin spent a year in the Biochemistry Department after obtaining his M.D. degree, to gain experience in research under the direction of Crandall and Gurin. Together they were able to isolate and characterize the enzymatic system for the oxidation of tyrosine first to homogentisic acid and then to fumaric acid and acetoacetic acid. This project, which was a major accomplishment in the study of intermediary metabolism, was certainly a by-product of the academic atmosphere which Wright had helped so much to establish.

The war years brought their inevitable restriction on fundamental research. Teaching of medical, dental, and veterinary students was accelerated and a research program on decontamination of foodstuffs by war gases was undertaken. However, several events occurred during this time that were eventually to have important repercussions on the future academic progress of the department. In the first place, the University of Pennsylvania was fortunate to be able to provide a scientific home for the great German biochemist and physiologist, Dr. Otto Meyerhof, who was forced to flee his native country with the rise of the Nazis to power. Through the efforts of the Rockefeller Foundation and of Dr. A. N. Richards and Wright Wilson, Dr. Meyerhof came to Philadelphia in 1940 and was appointed research professor in the Department of Physiological Chemistry at the University of Pennsylvania, where he carried on his work until his death in 1951.

Also, by 1940 the way was clear for one of the greatest breakthroughs in methodology that was to revolutionize biochemistry and, once and for all, establish it as a mature science in its own right. Investigators at Columbia University had demonstrated the immense power of the isotopes deuterium and N^{15} in the study of intermediary metabolism. The stable isotope of carbon, C^{13}, was soon proved to be even more useful, but, unfortunately, only small amounts were available through limited and private production. Gurin and Wilson were farsighted enough to realize the strategic importance of producing small amounts of this valuable substance. With the collaboration of the Physics Department a gas exchange apparatus was constructed for the concentration of C^{13} as $C^{13}O_2$, and a mass spectrometer was built. A whole range of problems in intermediary metabolism was open to exploration. As his bibliography shows, Wright with his students and colleagues studied the oxidation of fatty acids and acetoacetate, the metabolism of lactic acid and alanine in the phlorhizinized animal, and the precursors of the purine and pyrimidine bases of nucleic acids. Wright's main contributions were primarily concerned with the reactions of the biosynthesis of the pyrimidine compounds. He himself considered that one of his more important lifetime contributions was the finding that labeled CO_2 was incorporated into position 2 of the pyrimidines, because it is not thus incorporated into purines of the same nucleic acids.

Wright took a great interest in the training of graduate students. Unfortunately, the names of many of those who carried out their thesis work with him do not show in his bibliography. This is because the University at one time required the independent publication of a thesis by a Ph.D. candidate and also required him to submit a number of printed and bound copies of it. In order to save his students this extra cost Wright directed them to publish their theses in a scientific journal without his name attached and to submit reprints of the published article to the University. This was only one of the many manifestations of the consideration and kindness that Wright and his wife, Helene, displayed to the graduate students in the department.

At the conclusion of the war the graduate program in biochemistry was reorganized to accommodate students whose education had been interrupted by the hostilities. Dr. William C. Stadie, a long-time friend and colleague, shared with Wright the responsibility of the chairmanship of the Graduate Department of Biochemistry in the School of Arts and Sciences. His robust personality and good humor were much in evidence on the one day a week he visited the department for lunch and consultation. The curriculum in biochemistry for graduate students was revised to include lectures by Dr. Seymour Cohen in the new area of bacteriophages and nucleic acids. These lectures were well received by the students and were forerunners of a new discipline of biochemistry, namely molecular biology. Also, when Dr. Britton Chance became head of the Johnson Foundation, a strong program in biophysical chemistry was available for students in this important discipline. Thus, through these efforts, a comprehensive graduate program in biochemistry was developed on the campus of the University of Pennsylvania.

In 1948 there was a reorganization of the Health Sciences on the Pennsylvania campus. Dr. David Drabkin became Chairman of the Graduate Department of Biochemistry in the Medical School and Dr. James Jones the head of Biochemistry in the Veterinary School. The medical course, however, was always Wright's primary responsibility and concern. No laboratory instructor was more watchful and conscientious than Wright himself. He was particularly anxious that the medical students learn proper laboratory technique. One of the first experiments in the course was the Kjeldahl distillation. Lacking experience in setting up apparatus, the medical students frequently contrived jerry-built platforms for support of their receiving flasks. In gentle but no uncertain terms Wright lectured each unsuspecting victim on the proper method of constructing his apparatus. Obviously this small measure of discipline left no scars on his students, since they affectionately referred to him as "The Great White Father."

Wright's interest in isotopes involved him in several early activities to organize and foster research in this area. He was chairman of the Biological Section of the Isotope Research Committee, a national committee which was formed in 1945 for the purpose of sponsoring and aiding biochemical research with carbon and other isotopes by institutions and responsible individuals. The list of its membership in 1945 reads today like a *Who's Who* of the pioneers in the development of this important tool of biochemical research. One of the functions of this committee was the publication of a series of papers by leading investigators of this field on the topic "Preparation and Measurement of Isotopic Tracers." The Houdry Process Corporation collaborated with the Isotope Research Committee to supply investigators with C^{13} enriched compounds. Although this goal was never fully realized, the Houdry Process Corporation through the generous help of Dr. Sidney Weinhouse did perform many isotopic analyses for the group at the University of Pennsylvania.

By 1946 the first, small quantities of $C^{14}O_2$ were produced in the reactor at Oak Ridge National Laboratories. Wright was one of five scientists to receive a sample. Later he became the first chairman of the Radioactive Safety Committee at the University of Pennsylvania.

Wright received many honors in recognition of his accomplishments and service to his discipline of biochemistry. He was Secretary (1924-1925), Vice President (1952-1953), and President (1953-1954) of the American Society of Biological Chemists. He was a member of the Editorial Committee of the *Journal of Biological Chemistry* between 1939 and 1955 and a member of the Council of the Federation of American Societies for Experimental Biology. He was one of the founders of the Philadelphia Biochemists Club. In 1955 he was elected to the National Academy of Sciences.

In the same year he retired as the Chairman of the Department of Physiological Chemistry and became Emeritus Professor in 1957. His release from administrative responsibilities permitted greater attention to two of his hobbies, gardening and painting. Although the latter avocation was taken up rather late in life, he rapidly acquired a skill to match his real talent as a painter. Unfortunately, in the winter of

1957 Wright suffered an accidental injury from which he never fully recovered. In spite of this severe handicap he continued his research. Two papers were published in his later years with his wife, Helene, and a third paper with his son. Throughout this time he never lost his confidence or his good humor. No doubt the ministrations of a loving and gracious wife sustained his spirits in what otherwise were very trying times for him physically.

Wright was the father of Thomas Hastings Wilson, who is now Professor of Physiology at Harvard Medical School, and of Juliet Wilson Welch of California. In addition, he had seven grandchildren.

In the academic community his progeny are many. On the occasion of his sixty-fifth birthday Wright was honored at the meetings of the Federation of American Societies for Experimental Biology with a dinner by his students and colleagues. This gathering was undoubtedly a high point in his career. Upon retirement he was also honored with the presentation of his portrait, which now hangs in the Medical School of the University of Pennsylvania. As skillful as the artist was, he could not include on a single canvas the many facets of Wrights's personality that endeared him to his family, friends, and colleagues.

Finally on July 13, 1965, a courageous and youthful spirit departed an ailing body that could not longer support life. Undoubtedly Wright's greatest heritage was his own example to those who had the privilege of associating with him. A biography catches only a glimpse of the real man, with omissions of important events in his life and the failure to include the contributions of many close friends and associates. The effort of the two biographers was greatly aided by Helene Wilson, who has devoted many hours to gathering the factual information needed for this report.

BIBLIOGRAPHY

KEY TO ABBREVIATIONS

Am. J. Physiol. = American Journal of Physiology
Bull. Johns Hopkins Hosp. = Bulletin of the Johns Hopkins Hospital
Federation Proc. = Federation Proceedings
J. Am. Chem. Soc. = Journal of the American Chemical Society
J. Biol. Chem. = Journal of Biological Chemistry
Proc. Soc. Exp. Biol. Med. = Proceedings of the Society for Experimental
   Biology and Medicine

1914

The comparative chemistry of muscle: the partition of non-protein water-soluble nitrogen. J. Biol. Chem., 17:385-400.
The comparative chemistry of muscle: betaine from the scallop, periwinkle and lamprey: creatine from the lamprey. J. Biol. Chem., 18:17-20.
Claude Bernard. Popular Science Monthly, 84:567-78.
With P. B. Hawk. Fasting studies. XII. The ammonia, phosphate, chloride and acid excretion of a fasting man. J. Am. Chem. Soc., 36:137-46.
With P. B. Hawk. Studies on water drinking. XVIII. On the relation between water ingestion and the ammonia, phosphate, chloride and acid excretion. J. Am. Chem. Soc., 36: 1774-79.

1915

With Thornton Stearns and J. H. Janney, Jr. The effect of acid administration on parathyroid tetany. J. Biol. Chem., 21:169-77.
With Thornton Stearns and Madge D. Thurlow. The acid-base equilibria in the blood after parathyroidectomy. J. Biol. Chem., 23:89-121.
With Thornton Stearns and J. H. Janney, Jr. The excretion of acids and ammonia after parathyroidectomy. J. Biol. Chem., 23:123-37.

1917

With Edward F. Adolph. The partition of non-protein nitrogen in the blood of fresh water fish. J. Biol. Chem., 29:405-11.

With Edward F. Adolph. The partition of non-protein nitrogen in the blood of fresh water fish. J. Biol. Chem., 29:xviii. (A)

With E. D. Plass. Creatine and creatinine in whole blood and plasma. J. Biol. Chem., 29:413-23.

With D. R. Hooker and Helene Connett. The perfusion of the mammalian medulla: the effect of carbon dioxide and other substances on the respiratory and cardiovascular centers. Am. J. Physiol., 43:351-61.

1919

With Samuel Goldschmidt. The influence of oxygen administration on the concentration of the blood which accompanies the development of lung edema. Am. J. Physiol., 50:157-64.

With Walter Jones. *A Laboratory Manual of Physiological Chemistry.* Baltimore, Williams & Wilkins Co. 247 pp.

1920

Determination of amino nitrogen in compounds reacting slowly with nitrous acid. J. Biol. Chem., 41:iii. (A)

Studies in pyrimidine metabolism. Proc. Soc. Exp. Biol. Med., 17:179-80.

1921

With S. Bayne-Jones. Specific immunological reactions of Bence-Jones proteins. Proc. Soc. Exp. Biol. Med., 18:220-22.

1922

With S. Bayne-Jones. Immunological reactions of Bence-Jones proteins. I. Differences between Bence-Jones proteins and human serum proteins. Bull. Johns Hopkins Hosp., 33:37-43.

With S. Bayne-Jones. Immunological reactions of Bence-Jones proteins. II. Differences between Bence-Jones proteins from various sources. Bull. Johns Hopkins Hosp., 33:119-25.

1923

Determination of amino nitrogen in compounds reacting slowly with nitrous acid. J. Biol. Chem., 56:183-90.

Neutrality regulations in the body. Physiology Review, 3:295-334.

The determination of free amino nitrogen in proteins. J. Biol. Chem., 56:191-201.

A spontaneous crystallization of a Bence-Jones protein. J. Biol. Chem., 56:203-14.

Studies in pyrimidine metabolism. J. Biol. Chem., 56:215-27.

1924

With S. H. Liljestrand. The excretion of lactic acid in the urine after muscular exercise. Proc. Soc. Exp. Biol. Med., 21:426.

1925

With W. L. Long, H. C. Thompson, and Sylva Thurlow. Changes in the composition of the urine after muscular exercise. J. Biol. Chem., 65:755-71.

With S. H. Liljestrand. The excretion of lactic acid in the urine after muscular exercise. J. Biol. Chem., 65:773-82.

1926

With S. Goldschmidt. The influence of O_2 administration on the concentration of the blood which accompanies development of lung edema. Chapter 20 in: *The Medical Department of the United States Army in the World War; Medical Aspects of Gas Warfare,* ed. by M. W. Ireland, Vol. XIV, pp. 713-18. Washington, U.S. Govt. Print. Off. (Reprinted from Am. J. Physiol., 50:157-64.)

1928

With Eric G. Ball. A study of the estimation of chloride in serum. J. Biol. Chem., 78:1.

With Eric G. Ball. A study of the estimation of chloride in blood and serum. J. Biol. Chem., 79:221-27.

A Laboratory Manual of Physiological Chemistry. Baltimore,

Williams & Wilkins Co. 272 pp. (2d ed., 1932; 3d ed., 1937; 4th ed., 1941; 5th ed., 1944; 6th ed., 1947; 7th ed., 1952.)

1929

With E. G. Ball. A comparison of the composition of pancreatic juice and of blood serum under experimental conditions. Am. J. Physiol., 90:272. Thirteenth International Physiology Congress.

1930

Biochemistry. Chapter XX in: *Annual Survey of American Chemistry*, ed. by Clarence J. West, Vol. 5, pp. 317-32. New York, The Chemical Catalog Company, Inc.

Pages 119-28 in: *Methods and Problems of Medical Education*, 18th Series, Department of Physiological Chemistry, University of Pennsylvania, School of Medicine, Philadelphia. New York, Rockefeller Foundation.

With Charles G. Johnston. The effect of hemorrhage on the acid-base equilibrium of the blood. J. Biol. Chem., 85: 727-41.

With E. P. Laug. The determination of the pH of serum with the quinhydrone electrode. J. Biol. Chem., 87:xxvii-xxviii. (A)

1931

With William A. Wolff. The extractives of dog muscle. J. Biol. Chem., 92:lx-lxi. (A)

1932

With William A. Wolff. Anserine in mammalian skeletal muscle. J. Biol. Chem., 95:495-504.

With Edwin J. de Beer. The inorganic composition of the parotid saliva of the dog and its relation to the composition of the serum. J. Biol. Chem., 95:671-85.

Nitrogenous muscle extractives. Yale Journal of Biology and Medicine, 4:627-48.

With John G. Reinhold. The determination of cholic acid in bile. J. Biol. Chem., 96:637-46.

1933

With William A. Wolff. The determination of anserine in muscle. J. Biol. Chem., 100:cvi. (A)

1934

With John G. Reinhold. The acid-base composition of hepatic bile. I. Am. J. Physiol., 107:378-87.

With John G. Reinhold. The acid-base composition of hepatic bile. II. The changes induced by the injection of hydrochloric acid and inorganic salts. Am. J. Physiol., 107:388-99.

With John G. Reinhold. The acid-base composition of hepatic bile. III. The effects of the administration of sodium taurocholate, sodium cholate and sodium dehydrocholate (decholin). Am. J. Physiol., 107:400-405.

With Elinor Moore. The basic extractives of pecten muscle. J. Biol. Chem., 105:lxiii. (A)

1935

With Edwin J. de Beer and Charles G. Johnston. The composition of intestinal secretions. J. Biol. Chem., 108:113-20.

With Phyllis A. Bott. Lactic acid formation in liver. J. Biol. Chem., 109:455-62.

With Phyllis A. Bott. The concentration of lactic acid in blood and liver of rabbits. J. Biol. Chem., 109:463-66.

With William A. Wolff. Carnosine and anserine in mammalian skeletal muscle. J. Biol. Chem., 109:565-71.

1936

With Elinor Moore. The nitrogenous extractives of pecten muscle. J. Biol. Chem., 114:lxxi-lxxii. (A)

1937

With Elinor Moore. Nitrogenous extractives of scallop muscle. I. The isolation and a study of the structure of octopine. J. Biol. Chem., 119:573-84.

With Elinor Moore. Nitrogenous extractives of scallop muscle. II. Isolations from and quantitative analyses of muscles from freshly killed scallops. J. Biol. Chem., 119:585-88.

With J. Logan Irvin. Synthesis of octopine (pectenine). Proc. Soc. Exp. Biol. Med., 36:398-99.

1938

With Samuel Gurin and Carl Bachman. The gonadotropic hormone of pregnancy urine. J. Biol. Chem., 123:xlix. (A)

With William A. Wolff. Basic nitrogenous extractives of necturus muscle. J. Biol. Chem., 124:103-6.

With John A. Zapp, Jr. Quantitative studies of carnosine and anserine in mammalian muscle. I. A method for the determination of carnosine and anserine. J. Biol. Chem., 126: 9-18.

With John A. Zapp, Jr. Quantitative studies of carnosine and anserine in mammalian muscle. II. The distribution of carnosine and anserine in various muscles of different species. J. Biol. Chem., 126:19-27.

1939

With Samuel Gurin and Carl Bachman. The nature of the carbohydrate in the gonadotropic substance of pregnancy urine. Science, 89:62-63.

With J. Logan Irvin. Studies on octopine. I. The synthesis and titrations curve of octopine. J. Biol. Chem., 127:555-63.

With J. Logan Irvin. Studies on octopine. II. The nitrogenous extractives of squid and octopus muscle. J. Biol. Chem., 127:565-74.

With J. Logan Irvin. Studies on octopine. III. The precursor of octopine in autolyzing scallop muscle. J. Biol. Chem., 127: 575-79.

With Samuel Gurin and Carl Bachman. The gonadotropic hormone of urine of pregnancy. I. A simple method of extractions and purifications. J. Biol. Chem., 128:525-36.

With Alton C. Kurtz. Saccharolactone as a reagent for precipitating certain amines. J. Biol. Chem., 129:693-99.

With Samuel Gurin and Carl Bachman. The homogeneity of gonadotropic hormone preparations isolated from pregnancy urine. J. Am. Chem. Soc., 61:2251.

1940

With Samuel Gurin and Carl Bachman. The gonadotropic hormone of urine of pregnancy. II. Chemical studies of preparations having high biological activity. J. Biol. Chem., 133:467-76.

With Samuel Gurin and Carl Bachman. The gonadotropic hormone of urine of pregnancy. III. Evidence of purity obtained by studies of electrophoresis and sedimentation. J. Biol. Chem., 133:477-84.

1942

With Harold P. Lundgren, Samuel Gurin, and Carl Bachman. The gonadotropic hormone of urine of pregnancy. IV. J. Biol. Chem., 142:367-70.

With S. Gurin. The intermediary metabolism of alanine containing C^{13}. Federation Proc., 1:114. (A)

1944

With Warwick Sakami. Studies on l-methylhistidine. I. A synthesis of di-l-methylhistidine. J. Biol. Chem., 154:215-22.

With Warwick Sakami. Studies on l-methylhistidine. II. A study of the metabolism of di-l-methylhistidine in the albino rat. J. Biol. Chem., 154:223-25.

1945

With John M. Buchanan, Warwick Sakami, and Samuel Gurin. A study of the intermediates of acetoacetate oxidation with isotopic carbon. J. Biol. Chem., 157:747-48.

With John M. Buchanan, Warwick Sakami, and Samuel Gurin. A study of the intermediates of acetate and acetoacetate oxidation with isotopic carbon. J. Biol. Chem., 159:695-709.

1946

With Adelaide M. Delluva. A study with isotopic carbon of the assimilation of carbon dioxide in the rat. J. Biol. Chem., 166:739-46.

With A. O. C. Nier and Stanley P. Reimann. *Preparation and Measurement of Isotopic Tracers.* (Symposium) Ann Arbor, Edwards Bros., Inc. vii + 108 pp.

With John M. Buchanan, Warwick Sakami, and Samuel Gurin. Intermediates of acetoacetate oxidation. Federation Proc., 5:126. (A)

1947

With John M. Buchanan, Warwick Sakami, and Samuel Gurin. Intermediates in the biological oxidation of isotopic aceto-acetate. J. Biol. Chem., 169:403-10.

With Samuel Gurin and Adelaide M. Delluva. The metabolism of isotopic lactic acid and alanine in the phlorhizinized animal. J. Biol. Chem., 171:101-10.

The use of C^{13} and C^{14} in studying metabolism in animals. Science, 105:637.

The use of C^{13} and C^{14} in medical research. Journal of the Franklin Institute, 244:209-19.

With Adelaide M. Delluva and Samuel Gurin. The metabolic fate of radioactive lactate in the phlorhizinized animal. Federation Proc., 6:302-3. (A)

With Dana I. Crandall and Samuel Gurin. Studies on the formation of isotopic acetoacetate in homogenized liver. Federation Proc., 6:246. (A)

1949

With Milton R. Heinrich and Samuel Gurin. Isotopic studies of the biosynthesis of nucleic acid components. I. Purines and pyrimidines. Federation Proc., 8:205. (A)

With Jerome D. Valentine and Samuel Gurin. Isotopic studies of the biosynthesis of nucleic acid components. II. Allantoin. Federation Proc., 8:262. (A)

1950

With Milton R. Heinrich. The biosynthesis of nucleic acid components studied with C^{14}. I. Purines and pyrimidines in the rat. J. Biol. Chem., 186:447-60.

With L. L. Weed and Mary Edmonds. Conversion of radioactive orotic acid into pyrimidine nucleotides of nucleic acid by slices of rat liver. Proc. Soc. Exp. Biol. Med., 75:192-93.

With C. S. Miller and S. Gurin. C^{14} labeled 4 (5)-amino-5 (4)-imidazolecarboxamide in the biosynthesis of purines. Science, 112:654-55.

With J. D. Valentine and S. Gurin. Biosynthesis of radioactive allantoin. Proc. Soc. Exp. Biol. Med., 75:794-96.
With Mary Edmonds and Adelaide M. Delluva. Metabolism of purines and pyrimidines in growing yeast. Federation Proc., 9:167. (A)

1951

With Lawrence L. Weed. The incorporation of C^{14}-orotic acid into nucleic acid pyrimidines *in vitro*. J. Biol. Chem., 189: 435.
With Lemuel D. Wright, Charles S. Miller, Helen R. Skeggs, Jesse W. Huff, and Lawrence L. Weed. Biological precursors of the pyrimidines. J. Am. Chem. Soc., 73:1898-99.
With Lawrence L. Weed. Incorporation of orotic acid-2-C^{14} into pyrimidines of nucleic acid *in vitro*. Federation Proc., 10: 267. (A)

1952

With Charles S. Miller and Samuel Gurin. Substituted imidazoles as precursors of the purines. J. Am. Chem. Soc., 74:2892-94.
With Mary Edmonds and Adelaide M. Delluva. The metabolism of purines and pyrimidines by growing yeast. J. Biol. Chem., 197:251-59.

1953

With Lawrence L. Weed. Studies of pyrimidine nucleotides with orotic acid-2-C^{14} and P^{32}. J. Biol. Chem., 202:745-48.
With John M. Buchanan. Biosynthesis of purines and pyrimidines. Federation Proc., 12:646-50. (Review article)
Investigation of the biochemistry of nucleic acids with the use of the spectrophotometer and the refrigerated centrifuge loaned by the society. Yearbook of the American Philosophical Society, pp. 183-84. Philadelphia, American Philosophical Society. (Also in reprint form.)

1954

With Lawrence L. Weed. Studies on precursors of pyrimidines of nucleic acid. J. Biol. Chem., 207:439-42.
With Cecil Cooper. Biosynthesis of pyrimidines. Federation Proc., 13:194. (A)

With C. Cooper. Studies on the biosynthesis of pyrimidines. American Journal of Medical Sciences, 227:102-3.

1955

With Cecil Cooper and Ray Wu. Studies of some precursors of pyrimidines. J. Biol. Chem., 216:37-49.

With Ray Wu. Conversion of ureidosuccinic acid to orotic acid in fractionated homogenates of rat liver. Federation Proc., 14:309. (A)

1956

With Ray Wu. Studies of the biosynthesis of orotic acid. J. Biol. Chem., 223:195-205.

With T. H. Wilson. Intestinal absorption *in vitro* of undylic and thymidylic acids. Biochimica et Biophysica Acta, 22:587.

1958

With T. Hastings Wilson. Studies *in vitro* of the digestion and absorption of pyrimidine nucleotides by the intestine. J. Biol. Chem., 233:1544-47.

With T. H. Wilson. Studies *in vitro* of digestion and absorption of pyrimidine nucleotides by the intestine. Proceedings of the Fourth International Congress of Biochemistry, Vol. 5, p. 157, Vienna. London, Pergamon Press.

1960

With R. L. Stambaugh. The chromatography of nucleotides, nucleosides, and pyrimidines and purines on activated charcoal. Journal of Chromatography, 3:221-24.

1962

With Helene C. Wilson. Studies *in vitro* of the digestion and absorption of purine ribonucleotides by the intestine. J. Biol. Chem., 237:1643-47.

1965

With Helene C. Wilson. Digestion of purine ribonucleotides by intestinal enzymes of the developing rat fetus. Am. J. Physiol., 209:1155-58.

Edwin B. Wilson

EDWIN BIDWELL WILSON

April 25, 1879–December 28, 1964

BY JEROME HUNSAKER AND
SAUNDERS MAC LANE

E DWIN BIDWELL WILSON, mathematician, theoretical physicist, statistician, and economist, was born at Hartford,
Connecticut, on April 25, 1879. He was the son of Edwin Horace and Jane Amelia (Bidwell) Wilson; his father was a
teacher and superintendent of schools of Middletown, Connecticut. As a student at Harvard, Wilson already set the style
of his wide-ranging scientific interests, taking a considerable
variety of courses, including a major in mathematics. He graduated, summa cum laude, in 1899 and then began graduate
work at Yale, where he received a Ph.D. degree in 1901. In
1900 he became instructor in mathematics at Yale, but took
leave during the year 1902-1903 to study mathematics in Paris,
chiefly at the Ecole Normale Supérieure. He then returned to
teach at Yale; in 1906 he became an assistant professor of
mathematics there. In 1907 he went to the Massachusetts Institute of Technology as associate professor of mathematics,
becoming a full professor in 1911, and professor of mathematical physics and head of the Department of Physics in 1917.

During World War I the Massachusetts Institute of Technology gave a course in aeronautical engineering for Army
and Navy officers with Professor Wilson in charge. He was

Lowell Lecturer on aeronautics in 1918. Following the death of President Maclaurin of M.I.T., he was one of an administrative committee of three faculty members (1920-1922) which had charge of administrative affairs until Samuel Stratton was elected president. Thereupon Wilson moved to the Harvard School of Public Health to become Professor of Vital Statistics.

On July 5, 1911, Wilson married Ethel Sentner, daughter of Lemuel J. Sentner, merchant of Edmonton, Alberta, Canada. They had two children, Enid and Doris Wilson, both of whom survive him.

He also had two sisters, the Reverend Eleanor Wilson and Dr. Jane Wilson Hall, and two brothers, Dr. P. T. Wilson and Dr. T. W. Wilson. Their high education and professional prominence may be of interest to geneticists.

In 1945 Wilson retired from the Harvard School of Public Health. In 1945-1946 he gave the Stevenson lectures on citizenship in Glasgow, Scotland. From 1948 until his death on December 28, 1964, Wilson served the Office of Naval Research in Boston as a consultant and adviser in the mathematical and physical sciences. Wilson's services to the Navy and the ONR were recognized by two decorations: from the Chief of Naval Operations, the Superior Civilian Service Award (1960), and from the Secretary of the Navy, the Distinguished Civilian Service Award (1964).

We now turn to examine the variety of Wilson's scientific work. He came on the scientific scene in the United States just when the emphasis on research and graduate work was beginning and when it was becoming clear that mathematical methods could be applied to a wide variety of scholarly and scientific fields. These possibilities immediately attracted him. He applied his sharp and critical intelligence to a succession of topics. The breadth and variety of his interests and accomplishments explains why Wesleyan University, when awarding him an honorary LL.D. degree in 1955, called him "the modern Renaissance man, taking all knowledge for his province." In this memoir we shall take up in succession his major intellectual interests, beginning with vector analysis, advanced calculus, and mathematics generally, then continuing with aerodynamics, statistics, and economics, and ending with his work for the *Proceedings of the National Academy of Sciences* and the Academy itself.

VECTOR ANALYSIS

Wilson's first major accomplishment was the preparation (1901) of the Gibbs-Wilson book, *Vector Analysis*. For some time it had been clear that mathematical physics needed a flexible method of handling vector quantities. Various competing techniques were at hand: Hamilton's quaternions, lavishly popularized by P. G. Tait and the Quaternion Society, Grassman's *Ausdehnungslehre,* and the physical ideas of Clark Maxwell and Heaviside. Josiah Willard Gibbs, the outstanding American mathematical physicist, had modified the techniques of Grassman to fit the ideas of Maxwell and Heaviside as well as his own work. His resulting vector calculus was presented in lectures at Yale and in an unpublished brief set of lecture notes ("Elements of Vector Analysis," 1881 and 1884). Heaviside had adopted Gibbs's notations. Wilson, the last student of Gibbs, brought the Gibbs lectures to a full and polished written form in the Gibbs-Wilson book, setting down all the basic ideas and notations, plus a great variety of physical applications. This book remained the standard text in its subject in this country for many years. In a sense it definitely settled in this country the late nineteenth-century controversy between quaternion notation and vector notation. To this day American physicists constantly use the boldface notation for vectors, with a dot for scalar product and $\times$ for vector product, exactly as initiated by Gibbs and Gibbs-Wilson. Internationally the argument about notation continued much longer. This one may see by examining the papers in the controversy between Wilson and the joint Italian authors, Burali-Forti and Marcolongo, as recorded in Wilson's articles in *L'Enseignement Mathématique* in 1909 and 1911.

Vector Analysis was a splendid book, but not all parts of it were equally successful. Two of the later chapters presented the theory of dyadics—unpublished work of Gibbs, done for the standard three-dimensional Euclidean vector space (which we shall call the space E). A dyadic Φ is a formal sum of formal products **a b** of vectors **a** and **b** of E; each dyadic Φ determines a linear transformation on E sending each vector **r** to a vector Φ **r** (for example, the dyadic **a b** sends **r** to **a** $[\mathbf{b \cdot r}]$); two dyadics Φ and Φ' are defined to be equal precisely when $\Phi \cdot \mathbf{r} = \Phi' \cdot \mathbf{r}$ for all vectors **r**. Thus the dyadics provided a sophisticated machinery capable of handling in invariant form all the properties of linear transformations, exterior algebra, and the like. Their definition (once the formal product **a b** is replaced by the symbol **a** $\otimes$ **b**) becomes exactly the modern definition of the tensor product E $\otimes$ E, done in an invariant style worthy of Bourbaki. However, this material in 1901 may have been too sophisticated for its intended audience and the invariant treatment of linear transformation by dyadics was often replaced by the more concrete manipulation of matrices relative to particular coordinate systems. The invariant approach thus forgotten returned only much later in different form with Hermann Weyl's insistence on describing vector spaces by axioms and not by bases (in *Gruppentheorie und Quantenmechanik* [1928]) and with Hassler Whitney's discovery of tensor products (1938).

At the International Congress of Mathematics in Heidelberg in 1904 Wilson gave an address summarizing Gibbs's unpublished research on multiple algebra. He reveals there that Gibbs had objected to the publication of the Gibbs-Wilson *Vector Analysis* by itself without including the related and more original work which Gibbs had done on multiple algebra. That subject has now been developed (in other ways and by other hands) as multilinear algebra; in 1904 it might well have been ahead of its time, so we can be happy that the *Vector Analysis* (even without the projected work on multiple algebra) did itself make a timely appearance.

ADVANCED CALCULUS

In the early 1900s many textbooks were available for the standard courses in differential and integral calculus, but for the next course in advanced calculus there were only various famous volumes, the *Traité d'Analyse* by different French authors, plus the translation by E. R. Hedrick of one of these (the Goursat-Hedrick *Course in Mathematical Analysis,* Volume 1, 1904; Volume 2, 1916). Wilson taught the advanced calculus course both at Yale and at M.I.T., often using the *Course d'Analyse* of de la Vallee-Poussin. Based on this experience he published his own *Advanced Calculus* in 1912—a solid, extensive, informative, and lively book which was accurate in its treatment of the foundations and suggestive in its wide coverage of applications. For a dozen years this book was (except for Goursat-Hedrick as noted above) the only available modern American advanced calculus text; for a number of years thereafter it was still the best such text. It had a wide influence on a whole generation of mathematicians and scientists who fondly remember what they learned in its pages.

MATHEMATICS

From 1902 to 1916 Wilson's research and expository work ranged widely over many fields of mathematics: Synthetic projective geometry, with a special attention to areas and volumes and the group of transformations preserving them (1903); the representations of unimodular matrices as products of involutions (1907); and properties of differential equations (1906-1908). His reviews of various mathematical books were sprightly and sometimes debatable. For example, in 1908 (in "Logic and Continuum") he noted Zermelo's important proof that the axiom of choice implied that any set (in particular the continuum) could be well-ordered. However, Wilson doubted Zermelo's proof of the equivalence of these two properties; Wilson's argument is made on grounds which today are not convincing.

Wilson did not hesitate in his criticisms even in the case of David Hilbert. Hilbert, outstanding professor of mathematics at the German center of Göttingen, had just delivered his famous address at the Paris conference (1900) on the principal unsolved problems of mathematics and had just published his book on the foundations of geometry—a book which finally corrected all the errors of Euclid. Then in 1902 Hilbert published in the *Mathematische Annalen* a new group-theoretic foundation for geometry (Volume 56, pages 381-422). Wilson, a young student at the Ecole Normale Supérieure, published a response in the journal managed by the mathematicians at Berlin—long-time rivals of Göttingen. Wilson's paper, "The So-called Foundations of Geometry," was a vigorous criticism of Hilbert's paper. He picked up some minor slips and inaccuracies but he also made a basic objection to Hilbert's use of set theory and logic, an objection which few would follow today.

Wilson's caustic tongue was not limited to pure mathematics. In 1914, reviewing an early paper of Einstein on general relativity, he begins thus: "Einstein no sooner had defined the principle of relativity and established it on a sound basis than he went about destroying it, as some would say, or generalizing it, as he says, so as to take account of gravitational phenomena."

The range of Wilson's interest in mathematics is well indicated by his extraordinary activity in reviewing books—he published over thirty reviews in the period 1911-1914 in the *Bulletin of the American Mathematical Society*. A typescript of his bibliography which includes these and other reviews by him may be found in the archives of the National Academy of Sciences.

In summary, concerning his own work in mathematics, Wilson wrote on November 4, 1964, to Saunders Mac Lane as follows (beginning with his current interests in publication):

"The increase in facilities for brief announcements, the greater speed of their publication, and the real difficulty of getting long papers printed may make it desirable to do what the *Proceedings of the American Academy of Arts and Sciences* did—specialize on longer papers to be published individually and made up into volumes when enough had been published to make a good sized volume. That is how much of Bridgman's work came out . . . G. N. Lewis and I did a 120-page paper on special relativity . . . (November 1912) with an original 4-dimensional non-Euclidean vector analysis which probably was the neatest and most comprehensive (I do not say comprehensible) way in which it was ever treated, at least up to that time.

"C. L. E. Moore and I did a Differential Geometry of Two-Dimensional Surfaces in Hyperspace . . . (November 1916) which was all new original stuff and in a subsequent review of the literature many years later was cited as the most important contribution in the field. It was about the last thing I did in pure mathematics."

In this letter Wilson noted the gradual shift of his own

interests away from geometry (and to mechanics). This shift may have begun in 1906. In 1908 he solved a problem of an oscillating chain suggested to him by one of his Harvard teachers, William Fogg Osgood, and in 1909 he prepared two papers giving a systematic exposition of some of the work of Gibbs on statistical mechanics. Both at Yale and at M.I.T. he regularly gave courses in mechanics, hydrodynamics, elasticity, electricity and magnetism, and optics, while in 1917 he managed to give lectures on general relativity despite the paucity of news from Germany because of the British blockade (see his paper in the *Astrophysical Journal*). All these activities form the background to his next major contribution, that to aerodynamics.

AERONAUTICS AT M.I.T.

In 1909, Wilson, then of the Mathematics Department, taught a course on theoretical fluid mechanics (called Hydromechanics) to the Naval graduate students of the Department of Naval Architecture. The Wright Brothers' first flights of 1908-1909 stimulated his interest in possible aeronautical applications. Lanchester's *Aerodynamics* was published in 1909 and there soon appeared in the literature a few mathematical-physical papers dealing with the new science of aerodynamics as a basis for flight.

Wilson encouraged two of his students to read these papers and to come to him for help when baffled by the mathematics. In the summer of 1912, these students discovered for themselves that aerodynamics alone did not account for the flight of an airplane, but that its path in space depended on the dynamics of a rigid body moving through a resisting medium in response to imposed forces. This led to intensive tutoring by Wilson, quite outside his regular course in classical dynamics.

That same summer, two of his students were working with a paper by Bairstow of the National Physical Laboratory, England, in which the stability of the oscillations of an airplane was determined by six simultaneous differential equations of motion, with coefficients that might be found by experiments with a model in a wind tunnel. The mathematics and the physical concept were not clearly related, and the problem was taken to Wilson, then vacationing near Ossipee, New Hampshire.

A very modern "progressive" educational experiment was established in which the intellectual appetite of the students was balanced against their need for ordinary food. Mrs. Wilson acted as an honest broker and worked out an arrangement by which a pint of wild strawberries would procure the professor's help as well as a fine supper.

This brief summer experience led Wilson into a serious study of the motion of an airplane under the influence of the external forces that might be imposed on it when encountering gusts in unsteady wind.

When President Maclaurin started a graduate course in aeronautical engineering in the Department of Naval Architecture in 1913-1914, Wilson taught the theoretical part, aerodynamics and dynamics, and others the experimental part. This collaboration led to pioneer work by Wilson on the dynamics of flight.

In 1915 President Woodrow Wilson appointed the National Advisory Committee for Aeronautics. Its First Annual Report to the Congress, printed as a Senate document in 1916, started off with a report by E. B. Wilson entitled "Theory of an Aeroplane Encountering Gusts." This original work by Wilson was the first analysis of the accelerations caused by gusts. Wilson worked out practical numerical solutions for a typical airplane encountering gusts of several types. The aerodynamic coefficients necessary for the solutions were obtained from model tests in the M.I.T. wind tunnel. For this, the model had to be oscillative, and a young research assistant, D. W. Douglas, worked up from Wilson's theory practical spring-controlled supports. (Later the Douglas Airplane Company produced many practical airplanes for World War I and thereafter, including such well-known planes as the DC3.) This 1915 work by Wilson was new and became the basis for many more such studies by others as the art advanced and computing machines became available to reduce the labor of the successive approximation method used by Wilson.

As the M.I.T. work in aeronautical engineering developed, Wilson offered a special graduate course and eventually published a text (*Aeronautics,* Wiley, 1920) covering the substance of his lectures on rigid and fluid dynamics as applied to aeronautics. This book was a boon to graduate students as it threw new light on the theory of dimension and based the equations of motion on moving axes through the c.g. of the airplane. Integration of the differential equations had to be done by approximate methods using coefficients obtained by wind tunnel model experiments.

STATISTICS

During World War I, Wilson became interested in the use of mathematics in statistical and public health questions. With the completion in 1922 of his administrative duties at M.I.T. and his transfer to the Harvard School of Public Health, he turned his full attention to mathematical statistics and related questions. His subsequent publications, many of them joint papers, cover many timely topics; for example, the analysis and improvement of a curve due to Soper describing the spread of epidemics, a systematic study of 2×2 contingency tables, and long-continued systematic researches with

Jane Worcester, especially on quantal response assays with special attention to estimation of the median lethal dose (LD 50, in Wilson's terminology). Toward the end of his activity he may have been out of touch with the community of mathematical statisticians which by that time had developed in this country—perhaps because he continued to publish in his beloved *Proceedings of the National Academy of Sciences* rather than in the specialized journals usually studied by statisticians. We may note here two of his notable contributions to statistics, one to the idea of confidence intervals, the other to the study of uncontrolled sources of variation.

First consider confidence intervals. In a paper published in 1927 on probable inference, Wilson first describes the accepted method of finding an interval to estimate a binomial probability p from its observed analogue p_0 measured in a population of size n. The common procedure, he notes, is that of calculating the observed standard deviation σ_0 from the observed probability p_0 by the usual formula and then choosing some multiple $\lambda\sigma_0$ of this standard deviation to give an interval of length $2\lambda\sigma_0$ about the observed probability p_0. Then the tables of areas under the Gaussian probability curve (or the criterion of Tchebycheff) yield a probability p_λ which is said to be the probability that the true value of p lies outside the given interval about p_0. Then Wilson says, in characteristic vein:

"Strictly speaking, the usual statement of probable inference as given above is elliptical. Really the chance that the true probability p lies outside a specified range is either 0 or 1; for p actually lies within that range or does not. It is the observed rate p_0 which has a greater or less chance of lying within a certain interval of the true rate p. If the observer has had the hard luck to have observed a relatively rare event and to have based his inference thereon, he may be fairly wide of the mark."

Wilson goes on to propose an improved type of probable inference, starting from the formula for the true standard deviation in terms of the true probability. By solving the appropriate equation (involving λ) for p, he obtains a different interval not about p_0 but about a slightly displaced point and states: "If the true value of p lies outside this interval, the chance of having such hard luck as to have made an observation so bad as p_0 is less than or equal to P_λ."

This formulation is a well-stated anticipation of the idea of a "confidence interval." This notion, basic to the modern development of statistical inferences, had also been anticipated by A. A. Cournot in his book *De la Theorie des Chances* (1843). It was continued in papers by Working and Hotelling, *J. Am. Stat. Assoc. Suppl.*, 24 (1929), by Hotelling, *Ann. Math. Stat.*, 2 (1931): 360, and in 1932 by Pytkowski, a student of Neyman. The full idea of confidence intervals was then published by Neyman and Pearson—see C. T. Clopper and E. S. Pearson, *Biometrica*, 26(1934):404-13, and J. Neyman, *J. Roy. Stat. Soc.*, 97(1934):558-625 (especially pp. 589-93)—and is now commonly attributed to Neyman and Pearson. E. B. Wilson himself returned to this subject only much later in a 1942 paper entitled "On Confidence Intervals," chiefly in order to observe that confidence intervals had been introduced "for what I take to be nearly the same notion that I was discussing [in 1927]." In 1952 Neyman, on page 222 of his *Lectures and Conferences on Mathematics, Statistics and Probability* (U.S. Department of Agriculture, 1952), suggested that in his 1927 paper E. B. Wilson had indeed had the idea of confidence intervals. Later again, Wilson himself quoted this remark of Neyman and then said (*Proc. Nat. Acad. Sci.* [1964], p. 293), "I would make no such claim." Hence we cannot with confidence estimate the exact extent and influence of Wilson's contribution to the idea of confidence intervals, but we can be sure that his insight did bring him close to this central development of modern statistics.

Wilson, as a result of his early Harvard background, had a long-standing interest in the career of C. S. Peirce. With Margaret Helferty in 1929 he reexamined some data which Peirce had taken in 1873 measuring the time lapse between stimulus and response for an observer who made about 500 responses every day for a period of 24 days. The data were "out-of-control" in the sense that the day-to-day variation was much larger than the within-day variation. The Wilson-Helferty restudy of these data led them (in 1931) to introduce a certain approximation (via a transformation) for the chi-square distribution. These papers have been the starting point for many further statistical researches. The work on approximating chi-square may be Wilson's best-known contribution to statistics—though his controversy with Raymond Pearl about the way to calculate least squares also attracted a great deal of attention.

As on other subjects, Wilson's views on statistics and statisticians were incisive. For example, in a letter to Mac Lane (June 12, 1955) he wrote:

"It is all right to develop the mathematical properties of aggregates, but that is pure mathematics and has to be judged as such. Statistics deals with data and has to be judged as such. The prime duty of the statistician is to see that his data give evidence of being suitable for treatment by a certain kind of mathematics."

ECONOMICS

Wilson's long-time interest in mathematical economics (see various papers in the bibliography) has been well summarized by Paul A. Samuelson. In his Nobel address, reprinted in *Science*, 173(1971):993-94, Samuelson says:

"I was struck by a remark made by an old teacher of mine

at Harvard, Edwin Bidwell Wilson. Wilson was the last student of J. Willard Gibbs' at Yale and had worked creatively in many fields of mathematics and physics; his advanced calculus was a standard text for decades; his was the definitive write-up of Gibbs' lectures on vectors; he wrote one of the earliest texts on aerodynamics; he was a friend of R. A. Fisher and an expert on mathematical statistics and demography; finally, he had become interested early in the work of Pareto and gave lectures in mathematical economics at Harvard. My earlier formulation of the inequality in Eq. 4 owed much to Wilson's lectures on thermodynamics. In particular, I was struck by his statement that the fact that an increase in pressure is accompanied by a decrease in volume is not so much a theorem about a thermodynamic equilibrium system as it is a mathematical theorem about surfaces that are concave from below or about negative definite quadratic forms. Armed with this clue, I set out to make sense of the LeChatelier principle."

THE PROCEEDINGS

At the autumn meeting of the National Academy of Sciences in 1913 a special committee of the Academy recommended the establishment of a journal to be called *Proceedings of the National Academy of Sciences*. The aim was to provide for prompt publication of brief first announcements of discoveries and of the more important contributions to research of members and of those nonmembers whose work appeared to some member to be of particular importance. E. B. Wilson became the first managing editor. In a letter to Mac Lane written shortly before his death, Wilson described the circumstances in these words:

"One question you raised some time back was who should go on with this work of mine when I was through. That I have never answered is not that I have not wondered about it myself.

"Things are very different now from what they were at the start. Then the Academy had few members and no building, no money, practically no staff, and no Research Council. The *Proceedings* seems to have been Hale's idea; Noyes and he were old M.I.T. friends; both were on the Committee to set it up, and Noyes was chosen Chairman of the Board. He was at M.I.T. and naturally wanted somebody nearby as Managing Editor with whom he could work easily. Remember that he thought the *Proceedings* was really to be edited. The first big change came when the Academy decided that it should not be edited. After that there was very little for Noyes and me to do together; we discussed the interpretation to be put on the instructions that were implied by the ANNOUNCEMENT and by the Committee reports and by the discussions in the Committee, which he knew all about—and that was about all, and most of these discussions were when Hale happened to show up at M.I.T.

"When Noyes went west to CalTech, I was left with the *Proceedings*. Pearl, whom I knew well, was made Chairman, but he for some reason never suggested that it would be better to have a Managing Editor in Baltimore—which perhaps was strange in view of his great interest in publications in general, scientific or not. Then when the deal was made with NRC to cooperate in the publication beginning with vol. 7, the *Proceedings* was put under an executive committee of three with me as chairman and Pearl to represent the Academy and Kellogg, the permanent Secretary of NRC, as the third member—and the Editorial Board simply went into eclipse, and so continued for many years.

"I always considered the Home Secretary as my superior officer in Washington—Arthur Day, Fred Wright, and now

Dryden. One thing seems to me to be vital, and that is to keep
the *Proceedings* out of the system of publication of the NRC
and directly under the Council of the Academy through having it attached to the Home Secretary's office."

Wilson was managing editor of the *Proceedings* for fifty
years, from its first issue, dated January 15, 1915, until his
death in December 1964. He served under various chairmen of
the Editorial Board: Linus Pauling when the Editorial
Board was returned to authority in 1950, then Wendell Stanley in 1955 and Saunders Mac Lane in 1960. Under all these
administrations Wilson carried on his managerial responsibilities efficiently, watching each paper for length, for accuracy,
and for the possible inclusion of inappropriate materials (for
example, controversial matters which he felt to be out of place
in a privileged journal such as the *Proceedings*). He was particularly responsible for the invited addresses, which could be
given more than the usual allotment of pages at the discretion
of the managing editor. During much of the time all the secre-
tarial work was done by Wilson and one of his daughters, but
toward the end he had the expert assistance of Mrs. Josephine
Williams as editorial associate; she was located in Washington
at the Academy.

Wilson's annual reports on the *Proceedings* to the Council
of the Academy are models of brevity and precision. He was
always careful to manage and not to make policy, though he
much enjoyed educating his editors on the fruits and failures
of past policy. His actions were careful and impartial, but privately he could be severely critical of shoddy papers or of symposia which did little to advance science. As he wrote to Mac
Lane (November 3, 1964):

"If the Academy wants to be important to government
(not just NRC) it should stage two hot research meetings a
year in Washington—hotter than the Government laboratories

could put up—and no symposia unless it be on problems now most needing solution and why. *At our level* we must not let science down into trivialities. We must spell out the most important work and put out the most important problems by the most important people."

Or again (on September 29, 1964):

"I don't suppose that we should discontinue publishing symposia. There is one kind of symposium which is highly valuable and that is the kind where the best experts in the field discuss and list not past but next steps in the advance of the sciences, for there are more scientists who can solve stated problems than those who can state the problems."

E. B. Wilson's last major project was the preparation of *The History of the Proceedings of the National Academy of Sciences 1914-1963,* published in 1966 in combination with a cumulative index. This full and sparkling report summarizes his lifetime contribution to the communication of scientific research.

THE ACADEMY

E. B. Wilson was elected to membership in the Academy in 1919. Over the years he served the Academy in many ways: on the committee on government relations and science (1929-1938), as chairman of the section of physics (1930-1933), as vice president (1949-1953), as a member of the Council (1953-1956), and as a member of at least four of the annual nominating committees for officers of the Academy. For twenty-five years, 1929-1954, he was chairman of the standing committee on the revision of the Constitution. He early became an expert on the content and meaning of the Constitution and Bylaws of the Academy. It was a rare annual meeting when Wilson did not try to point out clearly and vigorously what was or was not possible according to the current Bylaws. This was not that he believed in restrictive Bylaws. He staunchly defended the central interests of the Academy in the following language (in a letter to Mac Lane, September 29, 1964):

"I have always been astonished at how stupid some Academicians are about things not in their speciality. They want to put rules in the Constitution and Bylaws instead of taking them out as Jewett recommended and trusting themselves and their successors. . . . The early giants—Welch, Walcott, Hale, J. J. Carty, Gano Dunn, and later Frank Jewett, were all trying to so conduct matters that the essential business of the Academy as such should not be overrun by the business of its service agency NRC. So far as I have seen, we have now had a dozen years of just the opposite policy—or at any rate, *practice* which it is now proposed to write into the constitution and Bylaws as policy."

Or again, as in the following letter to Mac Lane, written on Labor Day, 1964, and given complete:

"I did not go to the business meeting of the Academy last April. I was trying to be sure that while in Washington I was doing all I could to gather the local material needed for the history. I went to little at the centennial—the first session (with you), the Convocation, the dinner.

"I have voted against the amendments. In doing so I have referred to the *last four paragraphs* of Frank Jewett's address (Proc. 48, p. 490) stating 'these were carefully thought out under responsibility for action, and therefore are not a priori wishful thinking.' We have in every particular therein specified gone in the past 17 years directly contrary to his recommendations and the present proposals are a step further away from them. It would be far better to propose to remove from the Constitution and Bylaws whatever provisions prevented us from doing as we think best at the present or any future time.

"This may be entirely hopeless and even foolish, but I thought you ought to know.

"I am an experimentalist, not with physical apparatus but with ideas and personnel and behavior. I like to see what works before I am formally committed. On the *Proceedings* the proposers had a complicated referee system which the Academy abolished leaving responsibility up to the members. It has worked pretty well. I do not understand the mania to tie our hands no more than did Jewett. Is it a relic of our doubtless theological origin?"

To summarize, then, Edwin B. Wilson was a man of sharp and incisive mind, able to say clearly and forcefully what he understood. In the perspective of time, his varied original contributions to science appear now in each case to be contributions fitting the natural development of the field of his then current interest, whether it be special relativity theory or the discovery of confidence intervals in statistics. Moreover, his contributions to the effective communication of scientific ideas were outstanding. His books on Vector Analysis, Advanced Calculus, and Aerodynamics and his work on the *Proceedings* were all superb, each in its own way. This breadth of interest does indeed qualify him as a Renaissance man.

MEMBERSHIPS

National Academy of Sciences (elected 1919); Member, Board of Directors of the Bache Fund, 1923-1964; Chairman, Section of Physics, 1930-1933; Vice President, 1949-1953; Member of the Council, 1953-1956

American Statistical Association (President, 1929)

American Academy of Arts and Sciences (President, 1927-1931)

American Philosophical Society (Lewis Prize)

Social Science Research Council (President, 1929-1931)

Royal Statistical Society, London (Honorary Fellow)

American Society for the Control of Cancer (Executive Committee, 1929-1964; 1954 Cancer Award of Massachusetts Division)

American Mathematical Society

Mathematical Society of Benares, India (Honorary Member)

American Association for the Advancement of Science

Phi Beta Kappa

Sigma Xi

Harvard Club of Boston

Econometric Society

American Economic Association

John Simon Guggenheim Foundation (Committee on Selection)

Tobacco Industry Research Committee (Scientific Advisory Board, 1954-1964)

Jackson Memorial Laboratory, Bar Harbor (Board of Directors)

BIBLIOGRAPHY

KEY TO ABBREVIATIONS

Am. J. Cancer = American Journal of Cancer
Am. Math. Monthly = American Mathematical Monthly
Ann. Math. = Annals of Mathematics
Boston Med. Surg. J. = Boston Medical and Surgical Journal
Bull. Am. Math. Soc. = Bulletin of the American Mathematical Society
J. Am. Med. Assoc. = Journal of the American Medical Association
J. Am. Stat. Assoc. = Journal of the American Statistical Association
J. Prev. Med. = Journal of Preventive Medicine
J. Wash. Acad. Sci. = Journal of the Washington Academy of Sciences
Proc. Am. Acad. Arts Sci. = Proceedings of the American Academy of Arts
    and Sciences
Proc. Am. Phil. Soc. = Proceedings of the American Philosophical Society
Proc. Nat. Acad. Sci. = Proceedings of the National Academy of Sciences
Quart. J. Econ. = Quarterly Journal of Economics
Sci. Monthly = Scientific Monthly
Tech. Rev. = Technology Review
Trans. Am. Math. Soc. = Transactions of the American Mathematical
    Society

1900

The decomposition of the general collineation of space into three skew reflections. Trans. Am. Math. Soc., 1:193-96.

1901

Vector Analysis. A textbook for the use of students of mathematics and physics, founded upon the lectures of J. Willard Gibbs. New York, Charles Scribner's Sons (2d ed., 1929). 2d ed. republished (unaltered) by Dover Publications, New York, 1960.

1902

The centenary of the birth of Abel. Bull. Am. Math. Soc., 9:154-56.

1903

Ueber eine von dem Begriff der Länge Unabhängige Definition des Volumens. Jahresbericht der Deutschen Mathematiker-Vereinigung, 12:555-61.

The synthetic treatment of conics at the present time. Analytic projective geometry. Bull. Am. Math. Soc., 9:369-76.

Hydrodynamic action at a distance. Bull. Am. Math. Soc., 10: 139-53.

A generalized conception of area: applications to collineations in the plane. Ann. Math., 5:29-45.

The so-called foundations of geometry. Archiv der Mathematik und Physik, 6(3):104-22.

1904

Projective and metric geometry. Ann. Math., 5:145-50.

The theory of waves. Bull. Am. Math. Soc., 10:305-17.

Spherical geometry. Am. Math. Monthly, 11:1-6, 23-28, 47-51, 75-80, 101-5, 123-28, 151-56. (Seven lectures)

1905

On products in additive fields. In: *Verhandlungen des dritten internationalen Mathematiker-Kongresses,* pp. 202-15. Heidelberg, 1904. Leipzig, Druck und Verlag von B. G. Teubner.

The congress of mathematicians at Heidelberg. Bull. Am. Math. Soc., 11:191-217, 247-63.

The Breslau meeting of the Deutsche Mathematiker-Vereinigung. Bull. Am. Math. Soc., 11:263-68.

Sur le groupe qui laisse invariante l'aire gauche. Nouvelles Annales de Mathématiques, 5(4):163-70.

1906

Note on integrating factors. Ann. Math., 7:155-60.

1907

On divergence and curl. American Journal of Science, 23:214-20.

Involutory transformations in the projective group and its subgroups. Ann. Math., 8:77-86.

The revolution of a dark particle about a luminous center. Ann. Math., 8:135-48.

Oblique reflections and unimodular strains. Trans. Am. Math. Soc., 8:270-98.

1908

The number of types of collineations. Jahresbericht der Deutschen Mathematiker-Vereinigung, 17:341-44.

Logic and continuum. Bull. Am. Math. Soc., 14:432-43.

Note on statistical mechanics. Bull. Am. Math. Soc., 15:107-15.

The equilibrium of a heavy homogeneous chain in a uniformly rotating plane. Ann. Math., 9:99-115.

On the differential equations of the equilibrium of an inextensible string. Trans. Am. Math. Soc., 9:425-39.

On the theory of double products and strains in hyperspace. Transactions of the Connecticut Academy of Arts and Sciences, 14:1-57.

On the principle of relativity. Philosophical Magazine, 16:419-22, 6th series.

1909

Notations rationnelles pour le système vectorielle. L'Enseignement mathématique, 11:211.

Applications of probability to mechanics. Ann. Math., 10:129-48.

Thermodynamic analogies for a simple dynamical system. Ann. Math., 10:149-66.

Review. Economics: Fisher on capital, income and the rate of interest. Bull. Am. Math. Soc., 15:169-86.

1910

A curious mechanical paradox. Am. Math. Monthly, 17:132-35.

The unification of vectorial notations. Bull. Am. Math. Soc., 16:415-36.

1911

Notations rationnelles pour le système vectorielle. L'Enseignement mathématique, 13:391-93.

1912

Advanced Calculus. A text upon select parts of differential calculus, differential equations, integral calculus, theory of functions, with numerous exercises. Boston, Ginn and Company. Republished (unaltered) by Dover Publications, 1959.

Review. Mathematical economics: Pareto's *Manuel d'Economie politique.* Bull. Am. Math. Soc., 18:462-74.

Some mathematical aspects of relativity. Proc. Am. Acad. Arts Sci., 48:389-507.

With Gilbert N. Lewis. The space-time manifold of relativity. The non-Euclidian geometry of mechanics and electromagnetics. Proc. Am. Acad. Arts Sci., 48:387-507.

1913

The unification of vectorial notations. Bull. Am. Math. Soc., 19:524-30.

1914

Review. Einstein and Grossman on general relativity. Bull. Am. Math. Soc., 20:273.

Infinite regions in geometry. Bull. Am. Math. Soc., 21:73-82.

On the theory of the rectilinear oscillator. Proc. Am. Acad. Arts Sci., 50:107-28.

1915

The Ziwet-Field notations in plane kinematics. Bull. Am. Math. Soc., 21:378. (A)

Discussion relating to Ziwet and Field vector notations in kinematics. Am. Math. Monthly, 22:121-24.

Linear momentum, kinetic energy, and angular momentum. Am. Math. Monthly, 22:187-93.

Theory of an airplane encountering gusts. Report No. 1 in: *First Annual Report of the National Advisory Committee for Aeronautics.* Washington, U.S. Govt. Print. Off.

Elementary mechanics. Science, 42:528-30.

1916

Ricci's absolute calculus and its applications to the theory of surfaces. Bull. Am. Math. Soc., 22:271. (A)

Changing surface to volume integrals. Bull. Am. Math. Soc., 22:336-37.

Critical spreads for flat disks in a normal wind: theory. Bull. Am. Math. Soc., 22:378.

A mathematical table that contains chiefly zeros. Bull. Am. Math. Soc., 22:378-79.

With C. L. E. Moore. A general theory of surfaces. Proc. Nat. Acad. Sci., 2:273-78.

Theory of an airplane encountering gusts. Proc. Nat. Acad. Sci., 2:294-97.

With C. L. E. Moore. Differential geometry of two dimensional surfaces in hyperspace. Proc. Am. Acad. Arts Sci., 52:270-368.

On notational equivalence. Bull. Am. Math. Soc., 23:169-72.

Space-time manifold of relativity: the geometric potential. J. Wash. Acad. Sci., 6:665-69.

1917

Classification of real strains in hyperspace. Bull. Am. Math. Soc., 23:442. (A)

Note on multiple algebra: the reduction of real dyadics and the classification of real homogeneous strains. J. Wash. Acad. Sci., 7:173-77.

Symposium on aëronautics. Theory of an aëroplane encountering gusts. II. Proc. Am. Phil. Soc., 56:212-48.

Generalized coordinates, relativity and gravitation. Astrophysical Journal, 45:244-53.

The mathematics of aerodynamics. Am. Math. Monthly, 25:292-97.

1919

Note on rotations in hyperspace. J. Wash. Acad. Sci., 9:25-28.

Radiationless orbits. Proc. Nat. Acad. Sci., 5:588-91.

1920

The variation of yawing moment due to rolling. Report No. 26 in: *Fourth Annual Report of the National Advisory Committee for Aeronautics, 1918.* Washington, U.S. Govt. Print. Off.

Theory of an aeroplane encountering gusts, III. Report No.

27 in: *Fourth Annual Report of the National Advisory Committee for Aeronautics, 1918*. Washington, U.S. Govt. Print. Off.

Aeronautics. New York, John Wiley & Sons, Inc. vii + 265 pp. (Rewritten and enlarged as *Introduction to Aeronautical Dynamics*, by Manfred Rauscher. New York, John Wiley & Sons, Inc., 1953.)

Space, time and gravitation. Sci. Monthly, 10:217-35.

1923

Statistics and the doctor. Boston Med. Surg. J., 189:804-6.

First and second laws of error. J. Am. Stat. Assoc., 18:841-51.

The statistical significance of experimental data. Science, 58: 93-100.

Electric conduction: Hall's theory and Perkins' phenomenon. Proc. Nat. Acad. Sci., 9:135-40.

1924

Dynamic stability as affected by the longitudinal moment of inertia. Report No. 172 in: *Ninth Annual Report of the National Advisory Committee for Aeronautics, 1923, Including Technical Reports 159-185*. Washington, U.S. Govt. Print. Off.

The development of a frequency function and some comments on curve fitting. Proc. Nat. Acad. Sci., 10:79-84.

With Willem J. Luyten. A statistical discussion of sets of precise astronomical measurements: parallaxes. Proc. Nat. Acad. Sci., 10:129-32.

With Ewald Tomanek. Is pneumonia increasing? Proc. Nat. Acad. Sci., 10:161-66.

With Willem J. Luyten. A statistical discussion of sets of precise astronomical measurements. II: Proper motions. Proc. Nat. Acad. Sci., 10:228-31.

Coulomb's law and the hydrogen spectrum. Proc. Nat. Acad. Sci., 10:346-48.

With Willem J. Luyten. A statistical discussion of sets of precise astronomical measurements. III: Masses of the stars. Proc. Nat. Acad. Sci., 10:394-98.

With Willem J. Luyten. A statistical discussion of sets of precise astronomical measurements. IV: The mass-ratio in binaries. Proc. Nat. Acad. Sci., 10:433-35.

Some statistical aspects of pneumonia. American Journal of Public Health, 14:931-34.

With Ewald Tomanek. Pneumonia in Pittsburgh. Proc. Am. Phil. Soc., 63:279-316.

1925

The population of Canada. Science, 41:87-89.

With W. J. Luyten. The frequency distribution on apparent magnitude of the non-Magellanic O-type stars. Proc. Nat. Acad. Sci., 11:133-37.

With Willem J. Luyten. The population of New York City and its environs. Proc. Nat. Acad. Sci., 11:137-43.

On the Boltzmann equation $\rho = \rho_o \exp (-w/kt)$. Proc. Nat. Acad. Sci., 11:264-66.

With Willem J. Luyten. The frequency distribution of some measured parallaxes and of the parallaxes themselves. Proc. Nat. Acad. Sci., 11:270-74.

The logistic or autocatalytic grid. Proc. Nat. Acad. Sci., 11:451-56.

Certain statistical constants for cancer. Appendix B, pp. 110-18 in: *The Course of Cancer Mortality in the Ten Original Registration States for the Twenty-One Year Period, 1900-1920*, by J. W. Schereschewsky. Public Health Bulletin No. 155, U.S. Public Health Service.

1926

Statistical inference. Science, 43:289-96.

Empiricism and rationalism. Science, 44:47-57.

With Julia Deming, M.D. Statistical comparison of psychiatric diagnosis in some Massachusetts state hospitals during 1925 and 1926. Bulletin of the Massachusetts Department of Mental Diseases, 11:6-19.

With C. R. Doering. The Elder Peirce's. Proc. Nat. Acad. Sci., 12:424-32.

1927

The public health significance of vital statistics. Nation's Health, 9:23.

The scientist and the psychiatrist. American Journal of Psychiatry, 7:23-26.

On the proof of Sheppard's corrections. Proc. Nat. Acad. Sci., 13:151-56.

Probable inference, the law of succession, and statistical inference. J. Am. Stat. Assoc., 22:209-12.

Some recent speculations on the nature of light. Science, 45: 265-71.

What is statistics? Science, 45:581-87.

Tuberculosis in Boston and elsewhere. Boston Med. Surg. J., 196:665-67.

1928

Mendelian inheritance with assortive mating. Proc. Nat. Acad. Sci., 14:137-40.

On hierarchical correlation systems. Proc. Nat. Acad. Sci., 14: 283-92.

The use and abuse of statistics. Tech. Rev., 30:347-49.

Too little mathematics—and too much. Science, 47:52-59.

Gentle southwest winds. Science, 48:174-76.

Physics and medicine. Tech. Rep., 31:91-92.

A problem in Keynes' treatise on probability. In: *Proceedings of the International Mathematical Congress,* ed. by J. C. Fields, pp. 789-93. Toronto, 1924. Toronto, University of Toronto Press.

1929

Probable error of correlation results. J. Am. Stat. Assoc., 24:90-93. (Supplement)

Social science research and the state university. National Association of State Universities Transactions and Proceedings, 27:193-98.

With Margaret M. Hilferty. Note on C. S. Peirce's experimental discussion of the law of errors. Proc. Nat. Acad. Sci., 15: 120-25.

Comment on Professor Spearman's note. Journal of Educational Psychology, 20:217-23.

1930

Morbidity and the association of morbid conditions. J. Prev. Med., 4:27-38.

Mathematics and statistics. Sci. Monthly, 30:294-300.

1931

Correlation and association. J. Am. Stat. Assoc., 26:250-57. (Supplement)

With M. M. Hilferty and H. C. Maher. Goodness of fit. J. Am. Stat. Assoc., 26:443-48.

With Margaret M. Hilferty. The distribution of chi-square. Proc. Nat. Acad. Sci., 17:684-88.

Reminiscences of Gibbs by a student and colleague. Sci. Monthly, 32:210-27.

1932

With Hans Zinsser. Bacterial dissociation and a theory of the rise and decline of epidemic waves. J. Prev. Med., 6:497-514.

With H. C. Maher. Cancer and tuberculosis with some comments on cancer and other diseases. Am. J. Cancer, 16:227-50.

The value of statistical studies of the cancer problem. Am. J. Cancer, 16:1230-37.

What is a profession? Journal of Business of the University of Chicago, 5:3-7.

A correlation curiosity. Science, 76:515-16.

1933

Some immediate objectives in sociology. Sociologus, 9:14-16.

On the invariance of general intelligence. Proc. Nat. Acad. Sci., 19:768-72.

Transformations preserving the tetrad equations. Proc. Nat. Acad. Sci., 19:882-84.

On overlap. Proc. Nat. Acad. Sci., 19:1039-44.

With R. R. Puffer. Least squares and laws of population growth. Proc. Am. Acad. Arts Sci., 68:285-382.

1934

Boole's challenge problem. J. Am. Stat. Assoc., 29:301-4.

With Jane Worcester. The resolution of four tests. Proc. Nat. Acad. Sci., 20:189-92.

On resolution into generals and specifics. Proc. Nat. Acad. Sci., 20:193-96.

Periodogram of American business activity. Quart. J. Econ., 48:375-417.

Mathematics of growth. Cold Spring Harbor Symposia on Quantitative Biology, 2:199-202.

Are there periods in American business activity? Science, 80:193-99.

1935

Heights and weights of 275 public school girls for consecutive ages 7 to 16 years, inclusive. Proc. Nat. Acad. Sci., 21:633-34.

With M. M. Hilferty. Size of completed families. J. Am. Stat. Assoc., 30:577-80.

Generalization of Pareto's demand theorem. Quart. J. Econ., 49:715-17.

With F. Talbot and J. Worcester. Standards of basal metabolism of girls (new data) and their use in clinical practice. Journal of Pedagogy, 7:655-61.

What is proof? Science, 81:371-73.

1936

With M. M. Hilferty. On the explosiveness and destructiveness of the 1918 epidemic. Proc. Nat. Acad. Sci., 22:120-22.

1937

With F. B. Talbot and Jane Worcester. Basal metabolism of girls; physiologic background and application of standards. American Journal of Diseases of Children, 53:273-347.

1938

How to study the social aspects of the depression. J. Am. Med. Assoc., 33:505-12.

The standard deviation of sampling for life expectancy. J. Am. Med. Assoc., 33:705-8.

1939

With Jane Worcester. The resolution of tests into two general factors. Proc. Nat. Acad. Sci., 25:20-25.

With Jane Worcester. The resolution of six tests into three general factors. Proc. Nat. Acad. Sci., 25:73-77.

With Jane Worcester. Team tests for generals and specifics. Proc. Nat. Acad. Sci., 25:358-64.

With Constance Bennett, Margaret Allen, and Jane Worcester. Measles and scarlet fever in Providence, R. I., 1929-34 with respect to age and size of family. Proc. Am. Phil. Soc., 80:357-476.

Pareto versus Marshall. Quart. J. Econ., 53:645-50.

With J. Worcester. Note on factor analysis. Psychometrika, 4:133-48.

1940

Methodology in the natural and the social sciences. American Journal of Sociology, 45:655-68.

Cancer among the causes of death. National Bulletin of the American Society for the Control of Cancer, 22:3-5.

The sampling error of the median. Science, 92:58-59.

What is social science? Science, 92:157-62.

With L. J. Henderson and C. Brinton. Symposium on social progress. Proc. Am. Acad. Arts Sci., 73:457-72.

The place of statistics in studies of child development. Child
Development, 11:319-25.

1941

The controlled experiment and the four-fold table. Science,
93:557-60.
With Jane Worcester. Contact with measles. Proc. Nat. Acad.
Sci., 27:7-13.
With Jane Worcester. Progressive immunization. Proc. Nat.
Acad. Sci., 27:129-35.
With M. Burke. Statistical situation in cancer. Bulletin of
the American Society for the Control of Cancer, 23:4-6.

1942

On confidence intervals. Proc. Nat. Acad. Sci., 28:88-93.
On contingency tables. Proc. Nat. Acad. Sci., 28:94-100.
With Jane Worcester. Note on the *t*-test. Proc. Nat. Acad.
Sci., 28:297-301.
With Mary H. Burke. The epidemic curve. Proc. Nat. Acad.
Sci., 28:361-67.
With Jane Worcester. Contingency tables. Proc. Nat. Acad.
Sci., 28:378-84.
With Jane Worcester. The association of three attributes. Proc.
Nat. Acad. Sci., 28:384-90.
Norms of growth. Science, 95:112-13.

1943

With Mary Burke. The epidemic curve, II. Proc. Nat. Acad.
Sci., 29:43-48.
With Jane Worcester. The determination of L.D.50 and its
sampling error in bio-assay. Proc. Nat. Acad. Sci., 29:79-85.
With Jane Worcester. The determination of L.D.50 and its
sampling error in bio-assay, II. Proc. Nat. Acad. Sci., 29:
114-20.

With Jane Worcester. Bio-assay on a general curve. Proc. Nat. Acad. Sci., 29:150-54.

With Jane Worcester. A table determining L.D.50 or the fifty per cent endpoint. Proc. Nat. Acad. Sci., 29:207-12.

With Jane Worcester. The determination of L.D.50 and its sampling error in bio-assay, III. Proc. Nat. Acad. Sci., 25: 257-62.

Statistics in determination of L.D.50 point bio-assay. Bulletin of the New England Medical Center, 5:157-59.

1944

Note on the *t*-test. Am. Math. Monthly, 51:563-66.

With Jane Worcester. A second approximation to Soper's epidemic curve. Proc. Nat. Acad. Sci., 30:37-44.

With Jane Worcester. The epidemic curve with no accession of susceptibles. Proc. Nat. Acad. Sci., 30:264-69.

With Jane Worcester. Note on stability of incidence of the "common cold." Science, 99:468-69.

1945

Obituary. George David Birkhoff. Science, 102:578-80.

With Jane Worcester. The law of mass action in epidemiology. Proc. Nat. Acad. Sci., 31:24-34.

A letter from Lord Rayleigh to J. Willard Gibbs and his reply. Proc. Nat. Acad. Sci., 31:34-38.

With Jane Worcester. The law of mass action in epidemiology, II. Proc. Nat. Acad. Sci., 31:109-16.

With Jane Worcester. The variation of infectivity. Proc. Nat. Acad. Sci., 31:142-47.

Vital statistics of the National Academy of Sciences. Proc. Nat. Acad. Sci., 31:200-3.

With Jane Worcester. The variation of infectivity, II. Proc. Nat. Acad. Sci., 31:203-8.

Willard Gibbs on soaring flight. Proc. Nat. Acad. Sci., 31:233-35.

With Jane Worcester. Damping of epidemic waves. Proc. Nat. Acad. Sci., 31:294-98.

With Jane Worcester. The spread of an epidemic. Proc. Nat. Acad. Sci., 31:327-33.

With Olive M. Lombard. Cycles in measles and chicken pox. Proc. Nat. Acad. Sci., 31:367-71.

1946

Contributions to public health statistics. Public Health, 59: 125-28. (Public Health-Society of Medical Officers of Health, Tavistock House, Tavistock Square, London W.C.1)

1947

The spread of measles in the family. Proc. Nat. Acad. Sci., 33:68-72.

1950

National Academy of Sciences: minutes of the meeting for organization, April, 1863. Proc. Nat. Acad. Sci., 36:277-92.

1951

Note on association of attributes. Proc. Nat. Acad. Sci., 37:696-704.

1952

Some observations on the error of bio-assay. Proc. Nat. Acad. Sci., 38:97-99.

Barnard's CSM test of significance. Proc. Nat. Acad. Sci., 38: 899-905.

1953

Significance levels for a skew distribution. Proc. Nat. Acad. Sci., 39:537-46.

Vital statistics of our foreign associates. Proc. Nat. Acad. Sci., 39:1295-98.

1957

With Mary H. Burke. Some statistical observations on a cooperative study of human pulmonary pathology. Proc. Nat. Acad. Sci., 43:1073-78.

1959

With Mary H. Burke. Some statistical observations on a cooperative study of human pulmonary pathology, II. Proc. Nat. Acad. Sci., 45:389-93.

1960

With Mary H. Burke. Some statistical observations on a cooperative study of human pulmonary pathology, III. Proc. Nat. Acad. Sci., 46:561-66.

1961

The last unpublished notes of J. Willard Gibbs. Proc. Am. Phil. Soc., 105:545-58.

1962

Note on the epidemiology of peptic ulcer. Proc. Nat. Acad. Sci., 48:1924-27.

1963

A critical look at statistical epidemiology. Cancer, 16:510-15.

1964

Comparative experiment and observed association. Proc. Nat. Acad. Sci., 51:288-93.
Comparative experiment and observed association, II. Proc.

Nat. Acad. Sci., 51:539-41. (Contains many footnotes relating to the history of science.)

Tobacco smoking and longevity.   Proc. Nat. Acad. Sci., 52:199-200.

1966

History of the Proceedings of the National Academy of Sciences 1914-1963. (Supplemented by an author index to Volumes 1-50.) Washington, D.C., National Academy of Sciences. v-vii + 296 pp.

S. Winstein

SAUL WINSTEIN

October 8, 1912–November 23, 1969

BY WILLIAM G. YOUNG AND
DONALD J. CRAM

SAUL WINSTEIN was born in Montreal, Canada, October 8, 1912, the son of Louis and Anne Winstein. His death came suddenly at his home in West Los Angeles on November 23, 1969, at the age of fifty-seven, at the height of his career. He leaves his wife, Sylvia, whom he married on September 3, 1937; a son, Bruce, a graduate student at the California Institute of Technology; and a daughter, Carolee, a student at UCLA. Dr. Winstein came to the United States in 1923 and became a naturalized citizen in 1929.

He graduated from Jefferson High School in Los Angeles in 1930, after which he received an A.B. degree in 1934 from the University of California at Los Angeles, followed by an M.A. degree in 1935 from the same institution. He received his Ph.D. degree in 1938 from the California Institute of Technology. After a postdoctoral fellowship at Cal-Tech, he spent 1939-1940 as a National Research Fellow at Harvard University, where he was associated with Professor Paul Bartlett. After a year as Instructor at the Illinois Institute of Technology in 1940-1941, he returned to his alma mater, UCLA, as an Instructor in 1941-1942, Assistant Professor from 1942 to 1945, Associate Professor from 1945 to 1947, and Professor from 1947 to 1969.

Dr. Winstein began his career after the notion of the chemical bond had been introduced by G. N. Lewis, and while this concept was being applied and elaborated by Linus Pauling and others. As an undergraduate he was introduced to research in physical organic chemistry by William G. Young. This association produced eight publications by the time Saul Winstein had his master's degree. His love of the field of physical organic chemistry deepened and broadened while he worked on the bromonium ion, and on silver and mercury olefin complexes with Howard Lucas for his doctorate. He often remarked in later years how as a young man he had studied and admired the research of Louis Hammett and Hans Meerwein. Clearly, many of the seeds of physical organic chemistry planted by these and other pioneers were carefully nurtured by Saul Winstein, and the species produced underwent mutations and selection under his critical care.

His life spanned what may turn out to be the maturing period for physical organic chemistry. He lived to see neighboring group involvement in cation formation grow from an idea, to a theory, to an integral part of the science, repeated over and over again in new structural contexts. His career was engaged centrally with research on this phenomenon. His research developed from pi-electrons of carbon-carbon double bonds as neighboring groups in his undergraduate research, to bromine as neighboring group in his graduate and postdoctoral work, and to methoxyl, acetoxyl, acetamido, pi-carbon, and sigma-bound carbon or hydrogen as neighboring groups during his middle years. This central theme matured in the form of the nonclassical cation, and found its most elegant expression in his concept and exemplification of homoconjugation and homoaromaticity. Although highly profitable excursions were undertaken into medium effects, radical reaction mechanisms, organometallic reaction mechanisms, ion-pair behavior, complex organic syntheses, and mechanisms of simple substitution and elimination reactions, throughout his scientific career he came back time and again to neighboring group participation in solvolytic reactions. From a program of research whose experiments were conceived on the basis of a superb central idea flowed a wealth of new molecular rearrangements, new stereochemical concepts, and new mechanistic insights. New instruments as they developed were put to work elucidating structures of compounds and of high-energy reaction intermediates alike, and were also used as kinetic probes. Molecular orbital theory served as a guide at many points. However, the new instruments and theory never were more than handmaidens to the major theme of organic reaction mechanisms and reaction intermediates.

Professor Winstein's specific discoveries involved compounds and intermediates of considerable structural beauty. The structures of the compounds shown on page 324 provide graphic testimony to his thorough command of synthetic methods of organic chemistry. The structures of the reaction intermediates shown on page 325 summarize the fruits of his balanced application of the techniques of kinetics, stereochemistry, radioactive labels, spectra, molecular orbital calculations, and tailor-made starting materials to the difficult problem of elucidating the structure of often fleeting high-energy species.

As Dr. Winstein's career unfolded, his research results started whole trends which can be identified with vast bibliographies involving many distinguished investigators the world over. His research created a school of thought and investigation that reached far past his personal contacts. Many terms and phrases which highlighted the discovery and elaboration of new phenomena or concepts have become so common that their origins are unknown to the younger generation of investi-

STRUCTURES OF ORGANIC COMPOUNDS

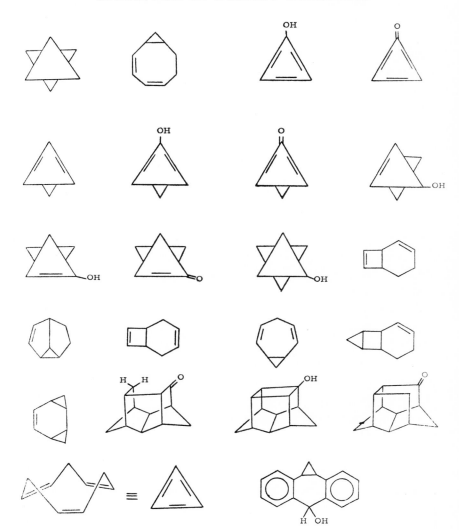

STRUCTURES OF REACTION INTERMEDIATES

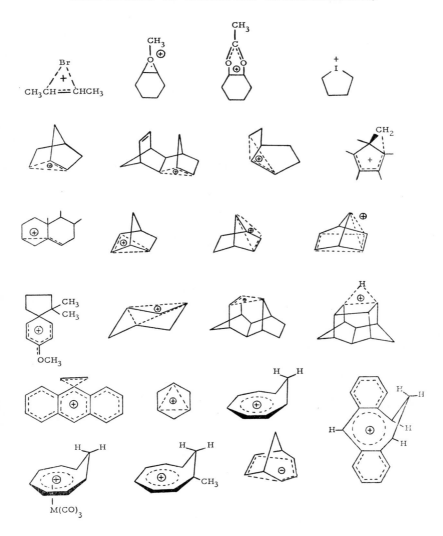

gators. Textbooks now abound with such phrases of his as "neighboring group participation," "solvent participation," "internal return," "anchimeric assistance," "intimate ion pair," "ion-pair return," "bridged ions," "nonclassical ions," and "homoaromaticity."

In the area of ion pairs and salt effects in organic chemistry, he again led the way. He was the first to appreciate the importance of the distinction between ionization and dissociation, and to recognize the difference in behavior of intimate and solvent-separated ion pairs in ion-pair reorganization reactions in organic chemistry.

Recognition of Saul Winstein's research accomplishments came in many forms. He was a principal speaker at symposia held in almost every country that has a research program of any size in organic chemistry. His lectures took him to Great Britain, Ireland, Canada, Japan, Germany, Italy, Israel, The Netherlands, Australia, France, Rumania, Russia, Czechoslovakia, and Venezuela. His more formal honors are as follows: ACS Award in Pure Chemistry, 1948; election to the National Academy of Sciences, 1955; Dickson Achievement Award as UCLA Alumnus, 1958; Richards Medal of the ACS, 1962; Docteur Honoris Causa degree from the University of Montpellier, France, 1962; California Museum of Science and Industry's California Scientist of the Year Award, 1962; election to the American Academy of Arts and Sciences, 1966; McCoy Award, 1966; Alumni Distinguished Service Award of the California Institute of Technology, 1966; ACS Norris Award in Physical Organic Chemistry, 1967; Franklin Memorial Award for Outstanding Contributions to Chemistry, 1968; and the National Medal of Science awarded posthumously in 1971. Had he lived a few more years, he undoubtedly would have received the highest awards the world has to offer a scientist.

Professor Winstein's impact as a teacher was no less impressive. A total of 72 students obtained their Ph.D. degrees under his supervision, and 86 postdoctoral fellows came from all parts of the world to collaborate with him. Of these, about 100 have joined the academic profession, and many are now noted investigators and teachers.

At the beginning, Saul Winstein taught the cultural course in chemistry at UCLA. At one time or another he taught almost every organic course offered there. His pedagogical impact was greatest perhaps in his advanced courses and contributions to seminars. Here his desire to "understand everything thoroughly" led him into cross-examinations of research ideas and results, which at one and the same time set standards and showed what can be known from the results of an experiment. His delivery of a seminar to the Thursday-night group at UCLA became an unforgettable experience for many students, colleagues, and investigators in physical organic chemistry from all parts of the world. His incisive insistence on clarity and his enthusiastic criticism were tempered as he grew older by perspective and, in instances, even by gentleness. What made his forthrightness always admirable was his visible interest in, and love of, the science, as well as his devotion to the idea of being correct. These qualities always enriched his questions and comments. He was a merciless worker who spent most of his daylight hours in personal contact with his co-workers. His long evenings were devoted to reading and writing. His outstanding qualities as a teacher were recognized by his being one of the first recipients of the Distinguished Teaching Award at UCLA. He was honored for his scholarship at the same institution by being elected Faculty Research Lecturer for 1955.

Professor Winstein contributed to the organizational aspects of his profession at several levels. He served for many years on the Editorial Board of the *Journal of the American Chemical*

Society, and was a charter member of the Editorial Board of the *International Journal of Chemical Kinetics.* He was also a member of the Honorary Editorial Advisory Board of *Tetrahedron.* He served on numerous committees of the Academic Senate of UCLA, and as faculty representative on the Executive Committee of the Alumni Association. In connection with the UCLA Fiftieth Anniversary celebration, he organized a symposium in physical organic chemistry dedicated to his first research supervisor, Professor William G. Young. His loyalty to the people, ideas, and institutions that contributed to his development was manifest.

In addition to his work with the alumni, he was active with other prominent members of the community in organizations such as the UCLA Art Council and Friends of Music. Irving S. Bengelsdorf, noted Los Angeles *Times* science writer, said of him: "Although single-mindedly devoted to science in general and chemistry in particular, Dr. Winstein was no ivory-tower recluse. He had an amazing ability to separate his professional world from his private life. Once out of the laboratory he loved to dance and entertain."

The noted author, Irving Stone, said of Saul Winstein at the memorial service: "I think this was a fortunate man, a man who realized his dream with nothing to go on but brains, character, integrity and self-discipline. . . . On three simple terms, fulfillment, a gentle man, and a man who gave himself both to love of his family and friends, and to his work, I can say how truly wonderful that he was born, that he grew up among us, that we had him for our co-worker and for our friend."

Dr. R. K. Lustgarten, a recent postdoctoral fellow of Saul Winstein, said of him: "My stay at UCLA probably represents as exciting a time as I will ever spend in chemistry, and a good part of the excitement came from simply being around Saul

Winstein. In my research report for Winstein, I included an epigram from the poet Cummings: 'Listen, there's a hell of a good universe next door—let's go!' Later, I reflected that this sentiment was superfluous—he'd known it all the time."

One cannot be a colleague of someone as dynamic as Saul Winstein for scores of years without gaining some knowledge of his character. Above all he was single-minded in all his enterprises. Whatever he did, he did intensely and effectively. He rejected sloppy reasoning, would not tolerate poorly designed undertakings, and grew restless when faced with ambiguity, arbitrary decisions, or amorphous arguments. He applied the same kind of reasoning and intensity to learning a new field of chemistry as to learning how to dance, and he applied the same standards of excellence to each endeavor. He dealt with matters either thoroughly or not at all. He applied his high standards to himself and those around him without discrimination. He was a tenacious competitor and was devoted to what his experiments and reasoning told him was correct. He never understood how others could be anything but reasonable. He lived as a real man in a real world on which he left a real impact.

BIBLIOGRAPHY

KEY TO ABBREVIATIONS

Chem. Ind. = Chemistry and Industry
J. Am. Chem. Soc. = Journal of the American Chemical Society
J. Org. Chem. = Journal of Organic Chemistry
Proc. Chem. Soc. = Proceedings of the Chemical Society

1933

With W. G. Young and A. N. Prater. The preparation of crotylmagnesium bromide. The effect of solvents on the yield of crotyl and allylmagnesium bromides. J. Am. Chem. Soc., 55:4908-11.

1935

With W. G. Young. The isolation of crotyl and methylvinylcarbinyl bromides. J. Am. Chem. Soc., 57:2013.

1936

With W. G. Young. The dibromide method of analysis of butene mixtures. J. Am. Chem. Soc., 58:102-4.
With W. G. Young. Allylic rearrangements. I. Crotyl and methylvinylcarbinyl bromides. J. Am. Chem. Soc., 58:104-7.
With W. G. Young and A. N. Prater. Allylic rearrangements. II. Crotyl and methylvinylcarbinyl-magnesium bromides. J. Am. Chem. Soc., 58:289-91.
With W. G. Young. Allylic rearrangements. III. The action of zinc on crotyl and methylvinylcarbinyl bromides. J. Am. Chem. Soc., 58:441-43.

1937

With H. J. Lucas. The rate of hydration of trans-crotonaldehyde. The equilibrium between trans-crotonaldehyde and aldol in dilute aqueous solution. J. Am. Chem. Soc., 59:1461-65.
With W. G. Young, J. F. Lane, and A. Loshakoff. Effect of solvent and metal on the coupling reaction of butenyl bromides. J. Am. Chem. Soc., 59:2441-43.

1938

With H. J. Lucas. The coordination of silver ion with unsaturated compounds. J. Am. Chem. Soc., 60:836-47.

1939

With H. J. Lucas. Retention of configuration in the reaction of the 3-bromo-2-butanols with hydrogen bromide. J. Am. Chem. Soc., 61:1576-81.

With H. J. Lucas. The reaction steps in the conversion of 2,3-diacetoxybutane to 2,3-dibromobutane. J. Am. Chem. Soc., 61:1581-84.

The reduction of α-bromocyclohexanone with aluminum isoproxide. J. Am. Chem. Soc., 61:1610.

The solvolysis of t-butyl chloride. Solvolytic reactions and the Walden inversion. J. Am. Chem. Soc., 61:1635-40.

With D. Pressman and W. G. Young. A mechanism for the formation of butenes from 2,3-dibromobutanes by the action of iodide ion. J. Am. Chem. Soc., 61:1645-47.

With H. J. Lucas. The loss of optical activity in the reaction of the optically active *erythro-* and *threo-*3-bromo-2-butanols with hydrobromic acid. J. Am. Chem. Soc., 61:2845-48.

With H. J. Lucas and F. R. Hepner. The coordination complexes of mercuric ion with cyclohexene. J. Am. Chem. Soc., 61:3102-6.

1940

With R. E. Wood. The dielectric constants of some pairs of diastereomers. J. Am. Chem. Soc., 62:548-51.

1942

With W. G. Young and J. D. Roberts. Allylic rearrangements. XIII. Kinetics and mechanism of conversion of butenyl chlorides to acetates and ethers. J. Am. Chem. Soc., 64:2157-64.

With R. E. Buckles. The role of neighboring groups in replacement reactions. I. Retention of configuration in the reaction of some dihalides and acetoxyhalides with silver acetate. J. Am. Chem. Soc., 64:2780-86.

With R. E. Buckles. The role of neighboring groups in replacement reactions. II. The effects of small amounts of water on the reaction of silver acetate in acetic acid with some butene and cyclohexene derivatives. J. Am. Chem. Soc., 64:2787-90.

The role of neighboring groups in replacement reactions. III. Retention of configuration in the reaction of the 3-bromo-2-butanols with phosphorus tribromide. J. Am. Chem. Soc., 64:2791-92.

The role of neighboring groups in replacement reactions. IV. The identity of various preparations of 1,2-dibromocyclohexane. J. Am. Chem. Soc., 64:2792-95.

With H. V. Hess and R. E. Buckles. The role of neighboring groups in replacement reactions. V. The effect of the neighboring acetoxy group on the course of replacement of the tosylate group of *trans*-2-acetoxycyclohexl *p*-toluenesulfonate. J. Am. Chem. Soc., 64:2796-2801.

1943

With R. E. Buckles. The role of neighboring groups in replacement reactions. VI. Cyclohexene ethyl orthoacetate. J. Am. Chem. Soc., 65:613-18.

With R. B. Henderson. The role of neighboring groups in replacement reactions. VII. The methoxyl group. J. Am. Chem. Soc., 65:2196-2200.

1946

With Dexter Seymour. The role of neighboring groups in replacement reactions. VIII. The reaction of stilbene dichlorides with silver acetate. J. Am. Chem. Soc., 68:119-22.

With Ernest Grunwald. The role of neighboring groups in replacement reactions. IX. Neighboring groups and reactivity. J. Am. Chem. Soc., 68:536.

With T. L. Jacobs, J. W. Ralls, J. H. Robson, R. B. Henderson, R. I. Akawie, W. H. Florsheim, Dexter Seymour, and C. A. Seil. Substituted α-dialkylaminoalkyl-1-naphthalenemethanols. I. Aminoketone method. J. Org. Chem., 11:21-26.

With T. L. Jacobs, J. W. Ralls, and J. H. Robson. Substituted α-dialkylaminoalkyl-1-naphthalenemethanols. II. 1-halonaphthalenes in the Friedel and Crafts reaction. J. Org. Chem., 11: 27-33.

With T. L. Jacobs, R. B. Henderson, and W. H. Florsheim. Substituted α-dialkylaminoalkyl-1-naphthalenemethanols. III. Reduction of substituted naphthyl halomethyl ketones to halohydrins, derived aminoalcohols. J. Org. Chem., 11:150-56.

With T. L. Jacobs, R. B. Henderson, J. H. Robson, and B. Day. Substituted α-dialkylaminoalkyl-1-naphthalenemethanols. IV. Substituted α-naphthylethylene oxides and derived aminoalcohols. J. Org. Chem., 11:157-62.

With R. F. Brown, T. L. Jacobs, E. F. Levy, H. R. Moss, and M. L. Ott. Substituted α-dialkylaminoalkyl-1-naphthalenemethanols. V. The preparation of some α-dialkylaminomethyl-2-chloro- and bromo-1-naphthalene-methanols. J. Org. Chem., 11:163-69.

With T. L. Jacobs, D. Seymour, and G. B. Linden. Substituted α-dialkylaminoalkyl-1-naphthalenemethanols. VI. Some Mannich ketones and derived propanolamines. J. Org. Chem., 11: 215-22.

With T. L. Jacobs, G. B. Linden, and D. Seymour. Substituted α-dialkylaminoalkyl-1-naphthalenemethanols. VII. Synthesis of some propanolamines by means of the Grignard reagents. J. Org. Chem., 11:223-28.

With T. L. Jacobs, R. B. Henderson, J. Bond, J. W. Ralls, D. Seymour, and W. H. Florsheim. Substituted α-dialkylaminoalkyl-1-naphthalene-methanols. VIII. 5, 6- and 7-chloro derivatives. J. Org. Chem., 11:229-38.

With E. Spaeth, T. A. Geissman, and T. L. Jacobs. Substituted α-dialkylaminoalkyl-1-naphthalenemethanols. IX. α-(2-dialkylaminoethyl)-α-methyl arylmethanols. J. Org. Chem., 11:399-404.

With T. L. Jacobs et al. 4-Substituted cinnoline derivatives. J. Am. Chem. Soc., 68:1310-13.

With T. L. Jacobs et al. Alpha-dialkylaminomethyl-4-quinolinemethanols substituted in the 2-position. J. Am. Chem. Soc., 68:1831-37.

With R. F. Brown, T. L. Jacobs, et al. Alpha-(2-piperidyl)-2-aryl-4-quinolinemethanols. J. Am. Chem. Soc., 68:2705-8.

With T. L. Jacobs *et al.* Alpha-piperidyl-4-quinolinemethanols substituted in the 2-position. J. Am. Chem. Soc., 68:2714-18.

1947

With Ernest Grunwald. Kinetics and mechanism of the reaction of hydrogen bromide with ethanol. J. Am. Chem. Soc., 69:2051-53.

With Frank Seubold. Free radical reactions of aldehydes. J. Am. Chem. Soc., 69:2916.

1948

With T. L. Jacobs and Bruce Day. Correction of structure for several supposed 2-substituted 1-naphthalene derivatives. J. Org. Chem., 13:171.

With Carolyn Hanson and Ernest Grunwald. The role of neighboring groups in replacement reactions. X. Kinetics of solvolysis of *trans*-2-acetoxycyclohexyl *p*-toluenesulfonate. J. Am. Chem. Soc., 70:812-16.

With E. Grunwald, R. E. Buckles, and C. Hanson. The role of neighboring groups in replacement reactions. XI. Some reactivities involving neighboring groups. J. Am. Chem. Soc., 70:816-21.

With Ernest Grunwald and L. L. Ingraham. The role of neighboring groups in replacement reactions. XII. Rates of acetolysis of 2-substituted cyclohexyl benzenesulfonates. J. Am. Chem. Soc., 70:821-28.

With Ernest Grunwald. The role of neighboring groups in replacement reactions. XIII. General theory of neighboring groups and reactivity. J. Am. Chem. Soc., 70:828-37.

With Rowland Adams. The role of neighboring groups in replacement reactions. XIV. The 5,6-double bond in cholesteryl *p*-toluene sulfonate as a neighboring group. J. Am. Chem. Soc., 70:838-40.

With E. Grunwald. The role of neighboring groups in replacement reactions. XV. Rates and medium effects in the alcoholysis and hydrolysis of α-bromopropionate ion. The carboxylate ion group. J. Am. Chem. Soc., 70:841-46.

With E. Grunwald. The correlation of solvolysis rates. J. Am. Chem. Soc., 70:846-54.

With A. Schlesinger. Exchange at the 6-position of i-cholesteryl methyl ether. J. Am. Chem. Soc., 70:3528.

1949

With W. G. Young and R. E. Kepner. Allylic rearrangements. XXIV. Abnormal bimolecular substitution. J. Am. Chem. Soc., 71:115-19.

With D. S. Trifan. The structure of the bicyclo-(2,2,1)-heptyl (norbornyl) carbonium ion. J. Am. Chem. Soc., 71:2953.

1950

With L. Goodman and R. Boschan. The role of neighboring groups in replacement reactions. XVI. The neighboring benzamide group in addition and substitution. J. Am. Chem. Soc., 72:2311.

With R. Boschan. The role of neighboring groups in replacement reactions. XVII. Complex neighboring groups. J. Am. Chem. Soc., 72:4669-77.

With H. M. Walborsky and K. Schreiber. Driving force of the homoallylic rearrangement in acetolysis of *exo*-dehydronorbornyl *p*-bromobenzenesulfonate. J. Am. Chem. Soc., 72: 5795.

With R. B. Henderson. Ethylene and trimethylene oxides. Chapter of treatise, *Heterocyclic Compounds*, pp. 1-60. New York, John Wiley & Sons, Inc.

1951

With W. G. Young and H. L. Goering. Allylic rearrangements. XXXII. The solvolysis and intramolecular rearrangement of α,α-dimethylallyl chloride. J. Am. Chem. Soc., 73:1958-63.

With T. L. Jacobs. 2-Hydroxycinchoninic acid. Organic Synthesis, 28:70-72.

Neighboring groups in displacement and rearrangement. Bulletin de la Société Chimique de France, C:55-61.

With C. Johnson. Oxidation-reduction. I. The kinetics of the reduction of iodine by titanous ion. J. Am. Chem. Soc., 73:2601-5.

With E. Grunwald and H. W. Jones. The correlation of solvolysis rates and the classification of solvolysis reactions into mechanistic categories. J. Am. Chem. Soc., 73:2700-7.

1952

With C. Johnson. Oxidation-reduction. II. Catalysis of the iodine-titanous reaction by quinones and phenazines. J. Am. Chem. Soc., 74:755-58.

With B. Morse, E. Grunwald, K. C. Schreiber, and J. Corse. Neighboring carbon and hydrogen. V. Driving forces in the Wagner-Meerwein rearrangement. J. Am. Chem. Soc., 74:1113-20.

With H. Marshall. Neighboring carbon and hydrogen. VI. Formolysis and other solvolysis rates of some simple secondary and primary benzenesulfonates. J. Am. Chem. Soc., 74:1120-26.

With B. Morse, E. Grunwald, H. W. Jones, J. Corse, D. Trifan, and H. Marshall. Neighboring carbon and hydrogen. VII. Reactivity of some alicyclic and bicyclic derivatives. J. Am. Chem. Soc., 74:1127-32.

With B. Morse. Neighboring carbon and hydrogen. VIII. Solvolysis of optically active α-phenylneopentyl derivatives. J. Am. Chem. Soc., 74:1133-39.

With M. Brown, K. Schreiber, and A. Schlesinger. Neighboring carbon and hydrogen. IX. Neighboring phenyl in benzylmethyl-carbinyl p-toluenesulfonate. J. Am. Chem. Soc., 74:1140-47.

With D. Trifan. Neighboring carbon and hydrogen. X. Solvolysis of endo-norbornyl arylsulfonates. J. Am. Chem. Soc., 74:1147-54.

With D. Trifan. Neighboring carbon and hydrogen. XI. Solvolysis of exo-norbornyl p-bromobenzenesulfonates. J. Am. Chem. Soc., 74:1154-60.

With L. Ingraham. The role of neighboring groups in replacement reactions. XVIII. Migration of the methoxy group. J. Am. Chem. Soc., 74:1160-64.

With K. Schreiber. Neighboring carbon and hydrogen. XII. Internal rearrangement in solvolysis of 3-phenyl-2-butyl *p*-toluenesulfonate. J. Am. Chem. Soc., 74:2165-70.

With K. Schreiber. Neighboring carbon and hydrogen. XIII. The solvolysis and internal rearrangement of 2-phenyl-1-propyl *p*-bromobenzenesulfonate. J. Am. Chem. Soc., 74:2171-78.

With C. Johnson. Oxidation-reduction. III. Reduction of sodium anthraquinone-*β*-sulfonate by titanous ion. J. Am. Chem. Soc., 74:3105-9.

With R. Heck. The role of neighboring groups in replacement reactions. XIX. Polarimetric acetolysis rate of *trans*-2-acetoxycyclohexyl *p*-toluenesulfonate. J. Am. Chem. Soc., 74:5584-86.

With C. A. Grob. Mechanism of mutarotation of 5,6-dibromocholestane. Helvetica Chimica Acta, 35:782-802.

1953

With R. M. Roberts. The role of neighboring groups in replacement reactions. XX. Some conversions of cyclopentane and indan derivatives. J. Am. Chem. Soc., 75:2297-2300.

With C. R. Lindegren, H. Marshall, and L. L. Ingraham. Neighboring carbon and hydrogen. XIV. Solvolysis of some primary arylsulfonates. J. Am. Chem. Soc., 75:147-55.

With C. R. Lindegren. Neighboring carbon and hydrogen. XV. Rearrangement as a sequel to neighboring group participation. Solvolysis of 2-methyl-2-methoxy-1-propyl *p*-bromobenzenesulfonate. J. Am. Chem. Soc., 75:155-58.

With R. Y. Mixer, R. F. Heck, and W. G. Young. *cis* and *trans*-propenylbenzene and their azeotropes with *n*-decane. J. Am. Chem. Soc., 75:4094-95.

1954

With M. Simonetta. Neighboring carbon and hydrogen. XVI. 1,3-interactions and homoallylic resonance. J. Am. Chem. Soc., 76:18-21.

With E. Clippinger, A. H. Fainberg, and G. C. Robinson. Salt effects and ion pairs in solvolysis. J. Am. Chem. Soc., 76:2597.

With E. Clippinger, A. H. Fainberg, and G. C. Robinson. The

nature and behavior of ion pairs in acetolysis. Chem. Ind., pp. 664-65.

With Leon Goodman. Neighboring groups in addition. II. Hydroxyl and acetoxy in allyl derivatives. J. Am. Chem. Soc., 76:4368-72.

With Leon Goodman. Neighboring groups in addition. III. The tertiary OH and O⁻ groups in α,α-dimethylallyl alcohol. J. Am. Chem. Soc., 76:4373-78.

1955

With L. L. Ingraham. Neighboring carbon and hydrogen. XVII. The pinacol rearrangement solvolysis of 2-methoxy-2-phenylethyl and related halides. J. Am. Chem. Soc., 77:1738-43.

With N. J. Holness. Neighboring carbon and hydrogen. XVIII. Solvolysis of the nopinyl p-bromobenzenesulfonates. J. Am. Chem. Soc., 77:3054-61.

With T. G. Traylor and C. S. Garner. Mechanisms of reactions of organomercurials. I. Stereochemistry of electrophilic displacement on cis-2-methoxycyclohexylneophylmercury by radio-mercuric chloride. J. Am. Chem. Soc., 77:3741-47.

With T. G. Traylor. Mechanism of reactions of organomercurials. II. Electrophilic substitution on saturated carbon. Acetolysis of dialkyl mercury compounds. J. Am. Chem. Soc., 77:3747-52.

With M. Shatavsky, C. Norton, and R. B. Woodward. 7-Norbornenyl and 7-norbornyl cations. J. Am. Chem. Soc., 77:4183.

With N. J. Holness. Neighboring carbon and hydrogen. XIX. t-Butylcyclohexl derivatives. Quantitative conformational analysis. J. Am. Chem. Soc., 77:5562-78.

Some recent aspects of carbonium ion behavior. Experientia Supplementum II, pp. 137-55.

1956

With E. Clippinger, A. H. Fainberg, R. Heck, and G. C. Robinson. Salt effects and ion pairs in solvolysis and related reactions. III. Common ion rate depression and exchange of anions during acetolysis. J. Am. Chem. Soc., 78:328-35.

With M. Shatavsky. Neighboring carbon and hydrogen. XXI.

Anti-7-derivatives of norbornene as homoallylic systems. J. Am. Chem. Soc., 78:592-97.

With M. Shatavsky. 2,6-Homoconjugate addition to bicycloheptadiene. Chem. Ind., pp. 56-57.

With T. G. Traylor. Mechanisms of reactions of organomercurials. III. Preparation and substitution reactions of bridgehead mercurials. J. Am. Chem. Soc., 78:2579-2603.

With R. Heck, S. Lapporte, and R. Baird. Ar_7-5 and Ar_2-6 aryl participation in ionic and free radical processes. Experientia, 12:138-45.

With A. H. Fainberg. Salt effects and ion pairs in solvolysis and related reactions. IV. Salt effects in acetolysis of neophyl and p-methoxyneophyl halides and arylsulfonates. J. Am. Chem. Soc., 78:2763-67.

With A. H. Fainberg. Salt effects and ion pairs in solvolysis and related reactions. V. Special salt effect in acetolysis of 2-anisylethyl p-toluenesulfonate. J. Am. Chem. Soc., 78:2767-70.

With A. H. Fainberg. Correlation of solvolysis rates. III. t-Butyl chloride in a wide range of solvent mixtures. J. Am. Chem. Soc., 78:2770-77.

With G. C. Robinson and A. H. Fainberg. Salt effects and ion pairs in solvolysis and related reactions. VI. Additional examples of special salt effects in acetolysis. J. Am. Chem. Soc., 78:2777-79.

With A. H. Fainberg. Salt effects and ion pairs in solvolysis and related reactions. VII. Salt effects in acetolysis of some secondary arylsulfonates. J. Am. Chem. Soc., 78:2780-84.

With E. Clippinger. Salt effects and ion pairs in solvolysis and related reactions. VIII. Special salt effects in acetolysis of cholesteryl and 2-(2,4-dimethoxyphenyl)-ethyl arylsulfonates. J. Am. Chem. Soc., 78:2784-88.

With D. Darwish and N. J. Holness. Merged biomolecular substitution and elimination. J. Am. Chem. Soc., 78:2915.

With W. G. Young and H. K. Hall, Jr. 1,2- and 1,4-dibromides from cyclopentadiene. J. Am. Chem. Soc., 78:4338-44.

With E. M. Kosower. Neighboring carbon and hydrogen. XXII. Homoallylic systems. The preparation and behavior of certain 3,5-cyclosteroids. J. Am. Chem. Soc., 78:4347-54.

With E. M. Kosower.   Neighboring carbon and hydrogen. XXIII. Homoallylic systems. 3,5-cyclocholestan-6 β-yl chloride.   J. Am. Chem. Soc., 78:4354-58.

With R. Heck.   Neighboring carbon and hydrogen. XXIV. Some methoxyl-substituted 2-aryl-1-alkyl benzenesulfonates.   J. Am. Chem. Soc., 78:4801-6.

With R. Boschan.   The role of neighboring groups in replacement reactions. XXI. Frontside participation of the acetoxy group. Catalytic effect of acetic acid on the reaction of glycols with hydrogen chloride.   J. Am. Chem. Soc., 78:4921-25.

1957

With F. L. Scott and R. E. Glick.   Amido, ureido and urethano neighboring group participation.   Experientia, 13:183-85.

Organic reaction mechanisms. Chapter 7 in: *Modern Chemistry for the Engineer and Scientist,* ed. by G. R. Robertson, pp. 146-67. New York, McGraw-Hill Book Co., Inc.

With E. T. Stafford.   *syn*-7-norbornenyl toluenesulfonates.   J. Am. Chem. Soc., 79:505.

With R. Baird.   The formation of dieonones through Ar$_1$-participation.   J. Am. Chem. Soc., 79:756.

With Richard Heck.   Neighboring carbon and hydrogen. XXVII. Ar$_1$-5 aryl participation and Tetralin formation in solvolysis.   J. Am. Chem. Soc., 79:3105-13.

With Richard Heck.   Neighboring carbon and hydrogen. XXVIII. Ar$_2$-6 participation in solvolysis of some ω-aryl-1-alkyl bromobenzenesulfonates.   J. Am. Chem. Soc., 79:3114-18.

With Richard Heck.   Neighboring carbon and hydrogen. XXIX. ρ/σ analysis of acetolysis of substituted neophyl aryl sulfonates.   J. Am. Chem. Soc., 79:3432-38.

With R. Heck, J. Corse, and E. Grunwald.   The role of neighboring groups in replacement reactions. XXII. Competition between *o*-MeO-5 and Ar$_1$3 participation in solvolysis of *o*-methoxyneophyl toluenesulfonates.   J. Am. Chem. Soc., 79: 3278-84.

With A. H. Fainberg and E. Grunwald.   Correlation of solvolysis rates. VIII. Benzhydryl chloride and bromide. Comparison of *m*

Y and Swain's correlations. J. Am. Chem. Soc., 79:4146-55.

With R. Baird. Isolation and behavior of *spiro*[-2:5]-octa-1, 4-diene-3-one. J. Am. Chem. Soc., 79:4238-39.

With Leon Goodman. Neighboring groups in addition. V. The benzamido group in 3-benzamidopropene. J. Am. Chem. Soc., 79:4788-92.

With A. H. Fainberg. Correlation of solvolysis rates. IV. Solvent effects on enthalpy and entorpy of activation for solvolysis of t-butyl chloride. J. Am. Chem. Soc., 79:5937-50.

With A. H. Fainberg. Correlation of solvolysis rates. V. α-phenylethyl chloride. J. Am. Chem. Soc., 79:1597-1602.

With A. H. Fainberg. Correlation of solvolysis rates. VI. t-butyl and α-phenylethyl bromides. J. Am. Chem. Soc., 79:1602-8.

With A. H. Fainberg. Correlation of solvolysis rates. VII. Neophyl chloride and bromide. J. Am. Chem. Soc., 79:1608-12.

1958

With J. Takahashi. Neighboring hydrogen, isotope effect and conformation in solvolysis of 3-methyl-2-butyl *p*-toluenesulfonate. Tetrahedron, 2:316-21.

With G. C. Robinson. Salt effects and ion pairs in solvolysis and related reactions. IX. The *threo*-3-*p*-anisyl-2- butyl system. J. Am. Chem. Soc., 80:169-81.

With A. H. Fainberg. Salt effects and ion pairs in solvolysis and related reactions. X. The 2-*p*-anisyl-1-propyl system. J. Am. Chem. Soc., 80:459-65.

With R. M. Roberts, J. Corse, R. Boschan, and D. Seymour. The role of neighboring groups in replacement reactions. XXIV. The acetoxy group. Preparation and reactions of the ketene acetal of *cis*-1,2-cyclohexandiol (2-methylene-*cis*-4,5-tetramethylenedioxolane). J. Am. Chem. Soc., 80:1247-54.

With E. Jenny. [14]C rearrangement, salt effects and ion pair return in solvolysis of 2-*p*-anisyl-1-ethyl *p*-toluenesulfonate. Helvetica Chimica Acta, 41:807-23.

With E. Allred, R. Heck, and R. Glick. Neighboring methoxyl participation in solvolytic nucleophilic substitution. Tetrahedron, 3:1-13.

With Leon Goodman and R. Boshchan. Neighboring groups in

addition. VI. The benzamido group in 3-benzamidocyclohexene. Stereospecific synthesis of trisubstituted cyclohexane derivatives. J. Am. Chem. Soc., 80:4312-17.

With Stanley G. Smith. Sulfoxides as nucleophiles. Tetrahedron, 3:317-19.

With Fulvio Gadient, E. T. Stafford, and P. E. Klinedinst, Jr. A tricycloheptonium non-classical cation. J. Am. Chem. Soc., 80:5895.

With T. G. Traylor. Mechanism of reduction of alkylmercuric salts with sodium stannite. J. Org. Chem., 23:1796.

1959

With Edward M. Kosower. Neighboring carbon and hydrogen. XXXIII. Reactivities of 3,5-cyclocholestan-6-yl derivatives. Strain and reactivity in homoallylic systems. J. Am. Chem. Soc., 81:4399-4408.

With R. Piccolini. Doublet character of O-H absorption in saturated alcohols. Tetrahedron Letters, No. 13, pp. 4-10.

With S. Smith and D. Darwish. Alleged S_N2 Finkelstein substitutions of t-butyl bromide. Tetrahedron Letters, No. 16, pp. 24-31.

With S. Smith and D. Darwish. Large salt effects in non-polar solvents. J. Am. Chem. Soc., 81:5511.

With Evan L. Allred and Joseph Sonnenberg. Homoallyl and homobenzyl alcohols by the hydroboration method. J. Am. Chem. Soc., 81:5833.

With R. Piccolini, L. de Vries, and R. Heck. The stereochemistry of the bis-cyclopentadiene-benzoquinone adduct and related compounds. Chem. Ind., 45:1416-17.

With Joseph Sonnenberg and Louis de Vries. The trishomocyclopropenyl cation. J. Am. Chem. Soc., 81:6523.

Homo-aromatic structures. J. Am. Chem. Soc., 81:6524.

1960

With John S. Gall, Masaru Nojo, and S. Smith. Racemization, acetolysis and radio-chloride exchange of two alkyl chlorides. J. Am. Chem. Soc., 82:1010.

With W. G. Young and S. H. Sharman. Allylic rearrangements.

XLVII. The silver ion-assisted hydrolysis of α and γ-methyl-allyl chlorides. Preservation of configuration in allylic cations. J. Am. Chem. Soc., 82:1376-82.

With C. Ordronneau. The 7-norbornadienyl non-classical cation. J. Am. Chem. Soc., 82:2084-85.

With M. Battiste. Cyclopentadienylmethyl derivatives as homoallylic systems. J. Am. Chem. Soc., 82:5244.

With Louis de Vries. Neighboring carbon and hydrogen. XXXIX. Complex rearrangements of bridged ions. Rearrangement leading to the bird-cage hydrocarbon. J. Am. Chem. Soc., 82:5363-76.

With C. F. Wilcox, Jr., and W. G. McMillan. Neighboring carbon and hydrogen. XXXIV. Interactions of nonconjugated chromophores. J. Am. Chem. Soc., 82:5450-54.

With W. G. Young and A. Gagneux. Rearrangements of allylic azides. J. Am. Chem. Soc., 82:5956-57.

With Robert L. Hansen. 1,5-hydrogen shift in a decahydrodimethanonaphthalene system. J. Am. Chem. Soc., 82:6206-7.

With Evan Allred and Joseph Sonnenberg. Preparation of homobenzyl and homoallyl alcohols by the hydroboration method. J. Org. Chem., 25:26-29.

With John S. Gall. Racemization and radio-chloride exchange of p-chlorobenzhydryl chloride in acetone. Tetrahedron Letters, No. 2, pp. 31-35.

With Masaru Hojo and S. Smith. Ion pairs, racemization, chloride exchange and the mass law effect in solvolysis of p-chlorobenzhydryl chloride. Tetrahedron Letters, No. 22, pp. 12-19.

With Lydia G. Savedoff, S. Smith, I. D. R. Stevens, and John S. Gall. Ion pairs, nucleophilicity and salt effects in bimolecular nucleophilic substitution. Tetrahedron Letters, No. 9, pp. 24-30.

With Robert L. Hansen. An Octahydrodimethanonaphthyl nonclassical homocyclopropenyl cation. Tetrahedron Letters, No. 25, pp. 4-8.

With L. J. Filar. Preparation and behavior of simple quinone methides. Tetrahedron Letters, No. 25, pp. 9-16.

With David Thompson and Peter Bruck. Dechlorination of isodrin and related compounds. Chem. Ind., 46:405-6.

With Peter Bruck and David Thompson. New carbonium ion routes to the bird-cage hydrocarbon and related compounds. Chem. Ind., 46:590-91.

1961

With S. G. Smith and A. H. Fainberg. Correlation of solvolysis rates. IX. *p*-Methoxyneophyl toluenesulfonate in a variety of solvents. Ionizing power of hydroxylic and non-hydroxylic solvents. J. Am. Chem. Soc., 83:618-25.

With Paul E. Klinedinst, Jr., and G. C. Robinson. Salt effects and ion pairs in solvolysis and related reactions. XVII. Induced common ion rate depression and the mechanism of the special salt effect. J. Am. Chem. Soc., 83:885-95.

Bicycloheptadiene dibromides. J. Am. Chem. Soc., 83:1516-17.

With Louis de Vries and Ray Orloski. Interactions of homoconjugated 1,4-chromophores in boat cyclohexane derivatives. J. Am. Chem. Soc., 83:2020-21.

With D. Kivelson, Peter Bruck, and Robert L. Hansen. Sterically increased C-H stretching frequencies in fused bicycloheptane and half-cage structures. J. Am. Chem. Soc., 83:2938-44.

With Joseph Sonnenberg. Homoconjugation and homoaromaticity. III. The 3-bicyclo[3.1.0]hexyl system. J. Am. Chem. Soc., 83:3235-44.

With Joseph Sonnenberg. Homoconjugation and homoaromaticity. IV. The trishomocyclopropenyl cation. A homoaromatic structure. J. Am. Chem. Soc., 83:3244-51.

With A. Ledwith and M. Hojo. Racemization and radiochloride exchange of *p*-chlorobenzhydryl chloride with mercuric chloride. Proc. Chem. Soc., p. 241.

With A. Ledwith and M. Hojo. Racemization and radiochloride exchange of *p*-chlorobenzhydryl chloride in acetone. Tetrahedron Letters, No. 10, pp. 341-46.

With Martin Feldman. Tropylium ion-aromatic hydrocarbon charge-transfer complexes. J. Am. Chem. Soc., 83:3338-39.

With Peter Carter. The π-route to a bicyclooctyl non-classical cation. J. Am. Chem. Soc., 83:4485-86.

With Paul E. Klinedinst, Jr., and E. Clippinger. Salt effects and ion pairs in solvolysis and related reactions. XXI. Acetolysis, bromide exchange and the special salt effect. J. Am. Chem. Soc., 83:4986-89.

1962

With Joseph Sonnenberg. Rearrangement of 6,6-dibromobicyclo[3.1.0]hexane. J. Org. Chem., 27:748-51.

With Richard Baird. Neighboring carbon and hydrogen. XLVI. Spiro-(4,5)-deca-1,4-diene-3-one from Ar_1^--5 participation. J. Am. Chem. Soc., 84:788-92.

With Anita Lewin. NMR spectra and conformational analysis of 4-alkylcyclohexanols. J. Am. Chem. Soc., 84:2464-65.

With Edwin C. Friedrich. Spirodienyl derivatives and benzenonium ions. Tetrahedron Letters, No. 11, pp. 475-80.

With Eddie Hedaya. Ionic decomposition of 2-alkoxy-2-propyl per-p-nitrobenzoates. Baeyer-Villiger-type reactions of a ketal and an orthoester. Tetrahedron Letters, No. 13, pp. 563-67.

With Martin Feldman. Planar cationic systems as charge-transfer acceptors. Tetrahedron Letters, No. 19, pp. 853-57.

With Elliot Vogelfanger and K. C. Pande. Demercuration route to the nortricyclyl cation. Chem. Ind., 2061-62.

With Elliot Vogelfanger, K. C. Pande, and Hans Ebel. Demercuration route to the norbornyl cation. J. Am. Chem. Soc., 84:4993-94.

1963

With Edwin C. Friedrich and S. Smith. Large salt effects and mechanism in acetone and ether. J. Am. Chem. Soc., 85:305-7.

With Robert S. Boikes. The hexahomobenzene problem. Tetracyclo[9.1.0.0^3,^{5}0^7,^{9}]dodecane. J. Am. Chem. Soc., 85:343.

With Phillip Radlick. cis-cis-cis-1,4,7-cyclononatriene, a homoconjugated six π-electron system. J. Am. Chem. Soc., 85:344.

With Richard Baird. Neighboring carbon and hydrogen. LI. Dienones from Ar_1^--3 participation. Isolation and behavior of spiro(2,5)octa-1,4-diene-3-one. J. Am. Chem. Soc., 85:567-68.

With Michael Cocivera. Ion pairs in elimination. J. Am. Chem. Soc., 85:1702.

With Paul D. Sleezer and W. G. Young. Electrophilic and nucleophilic substitution of allylic mercurials. J Am. Chem. Soc., 85:1890-91.

With Anita H. Lewin and K. C. Pande. The non-classical 7-norbornenyl cation. J. Am. Chem. Soc., 85:2324-25.

With J. W. H. Watthey. Isomerization of cyclononatrienes. J. Am. Chem. Soc., 85:3715-16.

With Richard J. Piccolini. Application of the LCAO method to some non-classical carbonium ions. Tetrahedron, 19:423-39.

With C. B. Anderson and Edwin C. Friedrich. The cis-cyclohexene acetoxonium ion. 2-Methyl-cis-4,5-tetramethylene-1,3-dioxolenium tetrafluoroborate. Tetrahedron Letters, No. 29, pp. 2037-44.

With C. B. Anderson. Oxidation of cyclohexene by thallic and other metal acetates. J. Org. Chem., 28:605.

With David S. Glass and Joachim Zirner. Dienyl and homodienyl 1,5-hydrogen transfer in cyclic trienes and homotrienes. Proc. Chem. Soc., pp. 276-77.

1964

With Phillip Radlick. Stereospecific synthesis of tricyclo[7.1.0. $0^{5,7}$]decan-3-ol. J. Am. Chem. Soc., 86:1866-67.

With P. Bruck, Phillip Radlick, and R. Baker. Three center nonclassical cation in the pentahomocyclopentadienyl system. J. Am. Chem. Soc., 86:1867-69.

With R. Baker. Nonclassical bridged ion in acetolysis of threo-3-anisyl-2-butyl p-bromobenzenesulfonate. J. Am. Chem. Soc., 86:2071.

With W. D. Kumler, Robert Boikess, and P. Bruck. Dipole moments, configuration and conformation of tricyclo[5.1.0.0^{3,5}]-octane derivatives and related compounds. J. Am. Chem. Soc., 86:3126-30.

With R. Baker and S. Smith. Dissociated ions and ion pairs in acetolysis of threo-3-anisyl-2-butyl p-bromobenzenesulfonate. J. Am. Chem. Soc., 86:2072-73.

With J. Zirner. Photoisomerizations of cyclooctatrienes and homotrienes. Proc. Chem. Soc., pp. 235-36.

With Bruce R. Appel. Ion pairs in reactions of trityl benzoate. J. Am. Chem. Soc., 86:2718-20.

With Bruce R. Appel. Ion pairs and dissociated ions from trityl benzoate in moist acetone. J. Am. Chem. Soc., 86:2720-21.

With Edwin C. Friedrich. Carbonium ion behavior of nopinyl derivatives. J. Am. Chem. Soc., 86:2721-22.

With Richard Heck and Phillip S. Magee. Reaction of the trityl cation with dimethylketene dimethylacetal. Tetrahedron Letters, No. 30, pp. 2033-36.

With K. C. Pande. Oxymercuration and oxythallation of norbornadiene and related olefins. Tetrahedron Letters, No. 46, pp. 3393-98.

With A. F. Diaz. Ion pairs in acetolysis of p-chlorobenzhydryl acetate. J. Am.Chem. Soc., 86:4484-85.

With F. P. Lossing. On the question of homoconjugation in 1,4,7-cyclononatriene. J. Am. Chem. Soc., 86:4485-86.

With Arthur F. Diaz. Racemization and radiochloride exchange of p-chlorobenzhydryl chloride in a series of solvents. J. Am. Chem. Soc., 86:5010-11.

1965

With E. Clippinger, Robert Howe, and Elliot Vogelfanger. The nonclassical norbornyl cation. J. Am. Chem. Soc., 87:376-77.

With A. Colter, Edwin C. Friedrich, and N. J. Holness. The apoisobornyl-*exo*-camphenilyl nonclassical cation. J. Am. Chem. Soc., 87:378-79.

With Robert Howe and Edwin C. Friedrich. The apoisobornyl bridged ion. Borohydride reduction of apocamphor. J. Am. Chem. Soc., 87:379-81.

On Brown's classical norbornyl cation. J. Am. Chem. Soc., 87:381-82.

With Bruce Appel, Ray Baker, and Arthur Diaz. Ion pairs in solvolysis and exchange. The Chemical Society, Special Publication No. 19, pp. 109-30.

With Peter Carter and Robert Howe. Preparation and solvolytic behavior of a bridgehead birdcage alcohol. J. Am. Chem. Soc., 87:914-15.

With Robert Howe. Homoenolization-homoketonization of a half-cage ketone. J. Am. Chem. Soc., 87:915-16.

With David S. Glass and J. W. H. Watthey. Isolation and valency isomerization of *cis-cis-cis*-1,3,5-cyclononatriene. Tetrahedron Letters, No. 6, pp. 377-83.

Ion pairs in solvolysis and exchange. Acta Científica Venezolana, 15:244.

With Jeremy Sprung and W. F. Libby. Reactions of thermal carbon atoms. J. Am. Chem. Soc., 87:1812-13.

With H. D. Kaesz, C. G. Kreiter, and Edwin C. Friedrich. Homotropylium ion and its molybdenum tricarbonyl complex. J. Am. Chem. Soc., 87:3267-69.

With L. Eberson, John Petrovich, R. Baird, and D. Dyckes. The neighboring anthryl group in solvolysis. J. Am. Chem. Soc., 87:3504-6.

With L. Eberson. Direct observation of the anthrylethyl bridged cation. J. Am. Chem. Soc., 87:3506-7.

With Terukiyo Hanafusa and Ludmila Birladeanu. Introduction of an angular methyl group by decarboxylative cyclopropane ring opening. J. Am. Chem. Soc., 87:3510-11.

With Peter Carter, F. A. L. Anet, and A. J. R. Bourn. The effects of steric compression on chemical shifts in half-cage and related molecules. J. Am. Chem. Soc., 87:5247-49.

With F. A. L. Anet, A. J. R. Bourn, and Peter Carter. Effects of steric compression on coupling constants. J. Am. Chem. Soc., 87:5249-50.

With Zvi Rappoport, Paul D. Sleezer, and W. G. Young. Allylic oxidation of olefins by mercuric acetate. Tetrahedron Letters, No. 42, pp. 3719-28.

1966

With David S. Glass and Robert S. Boikess. Dienyl and homodienyl 1,5-hydrogen shifts. Tetrahedron Letters, No. 10, pp. 999-1008.

With Arthur F. Diaz. Benzhydryl benzoate ion pairs from diphenyldiazomethane. J. Am. Chem. Soc., 88:1318-19.

With H. D. Kaesz and C. G. Kreiter. Novel reactions of olefin-metal carbonyl complexes. J. Am. Chem. Soc., 88:1319-20.

With C. G. Kreiter and J. I. Brauman. Ring inversion, ultra-

SAUL WINSTEIN 349

violet spectrum, and electronic structure of the monohomotropylium ion. J. Am. Chem. Soc., 88:2047-48.

With Anne Ehret. Cholesteryl perchlorate from carbonium perchlorate ion pair return. J. Am. Chem. Soc., 88:2048-49.

With William Kitching, Zvi Rappoport, and W. G. Young. Allylic oxidation of olefins by palladium acetate. J. Am. Chem. Soc., 88:2054-55.

With Ludmila Birladeanu and Terukiyo Hanafusa. A novel biscyclopropylcarbinyl system. J. Am. Chem. Soc., 88:2315-16.

With Ludmila Birladeanu, Terukiyo Hanafusa, and Brian Johnson. Rate and stereochemistry of solvolysis of a biscyclopropylcarbinyl system. J. Am. Chem. Soc., 88:2316-18.

With Arthur Diaz and M. Brookhart. Ground- and transition-state free energy relationships in sigma and pi routes to the nonclassical 7-norbornenyl cation. J. Am. Chem. Soc., 88:3133-35.

With M. Brookhart and Arthur Diaz. Structure of the nonclassical 7-norbornenyl cation. J. Am. Chem. Soc., 88:3135-36.

With C. G. Kreiter, A. Maasbol, F. A. L. Anet, and H. D. Kaesz. Valency tautomerism in metal-olefin complexes. Cyclooctatetraene-molybdenum, -chromium and -iron tricarbonyls. J. Am. Chem. Soc., 88:3444-45.

With R. Rieke, M. Ogliaruso, and Ronald McClung. Monohomocyclooctatetraene anion radical. A homoaromatic 9-electron system. J. Am. Chem. Soc., 88:4729-30.

With R. Rieke and M. Ogliaruso. Monohomocyclooctatetraene dianion. A homoaromatic 10-electron species. J. Am. Chem. Soc., 88:4731-32.

With Edwin C. Friedrich, R. Baker, and Yang-i-Lin. Homoconjugation and homoaromaticity. XVII. The nature and behavior of the unsubstituted trishomocyclopropenyl cation. Tetrahedron, Supplement 8, Part II, pp. 621-45.

With M. Brookhart and F. A. L. Anet. The behavior of the 3-phenyl-2-butanols in SO_2-FSO_3H-SbF_5. J. Am. Chem. Soc., 88:5657-59.

With M. Brookhart, F. A. L. Anet, and D. J. Cram. Phenonium and benzylic cations from 3-phenyl-2-butanols in FSO_3H-SbF_5. J. Am. Chem. Soc., 88:5659-60.

1967

Nonclassical ions and homoaromaticity. Special publication No. 21, The Chemical Society, pp. 5-45.

With Richard Leute. Solvolysis of 9-substituted 10-anthranyl systems. Tetrahedron Letters, No. 26, pp. 2475-80.

With Eddie Hedaya. The ionic decomposition of 2-substituted 2-propyl p-nitrobenzoates. Migration to electron-deficient oxygen and anchimeric acceleration of peroxide-bond heterolysis. J. Am. Chem. Soc., 89:1661-72.

With M. Brookhart and G. C. Levy. O-H chemical shift, conformation and electron delocalization in protonated carbonyl compounds. J. Am. Chem. Soc., 89:1735-37.

With M. Brookhart and M. Ogliaruso. The homoaromatic 1-hydroxyhomotropylium cation. J. Am. Chem. Soc., 89:1965-66.

With F. A. L. Anet, H. D. Kaesz, and A. Maasbol. The structure of cyclooctatetraene-iron tricarbonyl in solution. J. Am. Chem. Soc., 89:2489-91.

With M. Ogliaruso, M. Sakai, and J. M. Nicholson. Direct observation of a bishomocyclopentadienide anion. J. Am. Chem. Soc., 89:3656-57.

With Evan L. Allred. The role of neighboring groups in replacement reactions. XXVII. MeO-5 participation in some solvolysis reactions. J. Am. Chem. Soc., 89:3991-97.

With Evan L. Allred. MeO-5 participation in acetolysis. Ion and ion pair intermediates. J. Am. Chem. Soc., 89:3998-4008.

With Evan L. Allred. The role of neighboring groups in replacement reactions. XXIX. MeO-5 participation and lithium aluminum hydride reduction. J. Am. Chem. Soc., 89:4008-11.

With Evan L. Allred. MeO-6 participation and ion pairs in some solvolysis reactions. J. Am. Chem. Soc., 89:4012-17.

With M. Ogliaruso. Protonation of monohomocyclooctatetraene dianion. J. Am. Chem. Soc., 89:5290-91.

With R. F. Childs. A dibenzohomotropylium ion. J. Am. Chem. Soc., 89:6348-50.

With R. K. Lustgarten and M. Brookhart. Degenerate 5-carbon scrambling in the 7-norbornadienyl cation. J. Am. Chem. Soc., 89:6350-52.

With M. Brookhart and R. K. Lustgarten. Bridge flipping and

rearrangement of norbornadienyl and 7-methylnorbornadienyl cations. J. Am. Chem. Soc., 89:6352-54.

With M. Brookhart and R. K. Lustgarten. 7-Phenyl and 7-methoxynorbornadienyl cations. J. Am. Chem. Soc., 89:6354-55.

With M. Gasic, D. Whalen, and Brian Johnson. Nonclassical homoallylic cations and homoallylic ring expansions. J. Am. Chem. Soc., 89:6382-84.

With Dale Whalen, M. Gasic, Brian Johnson, and H. Jones. Single and double homoallylic ring expansions. J. Am. Chem. Soc., 89:6384-86.

1968

With A. J. Parker, M. Ruane, and G. Biale. Elimination reactions. The E2C mechanism. Tetrahedron Letters, No. 17, pp. 2113-18.

With G. A. Wiley, D. V. Braddon, and J. Dirlam. Methoxy substituent effects and anchimeric assistance in solvolysis of 2-benzonorbornenyl bromobenzenesulfonates. J. Am. Chem. Soc., 90:1901-3.

With A. F. Diaz and Ieva Lazdins. ^{18}O-scrambling in solvolysis of simple unactivated alkyl arenesulfonates. J. Am. Chem. Soc., 90:1904-5.

With Gordon Moshuk and Gary Petrowski. A classical anion radical from trans-fused bicyclo[6.1.0]nona-2,4,6-triene. J. Am. Chem. Soc., 90:2179-81.

With George C. Levy. Protonated β-phenyl ketones. Intramolecular π-hydrogen bonding. J. Am. Chem. Soc., 90:3574-76.

With Martin Feldman. Aromatic hydrocarbon-carbonium ion molecular complexes. Theoretica Chimica Acta (Berlin), 10: 86-89.

With Arthur Diaz and Ieva Lazdins. Correlation of k_Δ and k_s in solvolysis of 2-phenylethyl toluenesulfonate. J. Am. Chem. Soc., 90:6546-48.

With John Grutzner. The bicyclo[3.2.2]nonatrienyl anion. The anionic analog of the norbornadienyl cation. J. Am. Chem. Soc., 90:6562-64.

With R. F. Childs and M. Sakai. The observation and behavior

352 BIOGRAPHICAL MEMOIRS

of the pentamethylcyclopentadienylmethyl cation. J. Am. Chem. Soc., 90:7144-46.

With R. F. Childs. Ring opening and 5-fold degenerate scrambling in hexa- and heptamethylbicyclo[3.1.0]hexenyl cations. J. Am. Chem. Soc., 90:7146-47.

With R. K. Lustgarten and M. Brookhart. Direct observation of methyl-substituted 7-norbornadienyl and bicyclo[3.2.0]heptadienyl cations. J. Am. Chem. Soc., 90:7364-66.

1969

With Jean Lhomme and Arthur Diaz. The "σ"-route to the 7-norbornenyl ion. J. Am. Chem. Soc., 91:1548-49.

Nonclassical ions and homoaromaticity. Quarterly Reviews, 23: 141-76. (British Chemical Society 1967 Centenary Lecture)

With C. Dale Poulter. The cyclopropylcarbinyl—allyl rearrangement of a hexamethylcyclopropylcarbinyl system. J. Am. Chem. Soc., 91:3649-50.

With C. Dale Poulter. Solvolysis and degenerate cyclopropylcarbinyl $\rightleftharpoons$ cyclopropylcarbinyl rearrangement of a hexamethylcyclopropylcarbinyl system. J. Am. Chem. Soc., 91:3650-52.

With A. F. Diaz. Correlation of k_Δ and k_s in solvolysis of l-phenyl-2-propyl toluenesulfonate. J. Am. Chem. Soc., 91: 4300-2.

With W. G. Young, W. Kitching, and Brian Hegarty. Sulphur dioxide insertion: allylic and benzylic mercurials. Journal of Organometallic Chemistry, 20:253-56.

With I. Lazdins and A. Diaz. Trifluoracetolysis of simple primary alkyl toluenesulfonates. J. Am. Chem. Soc., 91:5635-37.

With A. Diaz and I. Lazdins. Solvolysis of primary tosylates in FSO_3H. J. Am. Chem. Soc., 91:5637-39.

With John P. Dirlam. Methoxy and nitro substituent effects and anchimeric assistance in solvolysis of tertiary 2-methyl-2-benzonorbornenyl p-nitrobenzoates. J. Am. Chem. Soc., 91: 5905-7.

With John P. Dirlam. Methoxy substituent effects in solvolysis of 2-phenyl-2-benzonorbornenyl p-nitrobenzoates. J. Am. Chem. Soc., 91:5907-9.

With John P. Dirlam, A. Diaz, William P. Giddings, and Gary C.

Hanson. Polarimetric rates in solvolysis of exo- and endo-2-benzonorbornenyl bromobenzenesulfonates. Tetrahedron Letters, No. 36, pp. 3133-36.

With C. Dale Poulter and Edwin C. Friedrich. Stereochemistry of the methylene iodide—zinc copper couple methylenation of cyclic allylic alcohols. J. Am. Chem. Soc., 91:6892-94.

With Philip Warner. Protonated 1,6-methanocyclodecapentaene, a potentially antihomoaromatic species. J. Am. Chem. Soc., 91:7785-87.

1970

With G. Biale, A. J. Parker, S. G. Smith, and I. D. R. Stevens. The E2C mechanism in elimination reactions. The absence of an extreme form of merged mechanism for elimination and substitution. A comparison of Saytzeff *vs.* Hofmann tendencies and of *anti vs. syn.* eliminations. J. Am. Chem. Soc., 92:115-22.

ACKNOWLEDGMENTS FOR THE PHOTOGRAPHS

Photograph of Victor Hugo Benioff
by elson-alexandre

Photograph of Edwin Garrigues Boring
by Fabian Bachrach

Photograph of Charles Judson Herrick
by Mc Keogh

Photograph of Walter Davis Lambert
by Harris & Ewing

Photograph of Howard Johnson Lucas
by Ballam-Wanek-King Studio

Photograph of Alden Holmes Miller
by Ed Kirwan Graphic Arts

Photograph of Thomas Gordon Thompson
by Office of Information Services
University of Washington

Photograph of Edwin Bidwell Wilson
by Atlas Photo Studio